THE COMPLETE CAPITATION HANDBOOK

How to Design and Implement At-Risk Contracts for Behavioral Healthcare

GAYLE L. ZIEMAN, EDITOR

CentraLink Publications
Tiburon, California
in cooperation with Jossey-Bass, Inc., Publishers

© 1995 by CentraLink in cooperation with Jossey-Bass, Inc., Publishers

CentraLink Publications
1110 Mar West Street, Suite E
Tiburon, California 94920-1879

Managing Editor: Adam Richmond
Production: Adam Richmond and Melanie Field
Interior Design: Suzanne Montazer, SLM Graphics
Cover Design: Beth Loudenberg
Copy Editor: Larry Beresford
Composition: Suzanne Montazer, SLM Graphics
Printer: Stellar Graphics, Inc./McNaughton & Gunn, Inc.

Library of Congress Cataloging in Publication Data

The complete capitation handbook : how to design and implement at-risk
   contracts for behavioral healthcare / Gayle L. Zieman, editor.
       p.   cm—(Managed behavioral healthcare library)
    Includes bibliographical references and index.
    ISBN 1-887452-03-6
    1. Psychotherapy—Practice—United States.   2. Insurance, Mental health—
United States.   3. Managed mental health care—United States.   4. Health
maintenance organizations—United States.
I. Zieman, Gayle L.   II. Series.
RC465.6.C65   1995   95-21334
362.2—dc20   CIP

Printed in the United States of America
10 9 8 7 6 5 4 3 2 1   00 99 98 97 96 95

DEDICATION

This handbook is dedicated to the Council of Behavioral Group Practices (CBGP).

The CBGP, under the sponsorship of the Institute for Behavioral Healthcare, is a consortium of almost 70 mental health practices that have joined forces to share ideas and resources in an open, nonproprietary forum. A large number of the associate authors represent members of the Council. The camaraderie of the CBGP, especially among Steering Committee members, was the catalyst that sparked the concept for this book.

May the member practices of the CBGP benefit from this text.

INFORMATION FOR AUTHORS

The Managed Behavioral Healthcare Library will publish an ongoing series of monographs and technical reports for behavioral healthcare executives. Our goal is to disseminate critical technical information rapidly and at an affordable price. These monographs and technical reports are designed to improve the professional effectiveness of our readers; colleagues whose work benefits the behavioral healthcare field and the patients and families that depend upon our excellence.

Please let us know if you or your organization would like to submit a monograph or technical report for publication in this series. To be considered for publication, your document must be clearly written, and contain pragmatic and actionable information that will provide immediate value to the reader.

We look forward to extending The Managed Behavioral Healthcare Library to our colleagues throughout the field, and we appreciate your participation in this collaborative education process.

For further consideration, please submit your monograph or technical report to:

Adam Richmond
CentraLink Publications
1110 Mar West Street, Suite E
Tiburon, California 94920-1879

CONTENTS

THE MANAGED BEHAVIORAL HEALTHCARE LIBRARY
FOREWORD FROM THE SERIES EDITOR

VISION — METHODS — ACTION — RESULTS

Dear Reader,

Behavioral healthcare has changed. The old and familiar professional landscape now seems disorienting and altered. The familiar landmarks that were well known to mental health administrators, clinicians, insurance executives, employee assistance program (EAP) directors, and academic researchers are fading off the map. Vanishing or gone are the employers that didn't pay attention to healthcare costs, insurance plans that would reimburse on a fee-for-service basis, the hospitals with beds filled by patients with coverage for long lengths of stay, the solo clinicians with full practices of affluent patients seeking long-term, insight-oriented therapy, and the community mental health centers that worked in a system of their own.

The scenery of today is different. Health maintenance organizations and managed behavioral health plans have replaced the insurance companies. Employers and purchasing cooperatives are bypassing even these new organizations and purchasing directly from providers. Clinicians are forming group practices. Groups are affiliating with facilities. Facilities are forming integrated delivery systems. Integrated delivery systems are building organized systems of care that include insurance, care management, and service delivery functions. Information systems are linking payors, managers, and providers into coordinated and comprehensive systems with new levels of accountability. The boundaries of the public sector are eroding, and the distinction between public and private has become more difficult to perceive.

Adjusting to this "brave new world" is challenging enough, and many mental health professionals are tempted to give up and opt out now. But for most of us the challenge will be worth facing. While this period of transition is fraught with difficulty and risk, there are an equal number of opportunities. Whenever a paradigm shifts, the stakeholders in the previous paradigm risk losing their place in the paradigm that emerges.

This, in a nutshell, is the problem that The Managed Behavioral Healthcare Library will help you and other readers solve.

In spite of the upheavals that are transforming the behavioral healthcare enterprise, many basic goals remain the same. In fact, managed behavioral healthcare has come about largely because our previous way of doing things failed to solve fundamental problems related to the cost, quality, access, and outcomes of care. The promise of "managed behavioral healthcare"—whatever this concept may eventually come to mean—holds out the hope of affordable, appropriate, and effective mental health and addiction treatment services for all. The various initiatives and efforts that are under way to reach this new plateau will result in a vast array of professional opportunities for the behavioral healthcare specialists whose talents are required to make this promise come true.

By reading the books and reports in The Managed Behavioral Healthcare Library, you will learn how to respond to the perils and possibilities that the shift to managed behavioral healthcare presents. The authors of this book and other volumes in this series recognize the need for direct and pragmatic solutions to the challenges posed by the changing paradigms of behavioral healthcare financing and services. Meeting this need inspires the work of the authors of this book and other volumes in The Managed Behavioral Healthcare Library, and it will be the goal of this book series to provide accessible and pragmatic solutions to the challenges encountered in the new landscape that will become the home for our efforts.

To help readers obtain the resources and solutions that are required, each chapter of each publication will be written by outstanding experts who can communicate in a pragmatic style to help you make a difference. In this way, The Managed Behavioral Healthcare Library will provide resources to help readers meet each of the key challenges that are posed by the new behavioral healthcare landscape. This volume and others that are planned will help you improve your effectiveness at pricing, financing, and delivering high-quality, cost-effective care. Future volumes will provide straightforward solutions to the ethical challenges of managed behavioral healthcare, and offer advice about practice management and marketing during a period of industry consolidation.

You can look forward to still other books and reports about developing and managing a group practice, creating workplace-based behavioral healthcare programs, measuring outcomes, computerizing delivery systems, and still other documents that provide you with useful data to "benchmark" and compare your own organization or practice with others that face similar challenges.

Since the landscape of behavioral healthcare is in flux, professionals in this field need to be aware of the alternative future scenarios that might emerge, and develop the skill-sets for success within each one. For behavioral healthcare leaders, the vision to select the best options that are in accordance with shared values, and the skills to put these possibilities into practice will be critical. For this reason, the themes of vision, methods, action, and results will be incorporated in the volumes you read in The Managed Behavioral Healthcare Library.

VISION: In the context of the current debate and upheavals in healthcare, we have seen broad agreement regarding the importance of behavioral health security for all Americans, at an affordable price. The Managed Behavioral Healthcare Library will offer publications that show how universal coverage for affordable, appropriate, accessible, and effective mental health and addiction treatment benefits and services can be achieved.

METHODS: How can we operationalize the new paradigms, and the new models and systems of care that will be required to make the promise of managed care come true? New methods of benefit administration and health services delivery will be required to implement this vision within realistic financial limits.

At the broadest level, these methods include the core technologies used to manage benefits, to manage care, and to manage the health status of individuals and defined populations. At the level of front-line operations, these methods include continuous quality improvement, process re-engineering, outcomes management, public/private integration, computerization, and delivery system reconfiguration in the context of capitation financing. These are the skill-sets that The Managed Behavioral Healthcare Library will help you build through an ongoing series of pragmatic professional publications.

New methods of direct clinical care will also be required. Instead of treating episodes of illness, disease state management methods will allow clinicians in future managed and integrated behavioral healthcare systems to reduce morbidity and mortality for individuals and for groups. The Managed Behavioral Healthcare Library will also provide front-line clinicians and delivery system managers the skills that will enable our healthcare systems to truly provide scientifically validated bio-psycho-social treatment of choice in behavioral healthcare.

ACTION AND RESULTS: Knowing that we are in a period of change, and even having the desire to make the changes that are needed, makes little difference without actions based on methods that can produce results. Since you and the other readers of this library take action and produce results through day-in, day-out application of your professional expertise, The Managed Behavioral Healthcare Library will be action-oriented to provide the greatest possible benefit to you and your colleagues.

The book you are about to read, *The Complete Capitation Handbook*, lays the groundwork for the behavioral healthcare financing and delivery systems of the short- to intermediate-term future. This book was written by a generation of front-line leaders for whom capitated behavioral healthcare services are a way of life. The authors of this book belong to the Council of Behavioral Group Practices, a highly experienced and innovative consortium of single-specialty behavioral groups and mental health departments in multispecialty medical groups. Together, the members of this council serve approximately 15 million behavioral healthcare beneficiaries through capitated and other managed behavioral healthcare arrangements.

Thank you for selecting this book, and for taking advantage of The Managed Behavioral Healthcare Library.

Michael

Michael A. Freeman, M.D.
Series Editor, The Managed Behavioral Healthcare Library
President, Institute for Behavioral Healthcare
Editor-in-Chief, **Behavioral Healthcare *Tomorrow*** Journal

ACKNOWLEDGMENTS

A professional book of this nature is a labor of love, created by the many authors who contributed their time and expertise. I am most grateful to the associate authors, without whom this handbook would never have been possible.

I must also thank the Institute of Behavioral Healthcare (IBH) and CentraLink, whose enthusiastic encouragement and many resources were invaluable. Michael Freeman, M.D., IBH President, and Adam Richmond, Managing Editor of the **Behavioral Healthcare** *Tomorrow* Journal, lent unwavering support and energy in seeing this project through from proposal to published form.

Finally, hats off to Larry Beresford for his excellent editorial assistance, and to Allen Daniels, Ed.D., and Scott Ries, L.I.S.W., from the University of Cincinnati for graciously volunteering to edit specific chapters.

GLZ
Albuquerque, New Mexico
January, 1995

GRAPPLING WITH BEING AT RISK

1

NEARLY A CENTURY OF CAPITATION: HOW AND WHY

Gayle L. Zieman, Ph.D.

Capitation is not new. It predated World War I and was popular until the late 1940s, when it was overtaken by the newer indemnity insurance. Cost containment was not the central force behind early capitation agreements. Efficiency in providing comprehensive services to defined employee or community populations was the original goal, and insurers had almost nothing to do with its initial development. Instead, capitation was the brainchild of entrepreneurial doctors. History tells us that there is far more to capitation than reducing costs.

Capitation and managed care grew out of nascent prepaid health clinics serving employer groups. The prepaid concept was then strongly promoted during the 1970s by governmental attempts to broaden medical insurance coverage to a greater proportion of the population while avoiding a single-payor system. Since the 1970s, both capitation and managed care have also been encouraged by a host of economic and sociological forces.

NINE DECADES OF PREPAID HEALTHCARE

The concept of prepayment and the provision of a set package of medical services by a fixed provider group developed in the early 1900s as a means of delivering services to geographically remote populations. The early prepaid medical plans, called prepaid group practices (PGPs), served the industries of lumbering, mining, transportation, construction, and shipping (Mayer & Mayer, 1985; Shouldice & Shouldice, 1978).

In 1910 Drs. Thomas Curran and James Yokum, founders of the Western Clinic in Tacoma, WA, became the first medical professionals to provide healthcare under capitation. Curran and Yokum became pioneers in prepaid care when they agreed to provide all necessary medical care to a group of lumber mill employees for 50¢ per member per month. This was also the first employer carve-out. By 1911, another Tacoma physician, Dr. Bridge, had opened the Bridge Clinic to compete with the Western Clinic. Eventually Bridge established approximately 20 Bridge Clinics, which contracted for capitation in Washington and Oregon.

The Tacoma area also provided the first resistance to managed care, as the Pierce County Medical Society quickly organized to oppose the Western and Bridge Clinics and the concept of prepaid care.

In 1927 Dr. Michael Shadid of Elk City, OK, a small farming community, promoted a one-time capitation payment. Shadid sold shares in the construction of Community Hospital for $50 apiece. Each share entitled the holder to medical care at the hospital. The residents of Elk City enthusiastically supported the plan—but the county medical society did not. Shadid lost his membership in the society, and consequently in state and national medical societies as well. He was threatened with the suspension of his medical license, and it is reported (Shouldice & Shouldice, 1978) that for many years physicians seeking to work at Community Hospital had an unusually difficult time obtaining a license to practice in the state of Oklahoma.

Despite the opposition, Community Hospital grew and in 1934 the Farmers Union took over sponsorship of the program, renaming it Farmers Union Cooperative Association. Shadid brought an antitrust suit against the county and state medical societies. Twenty years later, Shadid and his associates settled out of court for $300,000 in a victory which established a legal precedent. Prior to Congressional sanctioning of prepayment through the

In early 1987 Gayle L. Zieman, Ph.D., and his partners at Mesa Mental Health in Albuquerque, NM, pondered how to transition from being expense-sharing solo practitioners to becoming an integrated group practice. They focused on how to develop a full-service, multidisciplinary mental health delivery system and concluded, "Why attempt to be on every insurer's provider list? We should be *the list!*" Shortly thereafter their fledgling network, comprised primarily of subcontracted providers, was selected by an HMO wishing to capitate all mental health services. The Mesa partners quickly perceived capitation as an exciting method to achieve clinical and financial control over service delivery. They were certain that the better mousetrap had just been discovered. They would have been emotionally deflated if they had known of capitation's involved history long before its rediscovery in the 1980s.

HMO (health maintenance organization) Act of 1973, all court actions contesting capitation were settled in favor of the prepaid plans.

In 1929 Drs. Donald Ross and H. Clifford Loos in Los Angeles, CA, established a standard fee-for-service clinic. However, they were soon approached by the Los Angeles Water and Power Department about a prepaid plan of healthcare for the department's employees. The plan was so successful that over the next two years other groups of municipal employees were added. Ross and Loos were also expelled from the Los Angeles County Medical Society for operating their prepaid clinic.

The Palo Alto Medical Clinic in Palo Alto, CA, was another early pioneer in managed care. (See Chapter 25.) Originally a partnership formed in 1930 between Drs. Thomas Williams and Russell Van Arsdale, the growing clinic became an integrated group practice functioning in direct contrast to the predominant solo practice model of the time. The Palo Alto Medical Clinic began capitation in 1947 when it entered into an agreement to provide complete medical care to the students of Stanford University on a prepaid basis. Soon there were other contracts with local groups for prepaid care. By 1970, approximately 16 percent of the patients treated by the Palo Alto Medical Clinic were under capitation.

The conflict over capitation soon escalated to a national forum. After a five-year study funded by several large corporations, the Committee on the Cost of Medical Care reported in 1932 that medical care, both preventive and therapeutic, should be furnished largely by organized groups of physicians, and the cost of medical care should be placed on a group prepayment basis—by insurance and/or taxation (Falkson, 1980). Shortly thereafter, the American Medical Association issued a statement strongly condemning prepaid healthcare. The controversy also provided a major impetus for the blossoming of indemnity medical insurance. Blue Cross of Texas became the first major indemnity insurer. Organized medicine accepted fee-for-service insurance as a lesser evil than prepaid care.

The beginnings of indemnity medical insurance, however, did not stop the growth of prepaid plans. In 1937 the Group Health Association (GHA) of Washington, DC, was started by the Home Owners Loan Corporation as a means of preventing mortgage defaults caused by large medical bills. After the District of Columbia Insurance Commissioner claimed authority over GHA and tried to close it down, a court battle ensued, with the resulting legal opinion that prepaid plans did not constitute medical insurance. The District of Columbia Medical Society attacked GHA—impeding physician recruitment, limiting hospital privileges, and threatening GHA physicians with expulsion from the society. GHA took the medical society to court. Four years later the U. S. Supreme Court decided in favor of GHA, and the medical society was then indicted by a grand jury for restraint of trade.

On the West Coast in the late 1930s, Dr. Sydney Garfield began medical practice at a construction site in the Southern California desert, where an aqueduct was being built to divert Colorado River water to Los Angeles. Garfield built a ten-bed hospital on skids, which was pulled along as construction progressed. However, he was frustrated that all seriously injured workers were required to be transferred to Los Angeles for care. After much effort, he convinced the project managers that he could treat all patients under a capitation arrangement funded through salary deductions.

Henry Kaiser, an industrialist with connections to the aqueduct project, was impressed with Garfield's program and asked for help in establishing a similar arrangement for workers constructing the Grand Coulee Dam in Washington State. After success at Grand Coulee, this capitation program, called the Permanente Health Plan, was expanded in 1942 to Kaiser's 90,000 ship-building employees in San Francisco, Oakland, and Portland. The end of World War II resulted in a sudden loss of ship-building employees to support the Permanente Health Plan. Threatened with ruin, the plan was opened to public enrollment. It was immediately successful.

During the 1940s and '50s several prepaid medical plans developed across the country. Encouraged by Mayor Fiorello La Guardia, the Health Insurance Plan of Greater New York began capitation in 1944 to serve municipal employees. Spurred on by a visit from Dr. Shadid of Elk City, OK, consumers in Seattle formed the Group Health Cooperative of Puget Sound in 1947. PGPs were also founded by the Teamsters Union in St. Louis (the Labor Health Institute plan); the United Mine Workers in Pennsylvania, Ohio, and West Virginia (called Miners Clinics); and the United Auto Workers in Detroit (the Community Health Association plan). In 1956 a role reversal occurred when the Group Health Mutual Insurance Company, a traditional indemnity insurer serving rural Minnesota and Wisconsin, added a prepaid clinic to its new corporate headquarters, thus launching Group Health Plan. By 1984 Group Health had become the largest HMO in the Minneapolis-St. Paul metropolitan area.

The independent practice association (IPA) model of prepaid care began in 1954 when the Medical Society of San Joaquin County, CA, established the Foundation for Medical Care, linking solo and small group practitioners into a network that provided prepaid care.

In 1967 another blue-ribbon panel, the National Advisory Commission on Health Manpower, intensely studied the existing PGPs and concluded that prepaid group healthcare was a superior means of delivering cost-effective care (Falkson, 1980). The committee recommended to President Johnson that group practices, especially prepaid group practices, should be encouraged. By the 1960s, however, indemnity insurance had grown in popularity such that it vastly overshadowed its prepaid predecessor. Medical providers and associations had succeeded in establishing strong negative connotations to prepaid group healthcare, especially with the label of socialized medicine. By 1970 there were only about 30 PGPs in 15 states, covering approximately 3 million lives.

THE LEGISLATIVE CATALYST

In Minneapolis during the late 1960s Dr. Paul Ellwood, the new executive director of the American Rehabilitation Foundation (the research arm of the Sister Kenney Institute), struggled with the paradox of competing incentives in healthcare. Ellwood observed that good medicine resulted in reduced hospital usage, an outcome contrary to the financial needs of the institute. He concluded that the existing fee-for-service system created perverse incentives in rewarding the provision of treatment but withdrawing financial rewards for the restoral of health. He concluded that the healthcare system needed to incorporate incentives for prevention and health restoration. He studied existing PGPs and concluded that they offered a better model for the alignment of incentives. While working on a healthcare financing proposal in 1969 he coined the term *health maintenance organization*.

Ellwood then sought support from key federal policymakers. He was fortunate to find the Nixon administration groping for a healthcare policy. There was strong public concern about rising healthcare costs and the functioning of the Medicare and Medicaid programs. President Nixon had been elected without a healthcare program in the Republican platform, and the creation of a healthcare proposal had been delayed by a six-month battle with the American Medical Association over approval for Nixon's appointee as Assistant Secretary for Health and Scientific Affairs within the Health, Education, and Welfare Department. Not only was the Nixon administration in need of a healthcare program, but it was also desperate to oppose a Democratic proposal calling for national health insurance.

The administration quickly latched onto the HMO concept. In February, 1971, President Nixon in his Health Message to Congress outlined a detailed proposal for active HMO development. The plan proposed to make HMOs an option available to 90 percent of the population through 1,700 HMOs.

Two years of political wrangling ensued. Finally, in December, 1973, President Nixon signed Public Law 93-222, the Health Maintenance Organization Act of 1973. The act established a plan for HMO development, but one that had been much weakened by two years of political debate and compromise. It provided for federal assistance to establish a number of demonstration projects, created loan programs to stimulate the emergence of HMOs, and prescribed a broad set of requirements for plans to become federally qualified and thus receive the government's seal of approval. The law also mandated a dual choice provision which required employers with 25 or more employees residing in the service area of an HMO to offer the HMO option along with standard fee-for-service plans, if so requested by an HMO. The HMO Act classified HMOs into three types based on the system of organizing providers: staff-model plans, group-model plans, and IPAs. The law required plans to offer up to 20 outpatient behavioral health services per year, but did not require benefits for inpatient psychiatric or addiction treatment, although most plans offered inpatient care. The original act was so restrictive, and the resistance from established medicine so fierce, that by 1977 only 183 plans were available nationally, covering less than 7 million Americans (Mayer & Mayer, 1985).

The HMO Act has been amended six times by Congress—in 1976, 1978, 1979, 1981, 1986, and 1988. In general, the modifications have reduced the many restrictions of the original act. The 1981 revision created a fourth plan category, the direct contract model, commonly known as the network model, thus permitting contracting with community-based medical groups.

Following the HMO Act, the 1974 Employment Retirement Income Security Act (ERISA) also stimulated the growth of prepaid plans. While ERISA was designed primarily to modify rules related to pension plans, it contained a provision exempting self-insured groups from state laws pertaining to health insurance benefits. This exemption inspired many large employers and organizations such as labor unions to underwrite their own health plans, often with a standard insurer (known as a third-party administrator) administering the plan.

Self-insured groups have often been able to substantially reduce premium costs since, under ERISA, a self-insured group can base premiums on the projected cost of services solely for its group. HMOs until recently were legally mandated to base rates on a community rating, the projected cost of services provided to all enrollees of the HMO. Invoking ERISA, a self-insured group or employer with a healthy work force can achieve savings while emphasizing preventive and wellness programs.

SOCIOLOGICAL EVOLUTION

In addition to the dramatic forces of legislation, a variety of sociological changes in recent years have advanced managed care and capitation.

The societal perception of prepaid group healthcare has changed dramatically from a disdainful view of such plans as socialized medicine during the 1950s through much of the 1970s. This change has taken many forms, and increasingly has promoted the acceptance of capitated care offered by integrated groups of clinicians.

As the pace and urbanization of American life have increased, individuals increasingly have expected from medicine the same service attributes demanded of other service industries: speed, efficiency, flexibility, and convenience. Solo practitioners and small group practices have been hard pressed to meet these demands. Integrated group practices, however, have been encouraged by prepayment arrangements and have offered the public many of these attributes, albeit with a loss in the individual relationship between patients and their personal physicians. Americans as a group have been willing to forego the more intimate relationship with a single family doctor in exchange for an office or clinic that meets the broad demands for convenience and efficiency.

Similarly, the simplicity of prepaid health coverage has caught on. Fixed co-payments, as opposed to the more complicated indemnity system of deductibles and responsibility for a percentage of fees, have been strongly endorsed by consumers. Having a defined and limited set of healthcare providers from which to choose has also become increasingly acceptable as the norm for how medicine works. Many Americans seem glad to be relieved of the task of having to pick a family doctor from among the overwhelming list of doctors in the telephone directory, and are willing to rely on their health plan to provide a limited panel of high-quality providers from which to choose.

Just as Americans have broadly endorsed replacing the five-and-dime store and the small neighborhood grocery with large discount stores and supermarkets, the healthcare clinic offering one-stop shopping has come of age. Identity by patients has shifted from strongest association with one's primary physician to identifying with a particular clinic or health plan. Quality is perceived as being ensured by the clinic, group practice, or health plan, not strictly by individual providers of care.

Americans have accepted what has been labeled *industrialized medicine.* Healthcare today is commonly expected to be provided by a network of linked providers offering a full continuum of services.

ECONOMIC FORCES

By the late 1980s, HMOs and preferred provider organizations (PPOs) had come into the spotlight as cost-saving methods for financing healthcare. While reducing costs was not the primary objective behind the development of PGPs, the economic efficiency of such plans catapulted them to the forefront. Managed care, especially HMOs and payment by capitation, are now touted as the economically viable vehicles for controlling costs and allowing coverage for all Americans.

When the HMO label was first conceived in 1969, healthcare costs accounted for approximately 6 percent of the gross national product. That figure swelled to well over 14 percent by early 1993 (Geisel, 1993). Between 1986 and 1993 healthcare insurance premiums rose at five times the rate of wage increases for nonsupervisory workers and at over three times the inflation rate (Major, 1994). Similarly, the average cost per employee for behavioral health and addiction treatment benefits almost doubled from 1987 to 1991: from $163 to $304 (Block, 1992).

In the battle to demonstrate cost control, HMOs and PPOs have done well. Compared to traditional indemnity plans, with and without utilization review procedures, HMOs and PPOs posted lower average premium increases for 1991 through 1993, with the projection that such plans will lead in restraining costs for the future (Major, 1994). Currently, economic forces are paramount in driving the movement toward healthcare delivery systems that are fully integrated and capable of working under prepayment.

Thus, the business of healthcare has returned to capitation.

QUALITY: THE FUTURE OF PREPAID CARE

Assuring quality has become central to American industry. Until recently healthcare remained outside of the quality movement, but no more. Total quality management, quality assurance, quality improvement, and continuous quality improvement are rapidly becoming mainstream in the practice of medicine, from the receptionist to the medical specialist. Employers, patients, and insurers now demand demonstrable evidence that quality is being maintained and that treatment will result in ongoing improvements. A diploma from a prestigious school and many returning patients are no longer acceptable measures of quality. Data, statistics, measured indicators, policies and procedures, standards of care, and clinical algorithms are now required. Today, demonstration of quality is challenging cost control as the primary task of healthcare. (See Chapter 10.)

The demand for measurable quality currently is a major force in advancing prepaid health financing and group practices. Fully integrated groups and networks of providers have enormous advantages in developing systematic procedures of clinical practice and in measuring performance. Accreditation standards for outpatient systems are now in place through the National Committee for Quality Assurance, with networks and insurers across the nation seeking accreditation much as hospitals now do through the Joint Commission on Accreditation of Healthcare Organizations.

The future will bring further reliance upon accountability and measured outcomes. Groups, networks, and systems which meet these requirements will be in demand. In the 1990s the quality movement may become as important in advancing group practice and capitation as legislative actions were in the 1970s.

REFERENCES

Block, L. (1992, June 8). Mental health expenses make employers anxious. *Business Insurance,* pp. 3, 6–9.

Falkson, J. L.(1980). *HMOs and the politics of health system reform.* Bowie, MD: Robert J. Brady.

Geisel, J. (1993, January 11). 94 health care outlays may hit $1 trillion. *U.S. Business Insurance,* p. 3.

Major, M. (1994, February). Managed care is credited for breaking the boom-bust cycle of premium costs. *Managed Healthcare,* pp. 44, 46–48.

Mayer, T., & Mayer, G. (1985). HMOs: Origins and development. *New England Journal of Medicine* 312(9): 590–594.

Shouldice, R., & Shouldice, K. (1978). *Medical group practice and health maintenance.* Washington: Information Resources Press.

2

BEHAVIORAL AT-RISK CONTRACTING IN A CHANGING HEALTHCARE ENVIRONMENT

Michael A. Freeman, M.D.

The financing of behavioral healthcare services is transitioning to capitation. This shift will require payors and providers to accommodate new ways of thinking, managing, and practicing. The challenges and dangers to be encountered in this transition are not yet fully known. However, it is certain that pursuing the journey with a sense of confidence, adventure, discovery, and creativity will enable at-risk contracting to foster innovations that result in improved quality and effectiveness for behavioral healthcare. This chapter explains the role of behavioral at-risk contracting during a transition period for healthcare benefits, financing, and delivery systems, with special attention to the overriding social goals and risks. It also discusses the change from managing benefits to managing care to managing health, and the new forms of care that will occur in the context of capitation. The characteristics of future, high-performance behavioral delivery systems that will succeed under capitation are explored and described.

Capitation or at-risk contracting has emerged as a key element of most state and national healthcare reform initiatives. This financing method is also central to market reform initiatives implemented by many employer health-purchasing cooperatives. However, providers, managed care organizations (MCOs), and beneficiaries of behavioral healthcare services express pointed concerns about capitation and at-risk contracting.

Providers worry about assuming risk, incurring financial losses, and being torn between pressures to control costs and obligations to provide high-quality patient care. MCOs are concerned that the quality of care might erode when quality management functions are transferred to the provider setting. Beneficiaries are concerned that the clinicians they depend on may have financial incentives to deny necessary and appropriate care.

CAPITATION AS A VEHICLE FOR IMPROVING BEHAVIORAL HEALTHCARE

These concerns reflect the apprehensions that result from uncertainty and change. Capitation and at-risk contracting introduce a significant paradigm shift into the financing and delivery of behavioral health services. While apprehension and concern may be appropriate, this paradigm shift may also produce positive results. For example, capitation can facilitate innovation and efficiency, reduce administrative waste and overhead, simplify operating systems, encourage preventive services, and support the integration of fragmented services into coordinated and organized systems of care.

An analogy from the field of urban planning makes the positive dimension of capitation contracting more concrete (Katz, 1994). Urban environments are often stressful, disorganized, confusing, unsafe, unappealing, difficult to use, and unresponsive to the needs of the people who live and work there. This urban fragmentation is a consequence of zoning rules that divide property into lots and create financial incentives for each property owner to maximize the value of his or her lot.

As a result of these incentives, property owners each build the biggest allowable structure, so that their lot can create the most revenue, with little regard for how their building affects the adjacent neighborhood, community, city, or region. Consequently, our urban environments are filled with buildings that extend to the lot line with no setback for vegetation. Houses are squeezed together, leaving little room for children to play. High-rises block out sunshine. Traffic corridors are frozen in gridlock, resulting in inadequate parking, pollution, and noise.

Lot-based zoning produces congested, fragmented, uncoordinated sprawls that work at the level of the individual lot but fail at the level of the

---

Michael A. Freeman, M.D., is the President of the Institute for Behavioral Healthcare, the national center of excellence for behavioral healthcare education and leadership development. He also serves as the Editor-in-Chief for the journal **Behavioral Healthcare Tomorrow**. Dr. Freeman is a practicing psychiatrist on the faculty of the Langley Porter Psychiatric Institute at the University of California Medical Center in San Francisco, CA. He has held a number of senior management positions in the managed behavioral healthcare industry, and serves as a managing technical advisor with Behavioral Health Alliance, where he provides technical expertise and support to purchasers, providers, and managers of behavioral health benefits and services.

region. Similarly, charge-based healthcare financing produced fragmented, uncoordinated, sprawling behavioral health and addiction treatment services that maximized revenue at the level of the provider unit but failed at the level of the system as a whole.

Health policy planners expect capitation and at-risk contracting to create a vehicle that will allow necessary and appropriate care to be provided in an integrated and accountable manner that optimizes the functioning of the system as a whole, even if it means suboptimizing the functioning of a specific service, facility, or subsystem (Torchia, 1994; Cronin & Milgate, 1993; Goldsmith, 1992; The Institute for Alternative Futures, 1992; McClure, 1993).

Our former healthcare system produced a cluttered sprawl of hospitals, clinics, and clinicians' offices. Patients with psychiatric or addictive problems did not know where to go and their clinical needs often were not met properly, because providers rendered inappropriate care in the wrong treatment settings in order to maximize reimbursement. Beds were often filled by patients who had been re-admitted soon after being discharged without follow-up care.

Capitated financing can accelerate the development of integrated delivery systems; coordinated, organized systems of care; systems that reach out and prevent mental illness from becoming acute; and systems with incentives to follow patients after they have been discharged. Such systems can produce satisfied patients and providers and healthier communities.

As we enter the "brave new world" of capitation and at-risk contracting, it is important to frame at-risk contracting in the context of a hopeful vision of a better behavioral healthcare future, and in an understanding of how it can allow us to accomplish objectives that were impossible in the past. These hopes, aspirations, paradigm shifts, and goals are built into theories, reforms, and programs at the state and national levels. It will be our responsibility to create safeguards against the potential adverse consequences of capitation as we use this method of financing to improve behavioral healthcare.

A Brief History of Alternative Care and Cost Management Strategies

During the 1980s and early 1990s, behavioral healthcare cost escalation became a crisis for self-insured employers (Foster Higgins, 1989; Fishman, 1990; "Escalating Mental Health Care Costs," 1990; "News Briefs," 1990; Rinaldo, 1990). As a result, three approaches to managing behavioral healthcare costs and services emerged. These three cost-containment strategies were: managing benefits, managing care, and managing health.

Managing Benefits.   The first generation of strategies to manage rapidly escalating costs revolved around management of benefits in a manner that bore very little correlation to the actual clinical needs of patients (Freeman, 1991). These "benefit design gimmicks" included familiar devices such as limits on outpatient and inpatient care, annual and lifetime dollar limits on coverage, exclusion of coverage for certain diagnoses and services, infinite manipulations of co-payments, deductibles, and out-of-pocket maximum payments, and various other financial incentives and penalties. Benefit design manipulations largely failed to control costs. Rather, they controlled short-term expenditures. However, cost shifting to the public sector and escalation of indirect morbidity and mortality costs have been undesirable consequences of this approach.

Understanding the difference between controlling expenditures and costs is critical for organizations that enter capitation contracts, because these contracts put delivery systems at risk for the health status and care needs of defined populations. The capitated care model is intended to shift behavioral healthcare systems from controlling expenditures to improving the health status of defined populations while controlling direct and indirect costs on a long-term basis.

Managing Care.   During the mid- to late-1980s the "carve-out" managed behavioral healthcare industry grew rapidly (Freeman, 1992). Specialized organizations began to learn how to manage care as an alternative to managing benefits. Self-insured employers became more willing to authorize unlimited or less limited benefit designs when they realized that the care could be managed for medical necessity and appropriateness, and delivered by qualified provider networks for a guaranteed fixed price.

By the mid-1990s, the success of managed care models presented new options for policymakers. Health planners desired to meet the behavioral healthcare needs of the 60 million Americans who lacked coverage for behavioral health and addiction treatment services, and national healthcare reform initiatives stressed affordable universal access as a goal (The White House Domestic Policy Council, 1993; National Advisory Mental Health Council, 1993; Harris & Bergman, 1988). Managed behavioral healthcare enjoyed measurable success at expanding and facilitating access, liberalizing coverage, increasing benefits, defining quality, measuring outcomes, increasing utilization (albeit in less costly settings), expanding or creating coordinated continuums of care delivery systems, and overcoming many of the barriers to excellence and affordability that had previously existed (Geraty, et al., 1994). To a large degree, private-sector managed care entities were able to build upon work initiated in Community Mental Health Centers and other public-sector entities (Feldman, 1994; Ray & Finley, 1994).

During the late 1980s and early 1990s specialized managed behavioral healthcare programs relied upon authorization of benefit expenditures for the provision of criteria-defined necessary and appropriate care, coupled with individual case management, structured provider networks, and network management methods. This care management paradigm focused on managing illness treatment services, and is now giving way to a new model that is focused on managing the health status of individuals and defined populations.

Managing Health.   Managed illness treatment services can only reduce expenditures to a certain extent. There is only a limited amount of "fat" to cut out of the system by improving efficiency and limiting unnecessary care. A basic level of psychiatric behavioral morbidity is genetically embedded in populations, and basic behavioral health service needs will not go away.

Planners of reformed healthcare systems realize that beyond managing care, our society can only achieve further cost reductions by keeping people healthy in the first place, and by empowering ill individuals to manage the course of their illness and function at their highest level (Fries, et al., 1993; McWhorter, 1993).

A primary goal of healthcare reform has been to establish universal coverage and access to assure the inclusion of the 60 million Americans who have been excluded from mental health and addiction treatment benefits. To include these 60 million people without increasing total direct expenditures, it is necessary for delivery systems to predict the onset and manage the course of mental and addictive illnesses in their covered groups so as to arrest all preventable utilization and prevent costly acute care crises.

Unlike medical and surgical care, most patients with mental or addictive disorders seek treatment in a moment of crisis. Managed behavioral care systems have developed crisis intervention protocols and ambulatory crisis centers in order to improve quality and reduce costs. In a post-managed care environment guided by principles of demand reduction, behavioral health system managers will improve quality and reduce costs by determining the root cause of crises, identifying at-risk individuals, predicting the onset of mental and addictive disorders, and managing the course of illness so that acute episodes of illness do not necessarily occur.

How to Manage Costs, Care, and Health Status

During the transition to full capitation and fully integrated delivery systems, behavioral healthcare professionals will be called upon to employ a variety of methods to manage costs, care, and the health status of individuals and defined populations. Mastering these disciplines will be critical to the success of the behavioral healthcare systems. A variety of methods for managing costs, care, and health status have been developed in different

Figure 2.1 Methods to Manage Care

Alternative Delivery Systems
Ambulatory Care Centers
At-Risk Contracting with Provider
  Groups
Automated Practice Guidelines
Brief Psychotherapy
Concurrent Review
Continuous Quality Improvement
Continuity of Care Planning
Contracted Provider Networks
Cost-effectiveness Research
Course-of-illness Care Management
  (not Episode-driven)
Credentialed Structured Network
Decredentialing Providers
Denial of Benefit Authorization
Discharge Planning
EAP-driven Managed Behavioral
  Health Plans
Expert Second Opinion
Grievance and Appeals Procedures
Home Care
Integrated Delivery Systems
Intensive Case Management
Interactive Data Management
Level of Care Criteria
Medical Necessity Criteria
Multidisciplinary Treatment Teams

Network Education and Training
Network Management
Network Reconfiguration
Outcomes Measurement and
  Management
Patient Satisfaction Surveys
Practice Pattern Analysis
Practice Standards and Guidelines
Prior Authorization of Admissions
Purchaser-Provider Coalitions/
  Product Specifications
Quality Assurance
Quality-based Network
  Management
Quality Management
Real-time Online Behavioral
  Information Systems
Specialized Mental Gatekeepers/
  Gateways to Care
Standardized Intake Evaluation
  and Assessment
Telephonic Concurrent Review
Telephonic Intake and Referral
Treatment Planning
Treatment Plan Authorization
Utilization Management
Utilization Review

Figure 2.2 Methods to Manage Health

Advice Nurses

Barrier-free Benefit Designs and Delivery Systems

Behavioral Health Consumer Education

Behavioral Health Prevention

Behavioral Health Promotion

Behavioral Medicine

CD-ROM Patient Education Systems

Claims Analysis to Identify High-Risk Groups

Computerized Therapeutic Learning Programs

Demand Reduction

Demographic/Epidemiological Risk Group Identification

Drug-free Workplace Programs

EAP Offset Programs

Educational Programs in the Workplace

Educational Programs for Health Plan Members

Employee Assistance Programs

Executive Assistance Programs

Family-Worklife Education Programs

Financial Incentives for Meeting Personal Health Management Goals

Impaired Professionals Programs

Individual Health Risk Assessment

In-Home Support Services

Interpersonal Skills/Support Groups

Habit Abatement Programs

Health Advisors/Individualized Consumer Education

Life Cycle-specific Flexible Behavioral Benefits

Medical Offset Programs

Newsletters and Print Communication

Outreach to High Utilizers

Parental Leave Programs

Payroll Stuffers for Employee Assistance/Education

Population-based Health Risk Screens

Post-traumatic Stress Debriefing Programs

Self-help Groups

Telephonic Warm Lines

Wellness Program

Workers' Compensation Stress Claim Prevention Programs

settings during the last three decades. These methods are listed in Figure 2.1 and are not elaborated upon in this chapter due to space considerations.

Figure 2.2 describes program options, drawn from current experience, for managing health by capitated behavioral healthcare systems. For example, these systems may use telephone-available advice nurses, barrier-free benefit designs, and accessible delivery systems so that psychiatric diseases and behavioral conditions can be *predicted* and managed, allowing beneficiaries to benefit from precare so as to prevent crises and acute episodes. Capitation will allow these systems to emphasize "behavioral health consumer education," prevention, promotion, behavioral medicine, and behavioral healthcare in primary care medical settings. Employee assistance programs (EAPs) may be transformed into member assistance programs, community assistance programs, and other services that help improve the health status of beneficiaries and prevent unnecessary utilization.

HOW HEALTHCARE REFORM CHANGES THE CONTEXT OF CAPITATION

Healthcare reform initiatives in regional markets and at the state and federal levels are creating the context in which capitation will emerge. The fundamental context-shaping initiatives include: (1) provisions that encourage the formation of *health-purchasing alliances;* (2) provisions that encourage *universal access to integrated public-private systems;* (3) provisions for the inclusion of *behavioral healthcare in primary care medicine;* and (4) provisions that encourage accountability according to agreed-upon *quality, outcomes, and performance standards.*

Health-purchasing alliances or cooperatives envisioned under *buy right* and *managed competition* market reform theories are emerging as a core context-changing feature of reforming healthcare markets (McClure, 1993; Wicks, et al., 1994; Starr, 1993). The California market is illustrative. Like markets in many other states, the California healthcare marketplace is reforming rapidly on its own, with some government coordination and policy development. Recent small-group reform initiatives in the California market have resulted in the formation of a voluntary Health Insurance Purchasing Cooperative (HIPC) that pools the purchasing power of individuals and members of small groups. This purchasing alliance has relationships with several credentialed health plans, and employees or other HIPC members may select any of the certified health plans under contract with the HIPC (Wicks, et al., 1994). Simultaneously, large groups have formed their own HIPCs, such as the Bay Area Business Group on Health (BBGH). Most HIPCs, including BBGH, require affiliated health plans to offer a standardized benefit package on an at-risk basis.

Plans that contract with a HIPC such as BBGH are forming comprehensive integrated delivery systems that are fully capable of providing care on an at-risk, capitated basis. This arrangement embodies many of the elements of managed competition, in which large purchasing organizations pool premium dollars and purchase from credentialed, coordinated, organized systems of care.

Purchasing alliances and informed volume-purchasing entities of different types represent a basic contextual feature of the healthcare system of the future. Details will differ from market to market and from state to state. While some states will experiment with single-payor models, and many environments will prohibit mandatory purchasing alliances, volume purchasing from certified plans is likely to become central to most reformed behavioral healthcare markets (Wicks, et al., 1994).

Public-private integration is a second contextual change that will have an impact upon capitated behavioral healthcare systems. Many states have implemented, or are implementing, public-private partnerships or Medicaid behavioral carve-out programs at this time. California, Massachusetts, Tennessee, and other leaders in this movement are experimenting with a variety of different Medicaid carve-out, or public-private integration models (Helf, 1994a; Helf & Leeds, 1994; Helf, 1994b).

Healthcare reform seeks to integrate public and private behavioral healthcare as a way to stop shifting costs between the private and public sectors, and as a means to create universal access. As a result, integrated delivery systems will find ways to fuse and integrate public and private financing and provider components. Integrated public-private systems will also be capitated systems. This means that behavioral providers and managers assuming responsibility for the totality of behavioral morbidity, mortality, and care needs of defined populations must develop the beneficiary services and systems that previously were excluded from coverage and services within systems for privately insured individuals (Frank, et al., 1994; Lehman, 1987).

The public sector historically has innovated and invented care management approaches for the severely mentally ill, and has often served as the undercapitalized "R&D laboratory" for private MCOs. As inclusion of the severely mentally ill changes the context for at-risk behavioral healthcare organizations, the challenge will be to effectively overlay new private-sector technologies and more streamlined, efficient organizations onto established intensive ambulatory care services. This melding may be very productive, yet it will require that risk be managed in effective, comprehensive, and long-term ways (Bartlett, 1993).

A third context-altering aspect of capitation will be pressure to include behavioral healthcare in primary care medical settings and comprehensive healthcare systems. Many private-sector behavioral healthcare organizations will shift their focus from "carve-out" to "carve-in" as large risk-bearing systems come to terms with the extensive utilization of primary care services by patients with behavioral health and addictive disorders (Regier, et al., 1993).

One final context-changing trend deserves comment: the increasing emphasis on the use of quality indicators, outcomes indicators, performance indicators, and "report cards" in many healthcare reform programs (MHSIP Ad-Hoc Advisory Group Task Force, 1994; Kenkel, 1994a; Kenkel, 1994b). A dramatic information technology revolution is creating the management and measurement tools required for integrated delivery systems to function effectively in capitated environments, where quality and outcomes must be measured. (See Chapter 10.)

Creating measurement-driven behavioral healthcare systems will require cultural, behavioral, and service delivery changes that will be stressful for the individuals involved in implementing these changes. Effective leadership and human resource management will be essential. Furthermore, massive capital investments will be required in order for healthcare systems to compete within this environment. Hospitals, clinics, delivery systems, and clinicians that do not have access to the required capital, and that continue to rely upon the technologies of the past, may become obsolete.

New diagnostic technologies, computerized patient records, electronic data interchange, "swipe" cards, decision-support systems using practice guidelines and protocols, and automated outcomes measurement systems are just a few of the innovations that will allow behavioral delivery systems to respond to quality measurement, outcomes measurement, and report-card mandates (Mandersheid & Henderson, 1994).

High-Performance Behavioral Delivery Systems

Behavioral healthcare systems that can flourish within capitation and at-risk contracts will need to have performance characteristics that allow them to simultaneously manage costs and provide quality services within a context of demand reduction and population health status improvement. Capitation and at-risk contracting are anticipated to accelerate the movement from the fragmented delivery systems that emerged within charge-based reimbursement programs, to the high performance or "virtual" delivery systems that will be required to manage population health status in a customer-focused manner. This evolution is demonstrated in Figure 2.3.

A full explanation of the performance characteristics of high-performance behavioral health systems is beyond the scope of this chapter. However, to illustrate the concept of performance enhancement, consider access as one performance indicator. In the fragmented behavioral service environment before managed care, few care systems provided structured intake, assessment, triage, treatment planning, and facilitation of service delivery in the appropriate treatment setting.

Managed care systems, which are coordinating and improving formerly fragmented services, offer facilitated access programs. They have solved many previous access problems by implementing sophisticated intake, assessment, and individual treatment planning. In managed care programs, facilitated access is followed by referral to an organized, coordinated

Figure 2.3   High-Performance Behavioral Health

	INDICATORS OF OBSOLETE DELIVERY SYSTEMS	INDICATORS OF IMPROVING DELIVERY SYSTEMS	INDICATORS OF HIGH-PERFORMANCE DELIVERY SYSTEMS
ACCESS	No intake and triage system, no treatment plans	Sophisticated intake and triage system with individualized treatment planning	Anticipation and management of illness averts the need for crisis intervention, intake, and triage
CARE	Practice pattern variation	Validated practice standards, guidelines, and protocols	Team ownership and continuous improvement of clinical processes
SERVICES	Fragmented, uncoordinated illness treatment services	Coordinated, vertically and horizontally integrated illness treatment systems	Organized behavioral health promotion and management systems that are backwards integrated into the workplace and the community
SYSTEMS	No continuum of care	Expenditure-effective continuum of care	Cost-effective continuum of health
OPERATIONS	Lack of process measurement, monitoring, and outcomes assessment	Process measurement, monitoring, and outcomes assessment in place	Continuous, data-driven process inprovement
TECHNOLOGY	Technology profit centers	Appropriate technology	Critical technology
COST	Cannot measure behavioral costs or expenditures	Can measure and manage behavioral expenditures but not costs	Can measure and manage both behavioral health expenditures and costs
KNOWLEDGE	Minimal learning and knowledge deployment	Rapid learning and knowledge deployment	Knowledge creation

continuum of care where service is delivered according to validated practice guidelines and where outcomes are measured (Marques, et al., 1994).

In the future, high-performance behavioral health systems will be called upon to anticipate and manage illness and avert the need for crisis intervention, intake, and triage. Moving from the acute care model to the "predict and manage" model provides access before crises arise and enhances overall system performance with regard to cost and outcomes.

Ultimately, in order to function in a capitated environment, behavioral health professionals will be obliged to work within *learning organizations* (Senge, 1990). These are organizations that are managed by people and teams that learn not only from what they read in the scientific journals and what they hear at conferences, but also from their own experience and the experience of their organization.

Using measurement to drive care management, studying the results of organizational performance, building upon current quality standards to improve, and developing knowledge that is very specific to a healthcare system's defined beneficiary pools will become core competencies of future high-performance, capitated behavioral healthcare organizations. High-performance behavioral systems will create their own knowledge in order to gain competitive advantage. This will contribute to customer retention, operating cost reductions, the creation of customer-defined excellence, and the differentiation of behavioral healthcare systems in the marketplace.

QUALITY LEADERSHIP WITHIN CAPITATION AND AT-RISK ARRANGEMENTS

This chapter concludes with a discussion of value and leadership. One danger of capitated contracting is that downward price pressure may cause behavioral healthcare to become a commodity. Provider oversupply coupled with downward price pressure can result in a free-fall of the price of behavioral health services, commodification, and decreased profitability. Behavioral healthcare organizations may face a choice between becoming clinically inadequate low-price leaders or providing value-added services, which may not be covered by third-party payors.

Behavioral health services historically have been based upon strong linkages between suppliers and consumers of care. The risk of disconnection that results from commodification is great. By creating value, adding value, and entering into what virtual corporations refer to as the "co-destiny relationship" between producers and consumers of care, these connections between customer and supplier can be preserved within capitated behavioral healthcare systems (Davidow & Malone, 1992). Systems that embark upon this pathway will become the high-quality value leaders of the future.

Value leaders must have a concrete model of value. Several models apply, depending upon the customer in question. For business customers and individual beneficiaries, value relates to increasing customer performance and decreasing customer cost (Porter, 1985). For purchasers and regulators, value may be a function of the relationship between quality and cost. For almost any customer, quality can be defined as conformance to requirements, keeping in mind that requirements are specified by the customer (Crosby, 1984). Within large integrated delivery systems, value will also be determined in terms of effectiveness as related to cost. Ultimately, under long-term capitation contracts value will be defined in terms of change in population health status as related to the cost of achieving this change.

A new model of the relationship between behavioral healthcare customers and suppliers is needed if we are to move from commodified low-cost to value-added delivery systems under capitation. The capitation contract is a relationship that unfolds over time. For this relationship to succeed, partnerships must be structured in ways that create alignment between purchaser, provider, and beneficiary for the benefit of all parties and the system as a whole.

The goal of these partnerships is to engage customers and suppliers—or payors, providers, and beneficiaries—in a co-destiny relationship in which all will prosper. Health-purchasing alliances, business coalitions, self-insured employers, and other payors will need to benefit. Managed care plans, health maintenance organizations (HMOs), and insurance programs must benefit as well. Integrated delivery systems need to benefit, and patients need to benefit, too. If mutual gain cannot be achieved, capitation contracting may fail to accomplish its social objectives.

The Healthcare Forum has identified six skills of leadership in healthcare that apply in this context (The Healthcare Forum, 1992). These skills include mastering change, systems thinking, shared vision, continuous quality improvement, redefining healthcare, and serving the public and the community.

1. *Mastering change* will become a core skill for leaders of behavioral healthcare organizations entering capitation-financed service arrangements. As this chapter has indicated, many of the premises that underlie previous strategic planning and operating methods do not fit within capitation and at-risk contracts. Virtually every aspect

of behavioral delivery systems will experience the impact of capitation. Consequently, leaders of these systems must be able to help their organizations view change as an opportunity to experiment with new options and alternatives, and to take calculated risks.

2. *Systems thinking* is a second critical leadership skill. Whereas fee-for-service financing encouraged providers to function on their own as small businesses, capitation will require providers to coalesce into organized systems of care. Consequently, leaders of capitated behavioral healthcare systems must be able to conceptualize and understand their organization as a whole. They must also be able to make difficult decisions that result in suboptimization of some operating units on behalf of optimizing the performance of the entire system.

3. *The ability to create and communicate a shared vision* is necessary for behavioral healthcare system leaders in order to facilitate the transformation of their organizations. Successful capitated delivery systems will rely upon the alignment of the system's professional staff around their shared vision. Creating this shared vision requires deep knowledge of customer needs and requirements, and participation of all stakeholders within the delivery system in the vision development process. In addition, system leaders that succeed in helping their organizations to develop a shared vision compatible with rendering capitated services must also be able to empower delivery system professionals to succeed at translating this vision into goals and objectives, and to succeed at implementing vision-driven programs and services.

4. *Continuous quality improvement* skills will also be mandatory throughout at-risk behavioral healthcare systems. Leadership commitment repeatedly has been found to be the critical success factor in helping organizations learn and implement quality improvement skills. Continuous quality improvement methods, tools, and programs provide the resources that capitated delivery systems can count upon to improve outcomes while reducing costs incrementally. Since leaders and the systems they lead will be accountable for costs and outcomes under capitation, the need for quality leadership will be great. (See Chapter 10.)

5. *Fundamentally redefining healthcare* will be essential for capitated behavioral organizations to succeed under capitation. Rather than simply managing benefits and managing care, successful risk-bearing organizations must be able to manage the health status of defined populations. Consequently, leaders of risk-bearing organizations must advocate for a definition of behavioral health services that

includes a focus on wellness, changing lifestyles, the holistic inter-
play of mind and body, and long-term disease state management.
Successful translation of this redefinition of the behavioral healthcare product into sales and marketing presentations and contract
negotiations will support the long-term viability of both risk-bearing
organizations and the defined populations that they serve.

6. *Serving the public and the community* is the final core competency for
transformational leaders in healthcare. Healthcare is an essential
activity of any civilized society. Capitation and at-risk contracting,
within the broader context of healthcare reform, are merely the
next evolution of our ongoing endeavor to empower the behavioral
healthcare enterprise to fulfill its mission in society.

As behavioral healthcare professionals embark upon the transition to
capitation, it is common to experience both a sense of fear and a sense of
excitement. The excitement of capitated, integrated, health-promoting behavioral healthcare can be offset by concerns about the ethical abuses and
rationing of services that capitation may foster. Exactly what new dangers
and challenges will be encountered on the journey are unknown. However,
it is certain that beginning this journey with a spirit of confidence, adventure, discovery, and creativity will aid in using the vehicle of capitation and
at-risk contracting to improve the quality and effectiveness of behavioral
healthcare.

REFERENCES

Bartlett, J. (1993). Behavioral healthcare tomorrow—Evolution or revolution?
Behavioral Healthcare Tomorrow 2(1): 30–34.

Cronin, C., & Milgate, K. (Eds.). (1993). *A vision of the future health care delivery system:
Organized systems of care.* Report prepared by the Washington Business Group on
Health, Washington, DC.

Crosby, P. (1984). *Quality without tears.* New York: McGraw-Hill.

Davidow, W., & Malone, M. (1992). *The virtual corporation.* New York: HarperCollins;
pp. 160–161.

Escalating mental health care costs a major threat to business bottom line. (1990,
August). *The Psychiatric Times*, p. 70.

Feldman, S. (1994). Managed mental health—Community mental health revisited?
Managed Care Quarterly 2(2): 13–18.

Fishman, H. (1990, August). Major psychiatric cases are 'catastrophic' for employers. *The Psychiatric Times*, pp. 15–17.

Foster Higgins. (1989). Report 5: Mental health and substance abuse benefits. *Foster Higgins Health Care Benefits Survey.*

Frank, R., McGuire, T., Regier, D., Mandersheid, R., & Woodward, A. (1994). Paying for mental health and substance abuse care. *Health Affairs* Spring(I): 337–341.

Freeman, M. (1991). Design gimmicks won't solve behavioral health care cost crisis. *Employee Benefit News* 5(8): 4–5.

Freeman, M. (1992). Perspectives on the future of network-based managed behavioral health care systems. *The Journal of the American Association of Preferred Provider Organizations* 2(2).

Fries, J., Koop, C. E., Beadle, C., Cooper, P., et al. (1993). Reducing health care costs by reducing the need and demand for medical services. *New England Journal of Medicine* 329: 321–325.

Geraty, R., Bartlett, J., Hill, E., Lee, F., Shusterman, A., & Waxman, A. (1994). The impact of managed behavioral healthcare on the costs of psychiatric and chemical dependency treatment. **Behavioral Healthcare Tomorrow** 3(2): 18–30.

Goldsmith, J. (1992, May/June). The reshaping of healthcare. *Healthcare Forum Journal*, pp. 19–27.

Harris, M., & Bergman, H. (1988). Capitation financing for the chronic mentally ill: A case management approach. *Hospital and Community Psychiatry* 39(1): 68–72.

The Healthcare Forum. (1992). *Bridging the leadership gap.* San Francisco: Author.

Helf, C. (1994a). Reform update: The states. **Behavioral Healthcare Tomorrow** 3(2): 72–75.

Helf, C., and Leeds, H. (1994). Reform update: The states—Data collection and practice parameters: Crucial reform components. **Behavioral Healthcare Tomorrow** 3(3): 72–74.

Helf, C. (1994b). Reform update: The states—Tenncare: Mental health advocates move to solidify benefits. **Behavioral Healthcare Tomorrow** 3(4): 61–64.

The Institute for Alternative Futures. (1992). *Healthy people in a healthy world: The Belmont vision for health care in America.* Alexandria, VA: Author.

Katz, P. (Ed.). (1994). *The new urbanism: Toward an architecture of community.* New York: McGraw-Hill.

Kenkel, P. (1994a, January 10) Health plans face pressure to find 'report card' criteria that will make the grade. *Modern Healthcare*, pp. 41–42.

Kenkel, P. (1994b, April 11) New England HMOs, employers proceed with 'report card.' *Modern Healthcare*, p. 18.

Lehman, A. (1987). Capitation payment and mental health care: A review of the opportunities and risks. *Hospital and Community Psychiatry* 38(1): 31–38.

Mandersheid, R., & Henderson, M. (1994). The new informatics of national healthcare reform. **Behavioral Healthcare Tomorrow** 3(1): 11–15.

Marques, C., et al. (1994). Quality and access in the managed behavioral healthcare industry. **Behavioral Healthcare Tomorrow** 3(5): 22–29.

McClure, W. (1993, May 3). *The national buy right strategy: A quality-based consumer choice plan for universal health care and coverage.* Report prepared by the Center for Policy Studies (revised).

McWhorter, C. (1993, May 3). Reform requires government assistance, not intervention. *Modern Healthcare,* p. 23.

MHSIP Ad-Hoc Advisory Group Task Force. (1994). *Mental health component of a health plan report card under national health care reform.* Washington: Author.

National Advisory Mental Health Council. (1993). Health care reform for Americans with severe mental illnesses: Report of the National Advisory Mental Health Council. *American Journal of Psychiatry* 150(10): 1445–1465.

News Briefs. (1990, May). *Business & Health,* p. 12.

Porter, M. (1985). *Competitive advantage.* New York: The Free Press.

Ray, C., & Finley, J. (1994). Did CMHCs fail or succeed? Analysis of the expectations and outcomes of the community mental health movement. *Administration and Policy in Mental Health* 21(4): 283–293.

Regier, D., Narrow, W., Rae, D., Mandersheid, R., Locke, B., & Goodwin, F. (1993). The de facto U.S. mental and addictive disorders service system. *Archives of General Psychiatry* 50: 85–94.

Rinaldo, D. (1990). "Utilization and cost patterns of the 1980s: Strategic implications for the 1990s." Report presented at the AMCRA meeting.

Senge, P. (1990). *The fifth discipline.* New York: Doubleday.

Starr, B. (1993, mid-September) Employers give managed competition a new spin. *Business & Health,* pp. 42–48.

Torchia, M. (1994, February). How Twin Cities employers are reshaping health care. *Business & Health,* pp. 30–36.

The White House Domestic Policy Council. (1993). *The President's Health Security Plan.* New York: Times Books.

Wicks, E., Curtis, R., & Haugh, K. (Eds.). (1994). *Designing health purchasing alliances/cooperatives—Federal policy issues and options.* Report prepared by the Institute for Health Policy Solutions and The Henry J. Kaiser Family Foundation.

3

GRASPING CAPITATION

Martin D. Dubin, Psy.D.

Healthcare can be thought of as a three-legged stool, with access, cost, and quality comprising the three legs upon which the system depends. In recent years the cost leg grew so far out of control that an adjustment was required. Healthcare capitation has become the tool to even out costs, making them more stable and predictable. This chapter explains capitation as a paradigm shift in the financing of behavioral healthcare, and its effects on providers and the provision of care. The factors to consider in assessing clinical and financial risk under capitation are also discussed.

The upward spiral of healthcare costs in the 1980s brought about the awareness that the usual economic laws of supply and demand did not universally apply to the fee-for-service medical system. Initial efforts to manage costs through utilization limits and price controls frequently were circumvented by providers. Capitation as a means of shifting cost and risk to the service provider has re-emerged (see Chapter 1), forever changing the underlying economics of the healthcare delivery system. No longer can provider and patient demands drive up the utilization of services without constraint.

What Is Capitation?

Capitation is best defined as the paid assumption of risk by a provider for delivery of a defined set of services to a designated population over a specified time period, with the payment calculated on a per-person basis (Cerne, 1994). Through capitation of behavioral healthcare, the entire cost for all services is contained to an established amount. Cost control and predictability are achieved. Capitation is intended to bring the payor and provider to the same side of the table, working together to achieve sound global budgets.

How Does Capitation Work?

In the fee-for-service system, the risk of paying for healthcare was borne by the insurance company and then shifted to the employer in the form of premium rates. The actual buyer and seller of services (the patient and doctor) bore none of the financial risk that they created. The payment was made by a third party, whose removal from the actual service transaction provided little opportunity for cost-effective purchasing. Under capitation, the entire risk is shifted to the healthcare provider, whose role has thus changed to include both the provision of quality care and the management of that care in a cost-effective manner. (See Figure 3.1.)

As risk is shifted in a capitated system, so are incentives. In the fee-for-service system, increased utilization was rewarding for providers. The more procedures were performed, the more financial compensation was received. The fee-for-service system had no natural incentive for providers to hold down the cost or utilization of services. A capitation arrangement, by contrast, incentivizes the maximization of value—the best quality for the lowest price. Maximizing value becomes the provider's overriding mission.

Figure 3.1 Value

$$Value = \frac{Quality}{Cost}$$

Martin Dubin, Psy.D., is the Chief Executive Officer of Psychological Resource Organization (PRO), a managed behavioral healthcare company headquartered in Denver, CO. PRO has a combination staff and network model clinical delivery system and has been providing full-risk capitation for over 10 years. Dr. Dubin is a licensed clinical psychologist who prior to his position with PRO had a full-time private practice and held undergraduate and graduate academic appointments.

That this represents a significant paradigm shift for healthcare providers cannot be overstated. For example, under capitation psychiatric hospitals are no longer in the traditional hospital business. Instead they are primarily in the business of rapidly stabilizing and treating patients so that they can be safely and effectively transferred to less costly treatment settings.

What Risk Is Being Assumed?

Providers, once accustomed to sitting at the head of the healthcare table, have recently found themselves anxiously looking for a seat anywhere. Unfortunately, this anxiety can lead providers to imprudently accept capitation without fully understanding or assessing the risks involved (Cerne, 1994; Mechanic & Aiken, 1989).

With capitation, a provider assumes behavioral healthcare responsibility—clinical and financial—for a specific population. A population is defined as the group of individuals covered by a particular healthcare payor, and might be further defined by a fixed geographic area, a particular employer's work force, a specific benefit plan, or any combination of these.

In behavioral healthcare, the contracted capitation rate is calculated by the estimate of annual clinical and management costs, plus a profit margin, divided by the number of lives in the population. (See Figure 3.2.) Translated to a monthly rate, known as the per member per month rate, this is the amount that the provider is paid in advance each month to provide all covered and necessary treatment and management services required by the population. (See Chapter 11 for a detailed discussion of capitation finances.)

The capitating provider and the contracting payor must be absolutely clear as to what services are included and what services are excluded. Does

Figure 3.2 Annual Capitation Costs

$$\frac{(\text{Administrative Costs} + \text{Clinical Delivery Costs} + \text{Profit Margin})}{\text{\# of Covered Lives}} = \frac{\text{Per}}{\text{Covered Life Rate}}$$

$$\frac{\text{Per Covered Life Rate}}{12 \text{ Months}} = \frac{\text{Per Member Per Month}}{\text{(PMPM) Rate}}$$

the capitated amount cover inpatient care and partial hospital care? What specific services are considered outpatient services? What about addiction detoxification? Physician and anesthesiologist charges for electro-convulsive therapy? Comorbid medical and psychiatric conditions?

The industry standard for such arrangements is a one-year or multiple-year contract between the provider group and the payor, usually an insurer or a large, self-insured employer. The contract is specific with regard to the services covered, the expectations of both parties, and how the transition of behavioral services for patients will occur at the beginning and the end of the contract term. Capitation contracts must be negotiated carefully with attention to the service, quality, management, and legal aspects of the agreement. (See Chapters 13 and 14 for a further discussion of the contracting process.)

How Can Risk Be Assessed?

Behavioral healthcare providers wishing to assume risk through capitation must be able to evaluate the risks, financial and otherwise, being assumed. It is most important to consider what defines and affects the risks of a particular contract or population. Realistic pricing and ongoing financial predictability are crucial to successful capitation.

The cost of providing professional treatment services, either through contracted rates per service or per treatment episode with clinicians or through clinical staff payroll costs, is central to assessing risk. The extent to which the capitating provider group has the ability to negotiate and fix the rates for professional services greatly affects the assessment of risk.

The utilization of inpatient, outpatient, and consultation services by the population is the single largest variable in determining risk. Past utilization histories for the population and accurate predictions of future utilization are used to assess risk and to plan utilization strategies for managing the population during the contract. Professional service utilization must be under predictable control if providers are to reliably estimate costs and risks (Smith & Loftus-Rueckheim, 1993).

Insurance underwriters have a long history of using sophisticated algorithms for estimating utilization based on population demographics. In behavioral healthcare, there are considerable epidemiological data on the incidence and prevalence of most major psychiatric and addiction disorders. This knowledge should be used in any assessment of risk. Historical utilization by members of the defined population to be capitated—including the chronically mentally ill, blue-collar workers, white-collar employees, employees' dependents, and individuals from different demographic groups—must also be reviewed. Historical utilization patterns for the population are most often available from the contracting insurer. National data are also published by the Group Health Association of America. (See Appendix B.) Variability in utilization based upon geography and local community standards of practice must be taken into account, too.

The sheer size of the population to be managed is important in being able to predict risk. The effects of adverse selection and outlier cases such as severely mentally ill patients or chronic users of services tend to be minimized in large populations. A few costly cases in a population of 10,000 can be disastrous, whereas a population of 100,000 is large enough to absorb their cost impact.

Additionally, the capitating provider group must assess its own ability to manage utilization on an ongoing basis. The degree to which a distinct system will be in place to assess patients' needs for care and the match between those needs and what the benefit covers is important in predicting and controlling risk. Once the care need and benefit issues have been assessed, systematically directing patients to the most appropriate level of care and following up to ensure efficient, quality treatment within the limits of the benefit structure are essential to predict risk and ensure success with capitation. (See Chapter 17 for more information on utilization management.)

The type of healthcare plan the population had in the past and will have under the capitated arrangement is very important. Whether the health plan is a health maintenance organization (HMO), point-of-service plan (POS), preferred provider organization (PPO), or managed indemnity plan will greatly affect past, present, and future utilization—and consequently cost. HMO plans most directly control utilization and have utilization patterns that are more predictable than POS, PPO, or managed indemnity plans.

The healthcare benefit design within any particular insurance plan also has a very significant effect upon the risks assumed. Benefit structures have the ability to alter the pattern of utilization as patients evaluate their out-of-pocket costs in their decision to seek and/or maintain healthcare services. Benefit design limitations and exclusions must be weighed carefully in a sophisticated risk assessment. Benefit designs with high co-payments and deductibles typically retard utilization in the short run. However, if they prevent patients from seeking services early, costs may actually increase as more intensive (and costly) services are required later.

How Can the Risk Be Contained?

Providers can reduce their exposure to risk by effective management and through contractual methods of risk containment. The first line of defense is to carefully construct the capitation contract so that all expectations, responsibilities, and services to be provided are clearly defined and lead to a predictable service delivery system.

To directly control risk, provider groups can seek contractual agreements with payors that set an upper limit on the amount of risk for which the provider is liable. These limits can be set on a cost-per-patient basis or may depend on annual factors of population cost or utilization. Such arrangements are frequently referred to as stop-loss, risk band, or risk corridor clauses. (See Appendix A for exact definitions.) When providers cannot obtain a stop-loss type agreement, they may desire to purchase re-insurance for the risk to be incurred in the capitation contract. Re-insurance is coverage specifically designed to insure against excessive financial loss in an at-risk contract. Provider groups and insurers may also establish performance targets in which the provider is positively and negatively incentivized in accordance with some previously agreed-upon measures of quality, access, or utilization.

As previously mentioned, providers must remember that built-in benefit design exclusions and limitations greatly reduce the provider's potential financial exposure—the provider is contractually restricted from paying for utilization that falls beyond the scope of the health plan benefits. The single most effective control over financial exposure and risk, however, is the sound and systematic management of utilization and clinical treatment by the provider group. There is no substitute for good management. The best precontract assessments of risk and contractual provisions are useless without active and dedicated management.

The details of risk assessment and management are discussed in the next chapter, where specific types of risk and methods for handling them are presented.

What Are the Advantages and Disadvantages of Capitation?

Capitation presents an opportunity for providers to take control over many aspects of behavioral healthcare. Under capitation providers are the primary determinants of level of care, need for services, type of service offered, and how treatments are provided. Along with the autonomy afforded providers, innovation and prevention are rewarded in a capitated system.

Prevention programs, which have always been an unrealized hope in behavioral healthcare, are truly incentivized. Since the providers fare better financially if services are not sought, preventing the need for services in the first place is desired. Pragmatically speaking, prevention programs initially will have to focus on problems that can be averted in the short term. However, longer term prevention programs may become a reality as capitation becomes widespread and routine.

Capitated systems can also provide wonderful opportunities for improving outcomes and reducing costs through collaboration between behavioral healthcare and traditional medicine. There are many problems in behavioral medicine, such as medical compliance, where the incentive provided by capitation for prevention can encourage collaboration. Re-integrating mental healthcare with general medicine can be a relatively quick outcome from capitation.

A disadvantage of capitation is the fact that providers are financially rewarded for delivering fewer services. This presents the potential for utilization to be dangerously reduced to levels that impair health status. It can be argued that under the fee-for-service system the provider and the patient were aligned with respect to quality and the provision of adequate levels of treatment services. However, neither the provider nor the patient had any incentive to work with the payor for efficiency or reasonable costs. Under capitation it can be argued that the payor and provider are aligned on costs, while the patient and provider remain aligned for quality. It is important that the payor is also incentivized for quality through the desire to protect member enrollment. Otherwise, the provider must constantly balance the competing demands of the ethical treatment contract with the patient and the financial contract with the payor.

This disadvantage of capitation, however, can be adequately controlled to protect patients by the emergence of specific professional performance standards and treatment protocols along with regulation, accreditation, and monitoring of quality measures.

Capitation continues to grow in prevalence and acceptance in behavioral healthcare. It is a healthcare system that provides rewards for prevention and returns predictability in cost to an area of healthcare that has often been viewed as a "black hole" into which patients and resources disappeared. Capitated behavioral healthcare systems, however, still must prove their value and predictability in terms of quality and access to care.

REFERENCES

Cerne, F. (1994). Shaping up for capitation. *Hospitals & Health Networks* 3(2): 28–30.

Mechanic, D., & Aiken, L. (Eds.) (1989). *New directions in mental health services* (No. 43). San Francisco: Jossey-Bass.

Smith, M. E., & Loftus-Rueckheim, P. (1993). Service utilization patterns as determinants of capitation rates. *Hospital and Community Psychiatry* 44(1): 49–53.

4

ELEVEN TYPES OF RISK
AND THEIR ANTIDOTES

Michael A. Freeman, M.D.

Beta risk, demand risk, infrastructure risk, and morbidity risk—these are some of the forms of exposure or liability that accompany capitation. This chapter describes 11 direct and indirect risks which providers will encounter in at-risk contracting. Methods to anticipate and manage each form of risk are discussed. These are the risks and risk management methods which any behavioral group, hospital, or integrated delivery system must consider and embrace in planning for or implementing an at-risk arrangement.

Providers who practice in capitated behavioral delivery systems must understand both the direct and indirect risks that they face, and how to use effective risk management methods to respond to them. Scott Fruchter, a behavioral delivery system consultant, identifies 11 types of direct and indirect risks to be considered by providers in capitated behavioral healthcare organizations. The following sections expand upon each of these risk categories and include suggestions on how each type of risk can be effectively anticipated and managed.

DIRECT RISKS OF CAPITATION CONTRACTS

Capitation creates both direct and indirect risks. Five types of direct risk are morbidity risk, demand risk, utilization risk, beta risk, and price risk.

1. *Morbidity Risk* is the true need for services due to the morbidity load, or the amount of illness, that exists in a defined population. Some morbidity risk is a result of genetically transmitted diseases such as bipolar affective disorder or panic disorder, while other morbidity risk is attributable to traumatic events, such as hurricanes and earthquakes, that may result in widespread post-traumatic stress disorder.

Managing morbidity risk requires professionals in the capitated organization who are skilled in the area of psychiatric epidemiology. Providers must be able to characterize, measure, and manage the actual behavioral health status and morbidity of the defined populations for which they are at risk. Epidemiological population health status assessment surveys provide the data that allow these clinicians to identify high-risk subgroups, to develop population-based health status improvement measures, and to establish services that can manage disease states throughout the course of illness—rather than providing episode-based acute care.

2. *Demand Risk* means that beneficiaries may want more treatment than they actually require—or perhaps less. Refusing requests for unnecessary and inappropriate care will challenge capitated clinicians who must also sustain the loyalty and satisfaction of both beneficiaries, who may desire excessive care, and payors, who seek cost-effective services. Beneficiaries covered by at-risk arrangements may also fail to seek necessary and appropriate care for a variety of reasons. These individuals may deteriorate clinically and require expensive, intensive care later. In both instances the goal of at-risk clinicians is to create alignment between need and demand, a goal that has been notoriously difficult to accomplish under fee-for-service financing systems.

There are many ways to mitigate demand risk. Providers in at-risk organizations can educate members about service availability and appropriate utilization, and they can implement wellness, behavioral health promotion, and self-care or disease-state management programs. At-risk providers may also provide referrals to community resources to help beneficiaries satisfy their demands

---

Michael A. Freeman, M.D., is the President of the Institute for Behavioral Healthcare, the national center of excellence for behavioral healthcare education and leadership development. He also serves as the Editor-in-Chief for the journal **Behavioral Healthcare** *Tomorrow*. Dr. Freeman is a practicing psychiatrist on the faculty of the Langley Porter Psychiatric Institute at the University of California Medical Center in San Francisco. He has held a number of senior management positions in the managed behavioral healthcare industry, and serves as a managing technical advisor with Behavioral Health Alliance, where he provides technical expertise and support to purchasers, providers, and managers of behavioral health benefits and services.

without burdening delivery systems. Special outreach programs can engage members who need care but are not receiving it while still at an early stage of illness that can respond to preventive interventions.

3. *Utilization Risk* is another direct risk for capitated delivery systems. Clinicians in a capitated system may be inclined to overprescribe or overuse services. Lack of agreement about treatment planning, differences in orientation and training between clinicians, and the lack of clinical process controls contribute to utilization risk.

Utilization risk can be mitigated by the use of clinical practice guidelines and protocols. Such guidelines and protocols should be part of an organization's broader continuous quality improvement program, designed to reduce practice pattern variation and improve clinical outcomes through adherence to critical paths for care delivery. Managed care techniques such as credentialing of providers, criteria-driven case management, and provider education programs can also help reduce utilization risk.

4. *Beta Risk* refers to the inevitability of catastrophic cases. Clinicians who operate within a tight budget may find that just one or two catastrophic cases can devastate an annual health services budget, and in some cases an entire organization. This is particularly true when the overall risk pool is small.

Special contractual provisions can help protect against beta risk by arranging for additional compensation when catastrophic events are not a result of negligence. Other contractual provisions may identify risk corridors, in which the payor will share the risk and also the savings beyond certain specified margins. Re-insurance provides another safeguard. This is a special insurance policy that pays the at-risk entity when costs exceed previously specified levels or when specified catastrophic events occur. Participation in larger risk pools and risk-sharing with other organizations can also safeguard against beta risk, since the risk of catastrophic events is offset by the funds allocated for a larger covered population.

5. *Price Risk* is the difference between the price that is determined by a capitation contract (the *cap rate*) and the actual cost incurred to provide the contracted services. Clearly, clinicians and organizations that cannot measure their costs of doing business are more vulnerable to price risk and underpricing.

The most important way to safeguard against price risk is to measure and understand operating costs so that realistic prices can be set. (See Chapter 11.) Operating systems may need to be refined in order to improve both efficiency and clinical quality.

INDIRECT RISKS OF CAPITATION CONTRACTS

Six types of indirect risks may impact upon financial performance within capitation contracts. These include regulatory risk, insurance risk, liability risk, contract risk, infrastructure risk, and professional risk.

1. *Regulatory Risk* refers to the risk attributable to current and future regulations that may have an impact upon the provision of behavioral health services. The fluid nature of healthcare reform initiatives makes it difficult to determine how the regulatory environment for behavioral healthcare will change. Current and future regulations related to government supervision, reporting, severity risk adjustment methods, mandatory or excluded coverage and services, and other factors may have a significant impact on all clinicians and entities in the behavioral healthcare industry.

   To mitigate regulatory risk, it will be important to understand the regulatory environment, comply with regulations, avoid audits, and exert influence on the regulatory process. Behavioral healthcare professionals can help to stabilize the regulatory environment by being politically active and proactive.

2. *Insurance Risk* refers to new and additional kinds of insurance that will be required to protect clinicians against new forms of liability that may result from capitated arrangements. For example, clinicians and risk-bearing organizations may be required to purchase officers' and directors' insurance, re-insurance for cost overruns, and perhaps different types of malpractice coverage. Ultimately, the cost of necessary insurance coverage plus related risk management activities must be factored into the cost of capitated business arrangements.

3. *Liability Risk* refers to time loss and work disruptions that occur because of the increased likelihood of a lawsuit as a result of capitated contracts. Since behavioral healthcare providers will be liable for adverse outcomes under at-risk contracts, extensive efforts will be necessary to maintain patient and customer satisfaction and prevent catastrophic events.

   To mitigate liability risk, it is important to develop efficient clinical practices that minimize the potential for adverse outcomes, dissatisfied customers, and litigation. These practices will include regular and positive communication with beneficiaries as well as other customers. Clinical programs should be based upon validated practice guidelines that are improved by outcomes measurements, collected on an ongoing basis, and linked to clinical quality improvement programs.

4. *Contract Risk* is the risk associated with contract provisions that impact on an organization's ability to do business. These provisions may include restrictions such as noncompetition agreements, payor cancellation provisions, retrospective rate adjustments, reporting requirements, and provisions for the timing of reimbursement payments.

Two approaches may be pursued to offset contract risk. First, special contractual provisions must be carefully constructed so as to improve, rather than impair, the operating effectiveness of the clinicians in risk-bearing organizations. (See Chapter 13.) Second, contracts should be constructed to create a financial reward for both parties to the extent that contract risk is reduced. For example, provisions related to reporting requirements can be based on a basic fee for an agreed-upon set of basic reports, with additional charges for additional reports. The additional charges should be high enough to create a disincentive for such requests, while still leaving the option open.

5. *Infrastructure Risk* refers to the cost of infrastructure that must be created in order to implement the capitation contract. Some of these costs will be "learning curve" costs because clinicians must change their clinical practices and facilities must change their operating methods in order to succeed under capitation. Other infrastructure costs will be related to new information systems, new facility requirements, and staff changes resulting from the shift to a capitated environment.

There are very few methods to offset risk of this nature. Managed behavioral health plans and behavioral healthcare delivery systems will need to be retro-fitted, retooled and re-engineered in order to function effectively in the new era of capitation contracting. The best that can be done is to accept the inevitability of change, benchmark from industry leaders, implement best practices, reduce the cycle time for implementing new operations, and allocate investment capital judiciously.

6. *Professional Risk* means the risk that a capitation contract may cause individuals or organizations to violate professional ethics or engage in other activities that damage their professional reputations. The ethical challenges of capitation and at-risk contracting are substantial. (See Chapter 18.)

Capitation contracts may create incentives for providers to not spend money, rather than to spend money wisely or appropriately. As a result, there is a very real risk that mediocre, low-priced delivery systems will compete for and capture market share by driving down capitation prices or rates for strategic reasons, at the expense of quality of life and clinical needs of beneficiaries. Therefore, it is critical that we anticipate potential ethical abuses and rededicate ourselves to the ethical standards of healthcare and behavioral healthcare at this time.

All behavioral healthcare professionals are vulnerable to professional risk. Unethical conduct will damage the industry as a whole and the beneficiaries who depend upon us. Consequently, explicit safeguards are required. All stakeholders must cooperate to develop standards of access, quality, outcome, and care; criteria for medical necessity and appropriateness; and standards of ethical practice and ethical pricing.

By understanding the direct and indirect risks of capitation contracts, providers can prepare to face these challenges and avoid adverse clinical and financial results. The 11 types of risk identified in this chapter, coupled with appropriate risk management methods, must be included in the process of planning for and implementing behavioral at-risk contracts.

Note: This chapter reflects concepts developed through personal communication with Scott Fruchter, M.B.A., C.E.B.S., Principal, CostEffex Benefits, 10921 Rosebud Ct., Baton Rouge, LA 70815-7808.

BUSINESS ORGANIZATION AND MANAGEMENT

5

DEVELOPING THE MIND-SET FOR CAPITATION

Alan A. Axelson, M.D.

Entering the world of capitated contracts requires clinical, administrative, and technical resources and expertise. Those systems that will survive and experience clinical and financial success must first develop a mind-set of teamwork, integration, alignment, and empowerment. They must practice principles of total quality management, working together as a group to deliver services that improve the health of the population that is their responsibility. This all must be done while continuing to struggle with the ethical dilemmas of being paid to improve behavioral healthcare of a community—rather than for delivering discrete service units such as a day of inpatient treatment or an hour of psychotherapy. Over the short run capitation can be used to restrict access to necessary care, or it can be a long-term opportunity to bring flexible, innovative treatment to needy patients and their families.

> *"I don't think we're in Kansas anymore, Toto."*
> DOROTHY GAYLE, *THE WIZARD OF OZ*

E ntering into a contract to provide services on a capitated basis requires new information systems, more complex and reliable communications, an expanded array of clinical programs, and additional emphasis on utilization and quality management. While the development of each of these systems is important, what underlies them is a new conceptual framework establishing the principles that determine how services are constructed and presented. They form reference points for daily clinical and administrative decisions. As with Dorothy in *The Wizard of Oz*, there are familiar aspects to many components but the aggregate is unfamiliar.

Many clinicians struggle with the new forms of healthcare delivery and payment. They are distressed about external interference in their practices, about service limitations that appear to be arbitrary, and about administrative hassles that occupy nearly as much time as direct clinical service.

Together these issues have prompted a number of different responses, such as complaints, frustration, plans for early retirement, consideration of new practice opportunities, and interest in developing new systems of care. What determines the response is certainly not clinical skill, commitment to patients, or concern for quality. Often it is the ability to conceptualize the new forces and factors at work in determining systems of care and methods of payment. The mind-set of how we define ourselves is a key determining factor in our future success.

We live in a social system that supports continued change and renewal. This is a well-established principle in business, aptly described by Tom Peters in his books (Peters, 1982). Businesses that broadly define their capabilities and apply their resources to meeting needs identified by consumers have flourished. Those that maintained a more narrow view of their products did not fare as well. Similarly, clinicians who see themselves only as outpatient individual psychotherapists are finding the demand for their services reduced or at least not as highly valued as they once were. Being able to think broadly and realistically about what the consumer and purchaser want in behavioral healthcare helps prepare professionals for developing these new models of service. While professional training may have put providers in a position to know a great deal about the types of treatment that are needed, this knowledge must be coupled with a sensitivity and responsiveness to the desires of payors and consumers. Often such desires are in conflict, such as between high quality, high accessibility, and low cost. The challenge is to take these sometimes unrealistic expectations and mold them into an acceptable compromise.

When reaching into new areas, it is often informative to learn about changes going on in other parts of business and social systems. William

Dr. Alan A. Axelson is the Founder and President of Inter-Care, a system of comprehensive behavioral health services in western Pennsylvania. Widely noted for his work with children and adolescents, Dr. Axelson has achieved recognition for innovative approaches to managed behavioral healthcare. He is active in the American Psychiatric Association and the American Academy of Child and Adolescent Psychiatry. Dr. Axelson graduated from the University of Pittsburgh's School of Medicine in 1966 and completed his adult and child residencies at Western Psychiatric Institute and Clinic. He is a member of the Steering Committee for the Council of Behavioral Group Practices.

H. Davidow and Michael S. Malone (1992) characterize the successful manufacturing and service organizations of the future as those that can produce immediately available, mass-produced, individually customized products at competitive prices. In listening to our customers' expectations about healthcare, this seems to be the direction of their expectations.

In beginning to entertain the idea of a capitated contract, it is helpful for providers to assess their current organizational strengths and motivations for entering into a capitated arrangement. Clinicians in a traditional, solo, fee-for-service outpatient or inpatient practice must be prepared for a longer developmental process to prepare themselves for participation in a prepaid service delivery program. Although capitation is a type of payment methodology, clinicians experienced in working as members of groups and teams in community-focused systems offering an array of services are better prepared for the transition.

In developing the necessary mind-set, an initial question might be: "Why do this?" Is capitation pursued in order to bring new methods of treatment organization and payment to an area where there is little penetration of either health maintenance organizations (HMOs) or managed care? Or is it done in order to survive in a consolidated market where a substantial portion of the services are already provided on a prepaid basis? The former scenario may be based upon an opportunity to gradually develop systems and gain experience with a fairly broad margin of error. However, with only limited experience when competing against well-established systems, providers in more consolidated markets will require a greater depth of financial resources, external expertise, and courage.

In a well-established system providing clinical services for a national managed care organization, there probably already exists a good understanding of managing patient accessibility, short-term focused treatment, and crisis intervention. Even a group practice with considerable managed care experience makes a big step when the management focus moves from the external managed care company to internalized clinical self-management. Hopefully, through understanding the process of integration and care-based management, truly effective and efficient systems of care are achieved.

CONTRACTS

Understanding and being comfortable with contracts is a key to success. The capitation contract is a legally binding agreement to deliver services under clearly specified terms and conditions for a price that is determined by a specific amount paid for each individual covered by the contract.

In the past the treatment contract often was simply a verbal under-standing between patient and clinician setting forth some basic parameters for the treatment process. Over the years, this understanding evolved into complex treatment plans spelling out specific objectives, resources, and in-dividual responsibilities. It was clear that providers' responsibilities were di-rected toward the welfare of their patients, generally providing them as much treatment as might benefit them, particularly when they had rich in-surance benefits that could pay the bill. Insurance benefits that paid for one category of service over and above another subtly or not so subtly in-fluenced what went into the treatment contract. The emphasis was provid-ing reimbursable care for individual patients with criteria for necessity being only broadly defined.

This approach was certainly consistent with the training received by clinicians, in which comprehensive evaluations covering all diagnostic pos-sibilities were encouraged and there was little attention paid to resource uti-lization. It has also been supported by the various codes of professional ethics, which emphasize responsibilities to the patient. Only recently has that attention been given to a second ethical component, acknowledging that in addition to responsibilities to individual patients, ethics must also address the healthcare needs of society as a whole.

Most contracts for prepaid general healthcare services are written to au-thorize reimbursement for services that are medically necessary. There is an emphasis on providing the appropriate intensity of service in a setting that is appropriate to the patient's needs. The contract specifically prohibits the use of more costly and intensive treatment settings for the convenience of the patient or the clinician. In general medicine and surgery, medical ne-cessity is being determined through the development of practice guidelines by therapeutic and medical advisory committees, recommending frequen-cies for diagnostic testing and determinations for when procedures move from the category of experimental to approved for general use.

Behavioral healthcare is struggling with the same issues of medical ne-cessity, but for behavioral healthcare the shift seems more dramatic. There are benefits limitations, such as those included in the Federal HMO Act ("crisis intervention and conditions that are amenable to short-term treat-ment"), as well as benefits limited to 20 outpatient visits and 30 inpatient days per year. With little public debate, services expected by patients and gener-ally provided by clinicians have been redefined as "no longer covered by the contract." Individuals who had been covered by well-managed indemnity contracts could expect to have access to behavioral healthcare services that consumed about 7 percent of the premium dollar. When they move to an HMO system, what is considered medically necessary is now redefined to a level of services that often consumes only 2 to 3 percent of the premium dollar. Accepting responsibility for a capitated contract often means participating in this redefinition. Clarifying the expectations of the payor and how these expectations are to be communicated to patients is a key factor in any contract negotiation process. (See Chapters 12, 13, and 14.)

The whole process of contract negotiation and implementation may be quite foreign to clinicians who are used to the much simpler therapeutic contract with an individual patient. Clinicians now must be prepared to engage in the process of preparing a bid, understanding what is expected by the contractor, and evaluating the costs of different components of care —including what it will take to coordinate and manage the services. These skills are more like a building contractor's than a behavioral health professional's. Similar to the contractor, the clinician needs to understand costs and be willing to walk away from contracts where the financial expectations are unrealistic or require unavailable clinical resources. Also like the building contractor, providers must be prepared to accept the fact that not all contract bids result in securing the contract, and to consider these opportunity and development expenses as a cost of doing business.

CLINICAL CARE IN CAPITATION

The clinical care of the patients under a capitated contract puts the clinician in a new position. This position is both empowering and intimidating. It is empowering in the sense that clinicians can use their clinical judgment to select from an array of services that are most appropriate for each patient, without being concerned about external authorizations or benefit coverage. It is intimidating in the sense that decisions must relate to the most appropriate level of care and cost. Erring consistently by providing a higher intensity than necessary will bankrupt the provider organization. Erring on the side of being too restrictive places the patient at risk and jeopardizes the provider's professional responsibility and ethics.

Care-based management, where the provider or provider group combines the clinical professional responsibility for the care of the patient with the control of financial resources, focuses a great deal more responsibility on the individual clinician or the treatment team than past systems of distributing the decision making between the insurer, managed care company, treating clinician, and patient. Developing the mind-set to accept this shift in responsibility to the clinician may be one of the most difficult tasks for providers making the shift to capitation.

The services delivered to individual patients must be on target clinically, focusing on those issues that are most relevant to the patient's dysfunction. This may be different than for longer-term, fee-for-service patients, where problems unfold over time with one evolving into the next, but there is not much difference when compared to managed care contracts where there is strict management of outpatient services. What is different is the responsibility to be flexible in the quantity and intensity of services for a patient about to decompensate into a psychotic break. Frequent outpatient sessions may be the most cost-effective intervention. An extended crisis intervention session or in-home services might maintain a relationship that would otherwise deteriorate into a costly hospitalization. Outpatient therapists must know that they have reliable, timely inpatient backup. This allows them to handle more acutely ill patients in an outpatient setting.

In addition to clinical decisions, other factors to be considered include the need for services being available on a timely basis in geographically accessible locations. One must be prepared to balance the issues of consumer satisfaction with realistic boundaries necessary for cost control. Some patients have a strong sense of entitlement. In capitated contracts, there is a tie between the patient and clinician that requires very active efforts in customer service to maintain consumer satisfaction while also controlling costs.

The elements of cost and resources must be considered in many clinical decisions, particularly those that may involve a higher intensity of treatment. If a patient is left in a higher-cost hospital for a few days, will it shorten the overall length and cost of stay? Or is it better to move the patient to a facility where there is more clinical control? Do you trust an emergency room physician to gain the family's support for follow-up outpatient treatment rather than admission, or should you deploy a mobile assessment team or send an ambulance to transport the patient to one of your own clinical settings? Considering these factors, as well as the clinical picture, is required under capitated payment arrangements.

A few short years ago, particularly with adolescent patients who can be impulsive and present some risk, the standard of care was: "when in doubt, hospitalize." For those accustomed to this style of practice, setting careful limits on the use of expensive resources such as hospitalization can be quite unnerving. Compare the process with how emergency room physicians manage patients presenting with the complaint of chest pain. Although some cases are clear-cut, supporting a decision for hospitalization in a coronary care unit or discharge to outpatient follow-up, there are still a number of cases that require the physician's careful and critical clinical judgment. Certainly every patient with chest pain is not admitted for inpatient evaluation and observation. Likewise, not every adolescent at risk can be admitted to inpatient care. Therefore, it is important to establish systems and to train mental health clinicians, so that patients with clear-cut acute needs get the appropriate level of service, but those with less urgent problems consume no more than the appropriate amount of resources.

Clinical Population Management

The fee-for-service patient and even the network managed care patient is more or less an individual responsibility, one patient at a time. Being responsible for all behavioral health needs for a population of 30,000 to 100,000, starting *tomorrow*, will put clinical care into a whole new perspective. Resources must be deployed and managed to meet the needs not only of an individual patient, but of the population as a whole. Very new and different considerations come with the responsibility for managing a group of patients who need treatment today, as well as a population that, at the present time, is not symptomatic or has not identified itself as such, but may do so in the future. This presents an opportunity to apply and test treatment protocols observing the impact of more consistent and structured methods of evaluation and treatment, comparing the outcome of different methods and different clinicians.

Services delivered to large groups need to be managed by reviewing data, such as the percentage of the population utilizing services, the average number of outpatient visits per treatment episode, or the number of inpatient partial hospital and intensive outpatient days for behavioral health or addiction treatment. A higher number of emergency inpatient admissions can prompt an evaluation of whether there are barriers for early access to outpatient treatment or breakdowns of communication with the primary care physician group. A lower than average utilization of drug and alcohol services may indicate that this aspect of patients' problems is not being adequately evaluated in those patients presenting for behavioral health treatment. Identifying benchmarks and then comparing them by geographic location across years provides data necessary for the development of new services and the re-evaluation of current service effectiveness.

A continuous treatment process where there is mutual confidence and reliance is a key factor in cost-effective treatment. In many developed systems, individual treatment components are quite sophisticated and effective. Each setting offers special therapeutic expertise and resources, and effectively engages the patient in the treatment process. However, capitated systems cannot support the extended use of inpatient or even partial hospital treatment that is required for the patient to engage with, and then disengage from that particular treatment component. It is the responsibility of the staff to integrate the treatment of patients with severe conditions into a continuous process in which patients progress from one treatment level to the next with a sense of continuity and continued focus on treatment goals. Each treatment component must make the next component's job as easy as possible and support the patient's confidence in each aspect of the continuum of services.

Program boundaries can often become protective barriers when we try to integrate services. While this can be attributed to pettiness or lack of maturity, part of it is very typical organizational behavior. An organization taking on a capitation contract must be committed to becoming an integrated system, approaching each day with the challenge of making system integration work and nondefensively engaging in problem-solving when the inevitable breakdowns in communication and continuity arise. When a patient experiences a problem or engages in criticism, there is often a tendency to deflect either clinical or administrative responsibility—"That's a problem with the Billing Department; I don't have anything to do with that part of our organization." Under prepaid contracts, patients and payors have already purchased the service. To meet their expectations, an organization must function as an integrated system, with mutual responsibility between departments.

Evaluating Program Costs and Benefits

The capitation rate is fixed. All providers can do is spend capitation dollars to provide necessary and appropriate care, evaluating the cost and benefit of each treatment component. Paying for a treatment component that may have support within an organization, but really is not meeting the needs of the patient population, drains resources. If providers believe that getting a capitation contract will help to fill empty inpatient beds or revive a residential drug and alcohol treatment program, serious work must be done before even seeking the contract. There are benchmarks available to model utilization of inpatient services or partial hospital services for a given population. Carefully considering the cost of in-house services and the anticipated utilization may prompt reconsideration in strategy.

Despite all that is said and done about developing an appropriate mind-set, there may still remain the hope or wish that capitation will perpetuate some cherished aspects of "business as usual." Utilization reports and financial data after the second or third quarter may dictate difficult decisions that should have been made before signing the contract.

Be prepared to modify, reduce, or even close some favored treatment component. Accept data that indicate the need for an additional service component. Delays in handling calls after 5 P.M., increased utilization of hospital care over weekends, and delayed understanding of the need for drug and alcohol treatment services, for example, should prompt program changes and potentially the development of new services. Signing the contract to deliver the services, accepting the capitation payment, and then relying on the usual clinical services system will not work.

Responsibility for clinical and resource management is the key to a care-based system. Clinicians enter the role of clinical economists, factoring costs and financial incentives that impact on the behavior of the patient, the inpatient treatment unit, the partial hospitalization treatment team, and the outpatient therapist. An organization should be prepared to make these economic issues explicit with each staff member and provider and be prepared to actively engage patients and families in the process of making clinical economic decisions.

ETHICAL ISSUES

The clinical and economic perspectives, while important, are insufficient to establish a stable mind-set for the capitated system of care. Ethical considerations are part and parcel of daily policy administrative decisions and even daily clinical interchanges. Traditional patterns of care organization have supported well-tested and accepted ethical values. When the treatment contract is just between clinician and patient, there are not sticky problems about the boundaries of confidentiality. No one else would ever find out anything about the patient's psychiatric functioning, symptoms, or history. Diagnoses submitted to insurance companies traditionally have been modified to reduce the possibility of stigma associated with, for example, a bipolar disorder or schizophrenia. Many patients were diagnosed as suffering from one type of adjustment disorder or another. The vessel of confidentiality has now sprung many leaks as we justify inpatient treatment or additional sessions to an external reviewer. Under care-based and capitated contracts, clinician leaders must reassess what data need to be shared, how to obtain the patient's permission to provide feedback to a referring primary care physician, and who should collaborate in treatment. Hopefully, capitation contracts will reduce the need for sharing confidential information. (See Chapter 18.)

We must practice according to the responsibilities outlined by Edmond Pellegrino, M.D. (1986), who describes "a serious positive moral obligation on the physician to use both the individual's and society's resources optimally." In the case of individual patients, the clinician has the obligation inherent in his/her promise to act on the patient's welfare to use only those measures appropriate to cure his/her patient, or to alleviate suffering. What the clinician recommends must be effective—that is, must materially modify the natural history of the disease. It must also be beneficial—that is, to the patient's benefit. Social policies have contributed to this problem by providing full support for inpatient treatment while not adequately supporting outpatient treatment and a full array of intermediate levels of services. Participating in a capitated arrangement gives the clinician the opportunity to tailor services to be appropriate for the patient's particular need, allocating the pool of resources in new ways that have a better chance of being effective.

The ethics of financial responsibilities involved in capitation also make the economics of treatment decisions weigh heavily. Are financial decisions made with more professionalism and sensitivity in an interchange between the clinician and patient where the clinician must answer questions and gain support for the treatment plan, or when done remotely as a telephone reviewer says, "The symptoms you describe do not meet the criteria for inpatient treatment"? The latter situation transfers more responsibility to the remote reviewer and relieves the clinician, but it may be better for our patients and the profession if we struggle with these issues on a day-to-day basis in open dialogue with our patients. In professional meetings and other settings we can reshape the clinical and economic decision-making structures that relate to medical care.

Requiring the therapist to be both a caregiver and a care manager certainly complicates the treatment process, but it can sharpen the contract between therapist and patient, helping the patient to engage in an optimal treatment plan focused on dealing with only those issues forming the basis of medical necessity for treatment. Professionals must not become callous to the serious ethical dilemmas and believe they can avoid their responsibility by following policies or sterile criteria. Patients are people, suffering from treatable disorders, and we must be committed to their welfare.

Quality Management

In office-based, fee-for-service care it is hard to close the quality feedback loop. Patients often break off treatment or self-refer to another practitioner. In capitated systems the feedback loop is very direct. Consumers have already paid for their healthcare and therefore have high expectations for service. Appropriately organized systems of care have well-established programs that sample consumer satisfaction and various service and quality indicators. In developing the mind-set for capitated systems, providers must embrace quality management and develop a problem-solving attitude. Minimizing the importance of consumer satisfaction data, avoiding direct analysis of indicators, or failing to confront the issues of the quality and service will lead to complaints and grievances. While some complaints may stem from unreasonable expectations, a capitated delivery system must be ready to participate in the analysis of problems and to make the necessary changes indicated by the data. (See Chapter 10.)

Responsibility for quality only begins with the award of a capitated contract. The insurer and delivery system must continue to participate with the contractor in the process of accreditation and continuous quality management. Both have a vested interest in quality care and consumer satisfaction. Documentation, review, and quality feedback loops make the capitated system open to scrutiny. When it is appropriately administered, such a system addresses many of the concerns noted above in regard to ethical issues. Be willing to look at data and respond with problem solving.

Working Together

> *"It's easy to get the players.*
> *Gittin' them to play together . . . that's the hard part."*
> CASEY STENGEL

No collection of individuals can manage the number of consumers under a capitated system. The integration of an array of services with the availability of each component to play its role when needed is a requirement to make any capitation-based system successful. The staff necessary to carry out this integration process must function as a team, each understanding the roles that they play in supporting the roles of other team members. It is only when clinicians are able to work together across treatment components that the care delivered is both effective and efficient. While management services can supply many of the technical components of patient access, service authorization, reporting, credentialing, and claims payment, a clinical harmony is still necessary to develop a truly effective treatment system that can care for a volume of patients.

Group practices, where there is a shared investment and a group identity, provide one of the most effective ways to achieve this type of clinical coordination. The process of group members choosing each other and working through issues of practice organization, clinical focus, governance, and economics develops a core clinical delivery system that has the resiliency to deal with the ups and downs of contracted systems of care. There is a parallel for those who recognize some of the unique and powerful therapeutic forces available in group therapy in contrast to individual therapy. This process of growing as a group practice helps in dealing with the demands for mutual support, innovation, and courage necessary to take on clinical and financial risks. The process of open group interaction also helps in confronting ethical dilemmas, problems in program development, and the quality management issues that must be addressed.

An effective and efficient care-based delivery system requires that the members of the team each be empowered to exercise clinical and to some extent administrative judgment. If this empowerment of staff occurs in a system where there is insufficient leadership or alignment of purpose, a chaotic situation is created. Alignment followed by empowerment is a means for increasing the success and productivity of organizations. The mind-set must be to develop this increased productivity; otherwise, the new healthcare system will be one of restricted access rather than improved healthcare outcomes.

REFERENCES

Davidow, W. H., & Malone, M. S. (1992). *The virtual corporation.* New York: Harper Business; p. 3.

Pellegrino, E. (1986). Rationing health care—The ethics of medical gatekeeping. *Contemporary Journal of Health, Law and Policy* 10(3): 41–49.

Peters, T. (1982). *In search of excellence.* New York: Harper & Row; p. 2.

6

LESSONS LEARNED, PROBLEMS ENCOUNTERED

Richard C. Baither, Ph.D.
Paul A. Buongiorno, M.D.

Practice groups experience a wide array of difficulties in implementing capitation, especially in the first one or two years. The purpose of this chapter is to describe some of the problems that may be encountered in the early stages of capitation arrangements, in such areas as clinician adjustment, unexpectedly high utilization, associated medical costs, out-of-network services, inpatient versus outpatient utilization, data management, and billing difficulties. Based upon the authors' years of experience with a variety of capitation contracts, practical advice is offered to aid in averting or coping with each problem. This chapter is necessary reading for those about to embark upon capitation. The focus is on the difficulties experienced and on possible solutions.

As the practice group becomes more experienced with capitation, providers will slowly adopt a solution-oriented or brief therapy approach. This process can be encouraged by providing many educational opportunities, both within the group and at professional training seminars. Give providers frequent feedback about their treatment patterns, for example, individual length-of-treatment and length-of-stay performance. (Within the industry these numbers are calculated on a 12-month basis and do not represent what might be included in research as length-of-treatment data.) Providing these data will modify behavior in both subtle and direct ways, particularly if all practitioners are listed by name and discipline. (See Figure 6.1 on page 59.) There will be a few providers who resist this change and choose to leave the group. Expect such behavior; do not try to prevent it.

In the early stages of the authors' attempts to segregate the managed care product to a specific team, however, they found that the group became splintered and inefficient. It is important that the entire group embrace a managed care philosophy and be willing to learn new approaches to old problems. Group members must follow procedures developed for the good of the group's mission and purpose.

Be sensitive to the burnout providers may experience due to the rapid pace of urgent referrals, frequent turnover of patients (due to shorter lengths of treatment and more targeted customer concerns), and increased acuity of patient dysfunction. Managers need to encourage and support providers during this transition as they adopt and embrace these new philosophies. Group members must recognize that none of us is alone in this process.

In considering the development of special programs, recruit volunteers from within the group and elicit their ideas. Although staff currently may not be involved in the contemplated treatment modalities, some undis-

Richard C. Baither, Ph.D., is a clinical psychologist with the Northern Virginia Psychiatric Group in Fairfax, VA. He serves as a team leader, Capitation Contract Manager, and member of the management team, along with his involvement in planning and implementing the practice's managed care product line. Dr. Baither has been a peer reviewer and Director of Outpatient Case Management for American PsychManagement (now Value Behavioral Health). Currently he consults with Integrated Behavioral Care, a regional managed healthcare company serving the Baltimore, MD-Washington, DC, area, where he is the Director of Outpatient Case Management and a member of the Credential and Quality Improvement Committees.

Paul A. Buongiorno, M.D., is a graduate of Georgetown University School of Medicine, where he is currently a clinical assistant professor of psychiatry. He is the founder and Medical Director of the Chronic Pain Program at Fair Oaks Hospital. Dr. Buongiorno is also the President and Chief Executive Officer of The Northern Virginia Psychiatric Group in Fairfax, VA, and Medical Director of Integrated Behavioral Care, a preferred provider organization in northern Virginia. Additionally, he serves as President of Adult Behavioral Care, Inc., which specializes in geriatric psychiatry. Dr. Buongiorno is a consultant for and has played an integral part in implementing managed care at American PsychManagement (now Value Behavioral Health).

Figure 6.1 Length of Treatment

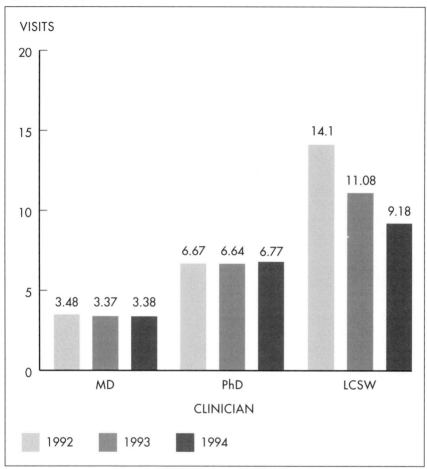

covered interests and talents and a developing sense of team spirit may be found by including everyone in the process.

Unexpectedly High Utilization

On several contracts the authors experienced higher utilization than had been projected initially. In some cases, for example, patients were unfamiliar with referral procedures and underutilized the system during the first year. As their familiarity increased and the transition was completed, utilization increased unexpectedly during the second year. After two years, utilization patterns generally stabilized. Do not overreact to short-term trends. Inaccurate precontract data can also compound utilization projection errors. Ask for the source and length of precontract information in budgeting for utilization. To prepare for these shortcomings, one may want to modify the risk or have a short contract period for added protection.

Additionally, it is common to fail initially to identify some population risk factors. For example, the authors found that employees of a large union contract had a higher incidence of substance abuse treatment than the normal population distributions. In evaluating a contract, it is important to reflect on the types of people that may be enrollees and the clinical problems that may be expected for this population. Obviously, it is more difficult to make such estimates about dependents.

It is also quite possible to experience different lengths of stay between different hospitals, independent of the treating provider. This may be due to a hospital's philosophy of care, administrative issues, or differences between an acute care general hospital and a freestanding psychiatric hospital. It is necessary to provide intensive education and to work with hospital administrators and staff to eliminate as many discrepancies as possible between institutions. Additionally, be certain that patients are referred to appropriate facilities.

As new staff are added to the group, educate them about capitation arrangements, monitoring procedures, and the experiences of other providers. They may also need assistance in identifying alternative care options, such as cost-effective group therapies, community resources, and solution-oriented therapies as opposed to psychodynamic methods.

Managing Medical Costs

Whenever carve-out arrangements are formed for psychiatric and addiction treatment based on financial targets, include an agreement about the processes for identifying and separating medical costs. For example, make sure both sides concur on medical and surgical costs for patients on psychiatric units and psychiatric consultations on medical and surgical units. If it is not possible to reach an agreement concerning medical versus psychiatric care, it may be necessary to transfer some patients to a medical unit. A common example is an alcoholic who is in alcohol withdrawal and needs intravenous librium. Is this a medical admission or a psychiatric admission? Or consider a patient with known organic brain dysfunction, who presents with acute behavioral management difficulties. Is this a medical or a psychiatric admission? Should a newly diagnosed dementia patient be considered a medical admission or a psychiatric admission? Make these very difficult situations as clear as possible on the front end. (See Chapter 14.)

Unmanaged Out-of-Network Care

Many insurance products allow enrollees to select out-of-network providers for care. It is not unusual for patients to go to the closest or most advertised inpatient facility without checking their behavioral health benefits. Some benefit plans also allow for transition to in-network providers within the first 24 to 72 hours of admission or at any time during the admission. Contact patients immediately about their options so that transition can occur as soon as possible. Patients in transition may not have received sufficient evaluation of the medical necessity for their admission. Managed care entities often do not perform medical necessity determinations until after they ascertain if the patient will be remaining out-of-network or transferring in-network.

There will also be a shift in utilization percentages between in-network and out-of-network care over time. This occurs as new employees are added or as employees become better educated about referral procedures. Conduct periodic reviews in order to account for these shifts in financial agreements. For example, one might project that out-of-network care initially may be 20 percent of care delivered but then find that it shifts to 25 percent during a particular period of time.

It is the authors' experience that out-of-network care should not be a part of the risk pool unless it is managed via utilization review or case management. It is very difficult to assure the diligence and consistency of utilization review services by a third party that is not at risk. At-risk providers may prefer, however, to have independent third-party reviewers available for appealed certification decisions or for second opinions concerning treatment plans.

Underfunding of Outpatient Care

Capitation arrangements often begin with an overfunding for inpatient care when alternative services previously were not widely used. The development and funding of outpatient alternatives should be budgeted for as the network matures. Monies can be set aside or taken from those projected for facility costs. An alternative is to consider waiving a portion of the co-payment for at-risk outpatients. Benefit plans may require higher co-payments for outpatient care. This prohibits some patients from following recommendations for intensive outpatient care and encourages them to seek inpatient care when it is not necessary. The authors have limited co-payments to one visit per week for at-risk outpatients when they are seen multiple times per week during restabilization.

Another capitation problem involves changes in benefit coverage or interpretation of coverage by the employer, managed care entity, or insurer, without additional funds being allocated to the network. Use clear contractual language in the contract with the managed care entity.

Data Difficulties

Maintaining separate data tracking between the managed care entity and the network provides a coordinated check and balance system. Errors of omission and commission may not be discovered in a timely fashion. The authors now meet with the managed care entity on a monthly basis to review all relevant data tracking forms and to ensure accuracy for both parties. Examples of relevant data to be tracked include: incurred but not reported services, in-network hospital admissions, out-of-network hospital admissions, psychiatric versus chemical dependency admissions, length of stay, inpatient days per thousand, bed days per thousand, admissions per thousand, level of care, and claims paid.

Billing Issues

At the most fundamental level the network must identify capitated patients from noncapitated patients at the first encounter. This enables the patient to access benefits and to determine the appropriate co-payment amounts. Identifiable insurance cards are clearly helpful.

Managed care companies may request a report of services rendered. Providing inpatient or intermediate care reporting on a monthly basis and outpatient reports on a yearly basis should be sufficient. Another issue in billing is determining primary versus secondary insurance coverage.

The Future

As capitation arrangements continue to change, new challenges will emerge. It is important to continually evaluate potential improvements and to plan for future inadequacies in the capitation requests of tomorrow.

7

KNOWING WHAT INSURERS WANT

Mark Donahue
Martha Titus Wirecki, L.C.S.W.

The key to success in the insurance business is effective risk management. Health insurance companies are in the business of assuming risk for a fixed price. Once the exposure has been assessed, the task of the insurer is to manage the risk. Escalating costs have made healthcare industry risks more difficult to manage. Insurers are handling cost and risk factors in two ways. First is the selection of a finite group of providers having the ability to efficiently deliver the full spectrum of behavioral healthcare services. Second is the shift in reimbursement from a fee-for-service arrangement to capitation, which means that the insurer and the provider share the risk. In this chapter, an insurer and a clinician analyze what insurers are seeking in capitation partners, including administrative structure, total quality management, structural integrity, and contract security.

For practitioners who traditionally have received new clients through the tried-and-true methods—referrals and the Yellow Pages—the notion of marketing to a sophisticated audience like a health insurance company (HIC) is daunting.

In the past, the initial concerns of new clients were likely to be: "When are you available?" "Can you help me with my problem?" and "How much will it cost?" But today HICs are more likely to ask about the computer system, client load, and response time to phone calls. It helps to know how HICs conduct their business and why increasingly they are turning to managed behavioral healthcare delivery systems (MBHDS) to deliver the total spectrum of behavioral healthcare services.

The key to success in the insurance business is effective risk management. HICs are in the business of assuming risk for a fixed price. The insurer must manage risk. Escalating costs in recent years have made healthcare industry risks more unpredictable and difficult to manage. HICs are handling cost and risk factors in two ways. The first step is the selection of a finite group of providers able to deliver the full spectrum of behavioral healthcare services. Second, reimbursement is shifting from a fee-for-service methodology to capitation.

The capitation of providers is a fundamental concept that must be understood and operationalized by an MBHDS. Through capitation arrangements, providers become partners with the insurer in the assumption of risk, so that cost and quality become a shared, risk-reward proposition. In some cases this may lead to a minimal-risk environment for the HIC. Increasingly, HICs are examining their operations and "make versus buy" decisions are becoming more prevalent. This is an opportunity for the MBHDS that develops and maintains an excellent relationship with the HIC.

The Beginning Contact

The initial contact with a potential insurance customer can happen in a number of ways. It may be a direct request for information by the insurer, a

Mark Donahue joined the Prudential in 1982 as a Marketing Representative at PruCare of Illinois. In 1984, he was promoted to Senior Marketing Representative. The following year he transferred to St. Louis as Director of Marketing. In 1986 Mr. Donahue joined the Chicago Group Office and worked in both managed and traditional product sales. In 1988 he was promoted to a team leader position within the Chicago office. In 1989 he was named manager for the Prudential Health Care System of Colorado, with a promotion in 1991 to Executive Director. Mr. Donahue graduated from the University of Michigan in 1978. He has also completed the Executive Program in Managed Care at the University of Missouri.

Martha Titus Wirecki, L.C.S.W., is a licensed clinical social worker whose experience includes clinical work in the public and private sectors. She received her Master's Degree from Smith College School for Social Work and in 1983 was a founding partner of Psychological Resource Organization, a managed behavioral healthcare delivery system in Denver, CO. Ms. Wirecki is an active lecturer, maintains a private practice, and is the Chief Operating Officer for Psychological Resource Organization. She carries advanced licensure in Clinical Social Work and is a Diplomate in Clinical Social Work and a member of the Academy of Certified Social Workers.

referral by the HIC's medical/surgical provider, a bit of information picked up on the grapevine, or part of a conscious, well-orchestrated marketing endeavor that involves research, prospecting by letter or telephone, or a professional network. Although "sales" may seem alien to the world of practitioners, this development of new business requires the same homework, persistence, patience, and attention to detail needed in any other sales environment. Many practitioners will passively respond only to information requested of them, but the proactive MBHDS aggressively seeks as much information about the HIC as possible. Once contact is made, practitioners can certainly use their well-developed interviewing skills to establish the basics.

The responses to preliminary questions in Figure 7.1 highlight what is important to the HIC and give the MBHDS a chance to identify new opportunities.

The Needs Assessment Tool

The next step, the preassessment stage, is to meet with key decision-makers at the HIC and complete the Insurer Needs Assessment Tool. (See Appendix E.)

HICs are as similar as they are different in their characteristics and accompanying needs. It is important to understand where the HIC lies on a spectrum of conceptual and operational issues, as well as to develop an appreciation for the pressures every HIC faces to remain competitive in the current healthcare environment.

Figure 7.1 Preliminary Questions

Who is currently providing services?

What scope of services is being provided?

How satisfied is the HIC with the current provider relative to:

● cost?
● quality?
● member satisfaction?

What additional services does the HIC require?

Who are the decision-makers for behavioral healthcare services?

Assessing the needs of the health insurance company begins with the most basic of questions. Knowing who actually makes the decision is critical.

The Needs Assessment Tool brings together the important components an MBHDS needs to understand as it contemplates entering a relationship with an HIC. Every MBHDS that contracts with an HIC becomes a representative of that company. The more comprehensive the understanding of the HIC by an MBHDS, the greater the capacity there is to develop a long-term, dynamic partnership.

Using the Needs Assessment Tool for the pre-assessment stage helps the MBHDS determine the HIC's key players and organizational priorities and gives it a chance to identify new opportunities to market to the HIC. It is from this base of information that both sides can decide whether to proceed to the more formal request for proposal (RFP) stage. (See Chapter 12.)

If discussions proceed to that stage, the Needs Assessment Tool should be revisited and the RFP targeted to the specific needs and interests of the HIC. Answers should be concise, clearly outlining a well-defined delivery system, with an understanding that the key considerations are cost, quality, member access, and the potential for a long-term partnership. A complete, accurate, and professionally presented RFP document should be delivered to the HIC by its deadline.

THE FUNDAMENTAL DELIVERY SYSTEM

Philosophy.   Of utmost importance to the HIC will be the compatibility of clinical philosophies. The MBHDS will need a well-defined philosophy that meets clinical practice guidelines, focuses on solutions, and is imbued with a well-defined, ethical value system. Many organizations develop a vision statement or a mission statement with input from those who will be expected to carry out the goals of the organization. Not only is the final product a useful guide for employees and providers, but the act of creating the statement promotes dialogue and elicits more "buy-in" from the participants.

Contrast this with a group of clinicians in a loosely structured group managing a flow of private patients; there is simply no comparison from the HIC's point of view. Sharing office space doesn't create the disciplined infrastructure required of a substantive delivery system fulfilling a capitated contract.

Clinical Delivery System.   An MBHDS must be prepared to offer a complete continuum of services, from the least restrictive to the most intensive modality. This is generally referred to as a *vertically integrated* system. The entire spectrum of services should include prevention, outpatient, intensive outpatient, partial hospitalization, residential, and inpatient services for mental health and addiction treatment. This continuum of services can be provided by a delivery system based upon a staff-provider model or a network-provider model, or some combination of the two. The staff model is often the most cost-effective. It provides a better environment for measuring quality and allows for continuous monitoring with the least amount of variance in the clinical delivery of care. This model is extremely labor-intensive and expensive from an administrative standpoint, particularly during the start-up period.

On the other hand, the network-provider model is even more costly, requires considerable administrative coordination, and offers fewer quality controls. It can be designed to provide the patient population a greater choice of clinical providers. It also gives the network administrator more flexibility in choosing providers and establishing geographic breadth and density.

Patient access is critical in the clinical delivery system. The elements described in Figure 7.2 should be defined, measured, and monitored.

Figure 7.2 Essentials of Patient Access

A telephone abandonment rate of less than 3 percent, 24 hours a day, seven days a week

Professional, respectful handling of intake information

Standards of timeliness in assigning appointments for emergency, urgent, and routine care

An emergency team providing active clinical interventions 24 hours a day, seven days a week

Aesthetically pleasing offices and clinical facilities in geographically convenient locations

Ability to interface with the primary care physician, particularly when psychotropic medications are being administered or patient noncompliance is an issue

Willingness and ability to provide a customer-responsive approach

Patient access means that there are the fewest possible barriers to receiving service. Often the "first step" is the hardest for a patient and any obstacle may seem like "too much."

The MBHDS must be able to provide utilization management, which includes utilization review and case management, to ensure quality and monitor costs *for every case*. Patients must be able to move seamlessly from one level of care to another without any disruption in treatment. All levels of care, including outpatient services, partial-care programs, residential programs, and inpatient services, must be accessible 24 hours a day, seven days a week, and must be philosophically compatible with the MBHDS.

In cases where existing community resources are inadequate, too expensive, or incompatible with managed care, it may be prudent for the MBHDS to create alternative programs. For example, many partial-care programs are hospital-based and reflect the costs of maintaining the larger infrastructure. When an MBHDS is providing service to 15,000 or more covered lives in a single community, it should consider developing in-house partial hospital programs. In many cases, this leads to comprehensive, quality-controlled programs with seamless care at a substantially reduced cost. With this model more services can be provided to those patients who present with debilitating, high-risk conditions.

As HICs integrate their products, they require expanded services from their MBHDS. Prevention programs, employee assistance programs, utilization management, and Medicare and Medicaid waiver products are becoming standard offerings for an MBHDS. The next generation of products will include programs addressing Workers' Compensation and short- and long-term disability. Anything that adds value to what the HIC has to sell—a primary care physician hotline, a professional newsletter, visibility in a professional publication—is welcomed by the HIC. It, too, must offer more in order to retain membership and compete for new business in a highly competitive market.

Total Quality Management.   A total quality management (TQM) program is a fundamental part of the delivery system for every MBHDS. (See Chapter 10.) Several years ago this was seen as an added-value feature, but it now has become an industry standard. Employers and HICs are no longer buying behavioral healthcare on the basis of cost alone, but are becoming adept at determining *value*. Value is defined as the predominance of quality (structure, process, outcome) relative to cost. (See Figure 7.3.)

The quality management committee should include key staff from the HIC, preferably a medical director, network coordinator, and quality improvement specialist, along with the medical director, officers, and management team of the MBHDS. This committee defines clinical monitors, sets performance benchmarks, and reviews compliance to the program. As a vehicle for partnering between the HIC and MBHDS, the program is open to review by every HIC customer. It represents the inner workings of

Figure 7.3 Essentials of a Successful Total Quality Management Program

Compatible definitions of "medical necessity" criteria

A process to review and manage high-risk patients

Tools for credentialing and recredentialing providers and facilities

Tools for routinely assessing patient and provider satisfaction

Defined procedures and policies regarding clinical grievances and appeals

Defined standards and performance audit tools for medical records

A quality management committee to oversee the entire quality management process

Fixed and fluid subcommittees that report to the quality management committee

Continuous quality improvement with decision-making power at all levels of the organization

A total quality management program is no longer an add-on, but has become an industry standard. A management committee must oversee the entire process.

the MBHDS operation, and makes the performance and responsiveness of the MBHDS highly visible.

It is the MBHDS' responsibility to embrace both the philosophical and financial commitment associated with an effective, formal total quality management program. An excellent foundation for such a program is the set of standards created by the National Committee for Quality Assurance (NCQA) or the Utilization Review Accreditation Committee (URAC). (See Appendix B for information on how to contact these agencies.) The level of compliance with these standards should be determined not only by HIC expectations, but by the mission and business strategy of the MBHDS.

Another significant measurement tool is the set of standards provided by NCQA called the Health Plan Employer Data and Information Set 2.0 (HEDIS), designed to assist employers in determining the value of their healthcare expenditures. It measures performance in five key areas: quality, access and patient satisfaction, membership and utilization, finance, and descriptive information. HEDIS holds providers accountable for quality service through a standardized measure of key practice guidelines. Currently, HEDIS has limited application in the behavioral healthcare delivery arena. However, it is important for the MBHDS to review these clinical guidelines and create the means to capture these data. HICs must provide HEDIS reports to their clients and will require those reports from their MBHDS.

A TQM program should incorporate a dynamic system addressing quality assurance or adherence to standards, risk management, and a continuous quality improvement *system*. Protocols need to be defined for all three areas. Aspects of care need to be identified, measured, and monitored within specific time lines. Communication between the organizations is essential, along with system flexibility in responding to customer and patient suggestions for improving care.

Administrative Structure. The MBHDS must have an internal administrative system which is efficient and accountable unto itself and to a larger organization. An integrated, functional business structure is necessary before the HIC will consider the MBHDS for capitation. See Figure 7.4 for the required components.

Figure 7.4 Elements of the MBHDS Administrative Structure

Ability to assume the financial, actuarial, and administrative risks associated with capitation

Ability to negotiate contracts with facilities at the most competitive reimbursement rates

Communication channels to health insurance companies

Defined procedures and policies regarding administrative grievances and appeals

Claims processing capability

Interface with the management information system to capture relevant data

Customer service capability to resolve patient questions or informal complaints

Provider relations department

Human resource capability to manage personnel policies and procedures and to comply with regulations in hiring, compensation, and benefits

Serving the needs of a health insurance company requires a new level of sophistication and a more complete infrastructure.

Figure 7.5 Management Information System Integrated Database

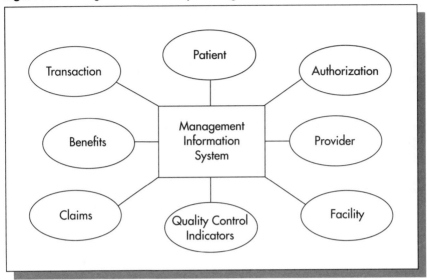

A fully integrated database will connect the systems that are essential to an accurate, user-friendly system. It is best to purchase or develop a system that can be expanded as the business grows.

Management Information System. The management information system (MIS) connects all of the databases used by the MBHDS. As the hub of patient data and claims processing, the system needs to be flexible, user-friendly, and expandable. All reports that are generated must be presented in a professional, pleasing format which can be understood by a non-MIS person, such as a clinical manager, health insurance executive, or benefits manager. The reports should include the type of product and benefit design, so that they will be understood if taken out of context.

Databases should include, at a minimum, patient information, authorizations, transactions, benefit descriptions, quality improvement monitors, facility information, provider credentialing, recredentialing, and profiling materials, as shown in Figure 7.5.

Records must be kept on the current book of business, with customer-specific utilization reports which minimally include: bed days per thousand, admits per thousand, outpatient sessions per thousand, and per member per month costs. Other standard reports would include quality information monitors, billing data, and provider credentialing, recredentialing, and profiling. (See Chapter 16.) The system needs to accommodate customized reports such as HEDIS measures or diagnostic distributions for individual HICs or large employer groups.

Outcomes Studies. Before the era of managed care, behavioral treatment outcomes were rarely examined. Payors did not request this data and the nature of the work was difficult to review and evaluate objectively. Escalating costs, rising expectations, and increasing sophistication have compelled employers and HICs to demand measurable outcomes and supporting documentation that demonstrate a commitment to improved clinical care. MBHD have the option of working with experienced companies which specialize in outcome studies or developing their own studies internally. (See Chapter 19.) The specialty companies have developed protocols and dedicated staff for the collection and analysis of formal data. Internal studies may be less costly but more difficult to administer with a high degree of consistency and motivation. The research should be tied into a feedback loop which positively affects the clinical delivery system. Designing an individualized outcome study with the HIC is an excellent way to strengthen the fundamental working relationship. (See Appendix H.)

Structural Integrity. The MBHDS needs to develop an internal structure which can function autonomously and in partnership with the HIC. This structure needs to encourage interaction on a case-specific basis, so that both entities can be used as reciprocal resources. This balance between autonomy and oversight is critical to the operational effectiveness of the delivery process. It must be viewed as a positive enhancement for patient care. One example is the written appeals process under which the MBHDS will be expected to function as an expert, reviewing and taking a definitive stand on patient appeals. This appeal is then subject to re-review by the HIC medical director or an independent consultant. This interactive capacity must be mutually respected or the working partnership is likely to erode.

Contract Security

A stable, long-term working contract between the MBHDS and the HIC is in everyone's best interests—especially the patient's. Every effort should be made to construct a win/win arrangement from the very beginning, to provide the best environment for contract security and continuity. This can be developed and maintained in a number of ways. It is important to establish contract stability as a specific goal and seek ways to ensure the mutual satisfaction of both organizations. This is particularly important with the number of mergers and acquisitions occurring in the healthcare environment. A well-established, secured contract may make the difference between opportunity and disaster for both the MBHDS and the HIC.

First and foremost is communication. A regularly scheduled meeting to review and discuss all administrative and operational issues is critical. Don't allow the MBHDS/HIC relationship to deteriorate into a mere vendor-supplier relationship. Suppliers are easily replaceable.

It is important that the MBHDS build relationships with key contacts at the HIC. Turnover and changing organizational priorities are likely to affect key HIC players, and an MBHDS would be wise to build its contacts and support as widely and deeply in the client organization as possible. This will positively impact on the working relationship, making it more pleasurable and services to the HIC customers more effective.

The best way to develop contract security is to continually add value to the systems and services offered by the HIC. One way to do this is to revisit the Needs Assessment Tool (see Appendix E) periodically to see that value, *as it is defined by the HIC,* is being delivered.

Although sometimes unsettling, the uncertainty and change in today's healthcare environment offer a great opportunity to the MBHDS. The end result rewards effective and ethical treatment, provides better value for the healthcare dollar, and promotes prevention and better health for the patients who rely on us for guidance.

Note: The authors wish to express their appreciation to Richard Kunnes, M.D., Senior Executive Practice Leader for the Wyatt Company and formerly President, Prudential Psychiatric Management, for his contribution to this chapter.

8

MARKETING FOR CAPITATION

Gayle L. Zieman, Ph.D.
Sean McMullan, R.N.

Capitation is the formation of a close and ongoing business relationship between a mental health group and an insurer, employer, government entity, or other purchaser. Seeking capitation contracts involves business relationship building, trust formation, and a joint understanding in which both parties develop mutually beneficial clinical and business solutions. Marketing is not primarily a sales procedure, but rather a process of creating visibility for the clinic or practice and then tailoring the delivery of treatment, quality procedures, and administrative systems to match the needs of purchasers. A commitment of significant time, energy, and resources is required to pursue capitation. The marketing process is a proactive investment procedure for the future.

Consumers of behavioral healthcare are no longer the primary force in the selection of providers. Insurers, employers, and governmental forces now designate the providers and design the systems by which care will be delivered. To prosper in today's healthcare environment, the providers of care must have business savvy.

Practice groups, whether single specialty practices or larger multispecialty clinics, must commit as much effort to business development as to the provision of care. The required business relationships with purchasers demand that providers recognize business administration and marketing as services equal in necessity and stature to clinical treatment. Clinicians can no longer claim to support the business staff—it's now a shared proposition. Administrative personnel bring a large portion of the business to clinicians, and the purchasers of care directly contract for administrative services in addition to patient treatment. Under capitation, clinical care, case management, and business administration are purchased simultaneously.

Marketing behavioral health services for capitation requires that the practice group have both a full-service delivery system and sophisticated business knowledge. Selling one's business management skills has become a critical component in obtaining and retaining capitation contracts.

Insurers and employers seek to capitate with providers that can demonstrate business competence in marketing, financial administration, and data management. They require that providers understand contracting, negotiating, cost accounting, computer systems, data reporting, and the cultivation of business relationships. To market a practice for capitation, a provider group or clinic must project a sound business infrastructure with integration among all parts of the group.

Capitation agreements are most often the result of relationship cultivation which has extended over months or years. A commitment to developing long-term relationships and treating purchasers as partners in the provision of care are necessary for both immediate and long-term success. The group must be prepared to be flexible over time to meet the purchaser's ongoing and changing needs. Seeking a capitation contract does not begin or end with the response to a request for proposals.

Gayle L. Zieman, Ph.D., and his colleagues at Mesa Mental Health in Albuquerque, NM, understand well the importance of marketing and sustaining business relationships. They have continued for almost eight years with their original HMO capitation arrangement and have subsequently contracted for five other capitation agreements. Dr. Zieman has been presenting workshops on managed care since 1990, in which he has stressed the importance of marketing and business relationships.

Sean McMullan, R.N., has been designing, promoting, negotiating, and implementing behavioral health capitation contracts since 1988, when he joined Mesa Mental Health in Albuquerque, NM. He has marketed full-service behavioral health delivery systems to a wide array of insurers and employers, and has developed a provider network across the state of New Mexico. Quality customer service and the formation of long-term relationships with insurers and employers are his focus. He received his nursing degree in 1984 from Golden West College in California and has over 20 years of experience in the mental health field.

Provider groups must directly commit financial and time resources to capitation development. Doing so is a critical investment in the group's business and clinical future. The group must possess a distinct marketing strategy, understand the components that are sold in capitation, and articulate well why it desires capitation.

Why Desire Capitation?

Groups lacking a disposition toward business savvy may well question the value of building the business infrastructure necessary to attract capitation. What is the worth of capitation to a practice group? Why do it?

Capitation has two major advantages in today's healthcare environment: market security and retention of autonomy. Financially, capitation is a means of holding onto and increasing market share. As the purchasers of healthcare move toward selling the care for entire populations, provider groups must be prepared to accept the responsibility of managing the treatment needs of large groups over time. Capitation is becoming the most common means of financing the care for entire populations of enrollees. Groups that do not become capitation-ready are likely to face dwindling business activity.

Retention of autonomy is also central to why provider groups desire and grow with capitation. Clinicians typically wish to preserve the traditional independence of medicine to decide on treatments and conduct case management. Today in noncapitated arrangements much of that autonomy is gone; the clinician must focus on satisfying the demands of outside utilization reviewers. By accepting the role of self-case management which is inherent in capitation, providers can regain much of the control in deciding upon treatments and lengths of stay. Avoiding external utilization review is a powerful reward for practices to seek and succeed under capitation.

Two ancillary advantages to capitation are the abilities to diversify revenue sources and to increase efficiency. Capitation provides a steady monthly income that allows for financial stability to complement traditional fee-for-service payments, which fluctuate with the actual provision of care. A predictable income stream allows a provider group to think creatively about how to work more efficiently. Under capitation, working more does not increase income, but working smarter can. Capitation highly encourages the prevention of illness and the use of effective treatments with the lowest expenditure of resources.

Creative providers enjoy the challenge of using financial predictability as a springboard to designing services that result in greater efficiency in care. Creative providers also recognize that to undertreat the population or severely limit access to care will result in large resource expenditures in the future. Mastering how to achieve the balance between efficiency, quality, and financial viability under capitation is a self-motivating learning process for many; a reason in itself to actively market for capitation contracts.

Provider groups must articulate to potential capitation partners why they want capitation arrangements. Insurers and large employers will understand the reasons outlined here.

THE COMPONENTS SOLD IN CAPITATION

Prepaid clinical services for an entire population of subscribers are not the only services sold in a capitation agreement. A willingness to share the risk of financing care, the desire for a long-term business relationship, and an ongoing commitment to seeking the most efficient care are also prime components that a provider group must confidently sell to an insurer or employer. To market successfully, the practice must convince a potential capitation contractor that an agreement will result in a multiyear partnership of sharing risk and a program of continuously improving the quality and cost-effectiveness of care. Marketing efforts must portray the group as willing and capable of sharing risk and as a flexible, ethical business with which a long-standing business partnership would be mutually productive.

Specifically, the practice or clinic must directly market its capabilities and services in the following clinical and business areas:

- responsiveness to patients' needs and desires;
- the provision of a full continuum of care adequate to meet the treatment needs of the population (This must include emergency services and the ability to service well the age spectrum of the population.);
- having adequate geographic service availability to serve the capitated population;
- having a system for easy access by patients, with swift triage of patients to the appropriate level of care;
- a sound quality assurance and improvement program that will provide ongoing enhancements to the delivery of care;
- a system for patient and contractor complaints and their resolution;
- a well-rounded outcomes management system providing direct accountability for the services provided. Capitation contractors want frequently issued, easily interpreted data showing patients'

symptomatic and functional improvement as well as satisfaction
with the services received;

- an openness to sharing utilization and outcomes data;
- responsiveness to the needs and desires of the contractor; and
- financial soundness and adeptness at managing risk.

In addition, many contractors will want to know that the provider
group is capable and willing to provide special services such as on- or off-
site employee assistance program (EAP) counseling (see Chapter 21), prevention programs, and psychoeducational training to the population.
Selling—and continuously demonstrating—flexibility is critical.

Initial Marketing Strategies

Capitation arrangements are finalized only after much hard work and discussion.

A Commitment in Advance of Time and Resources Is Necessary.   Seeking capitation contracts is at least a half-time job. A skilled marketing person who is
very knowledgeable about behavioral healthcare and business practices is
needed. Neither a business degree nor a behavioral health professional
background alone will ensure success. To market successfully, the provider
group must select an individual who projects trust as well as business and
professional knowledge. The group must then allow this individual to develop the necessary relationships. Have a *rainmaker* who can sell the group.

Initial Contacts Must Be Direct and Personal.   Brochures and surveys are not
significantly productive. Meetings, lunches, golf games, and small joint projects are the means of establishing contact.

Visibility Is Important.   Overt visibility as in brochures, advertisements, and
sponsorships can be helpful, but this should not be the main source of
recognition for the group. Participation in health fairs and joint sponsorship of events such as free health clinics are good sources of direct marketing. Over time, subtle visibility is extremely powerful. Recognition
within professional associations, local business groups, and civic associations can be important to developing the image of the practice group as a
business worthy of attention. Remember, capitation contracts are not sold
primarily by a group's public name recognition, but rather by recognition
in the business and professional communities.

Most important in the initial marketing phase is to follow a distinct plan. The plan should have the following elements:

1. *Complete a Market Analysis.* Learn to whom to market. This requires a systematic program of contacting the local and national provider relations personnel for the major insurers and the benefits managers of large employers. Learn which employers are self-insured and which are interested in behavioral health carve-outs. Find out which insurers are dissatisfied with their provider panels or fee-for-service payment arrangements. Learn which insurers and employers desire an exclusive relationship for the provision of behavioral healthcare.

2. *Listen and Be Helpful.* Learn what is important to insurers and employers. Their problems are opportunities for a provider group or clinic to solve. An approach focused on how the provider group can help with behavioral health service problems is important.

3. *Know the Competition.* This is vital. Who else provides or is interested in providing behavioral health services on a capitated basis? What are their strengths and weaknesses? Why would an insurer or employer choose one group over the competition?

4. *Target Key Contacts.* Frequent, predictable contacts with principal benefits managers, insurer provider relations personnel, and hospital executives is part of building visibility and maintaining a ready presence. Active participation in local groups such as EAP associations, hospital cooperatives, and business consortia can be an excellent vehicle for maintaining contacts. Remember that the foundation to capitation arrangements often is years of building relationships and trust with the decision-makers.

5. *Network with Other Professionals, Including Competitors.* Do not shun the competition; get to know them. Learn what they do well and not so well; this is a part of marketing. Also, being cooperative with competitors lends a sense of professionalism, courteousness, and flexibility to your reputation. A practice group must be perceived as a team player before any purchaser will desire to contract with it.

6. *Include Clinicians and Shareholders in Marketing.* While a marketing effort must have a lead person, that individual should be perceived as having strong and broad support from within the provider group. Showcasing key clinicians and group principals in meetings with potential contracting sources is a powerful way of demonstrating the group's strengths and solidarity. Additionally, it allows the key clini-

cians and shareholders to see firsthand the activities of the marketing director, who is often falsely assumed to have an easy, carefree position.

7. *Focus on the Here-and-Now and the Future.* Business relationships are based on current strengths and are forward-looking. Recalling good or bad aspects from the past is not helpful. Potential contractors want to know what a group and its competitors can provide from this day forward.

ADVANCED MARKETING STRATEGIES

Be willing to spend time with potential contractors analyzing their needs. Find out what problems they have that capitation can solve or reduce. Be educational—help them to brainstorm and articulate ideas. Determine what factors are central to them: cost, quality, access to care, or better case management. Discuss joint solutions. After a period of time in this process the product they desire and the services that your provider group can provide may become so well-matched that you have become the automatic leader in the competition—even before a request for proposals is issued.

Often it is helpful to show how modifying a benefit package can be advantageous. Insurers seldom want to loosen the benefit package out of fear that this will result in runaway costs. Show which benefit changes can result in better or more efficient care. Insurers and employers often have limited or inaccurate knowledge about the behavioral health treatment process, EAP services, prevention, psychoeducational programs, group and family psychotherapies, and the cost-saving potential of newer but more expensive medications. Teach them. Then build appropriate benefit modifications into a future capitation agreement. (See Example 8.1 on page 82.)

The Formal Proposal

Once an insurer or employer definitely decides to seek a group with which to capitate, a formal request for proposals almost always comes into play. It is important to take the proposal seriously, since competitors can and will submit proposals which are very professionally written.

The proposal must clearly articulate the group's capabilities and stress how it will provide a full care delivery system meeting the purchaser's needs. The proposal should also address any current weaknesses of the group in meeting these needs, and should identify a plan and commitment for remedying them. The use of subcontracted or subcapitated providers to

Example 8.1 Modifying the Benefit Package: The Mesa Mental Health Experience

Beginning in 1988 with the very first capitation contract awarded to Mesa Mental Health, a full-risk professional service agreement for 30,000 health maintenance organization (HMO) enrollees, the benefit packages administered by Mesa Mental Health have included the expanded features listed below. Through the years, contract renewals (three contracts are now for five-year periods) have maintained this expanded benefit package. While the insurers were always initially skeptical, we have been able to impress upon them the rationale behind each feature in improving care without adversely impacting on it. Universally, our contracting partners have agreed to the following benefit modifications:

Twenty Hours versus 20 Visits. While the standard HMO outpatient benefit is for up to 20 visits in a benefit year, this method of counting service units can result in adverse outcomes for patients, especially those with chronic disorders for whom medication check-ups are important. A patient with schizophrenia or bipolar disorder may not keep a routine 15-minute medication appointment if he or she knows that this one visit is one-twentieth of the entire allowed services for the year. Yet medication adjustments may be extremely important in averting crises and the use of inpatient services. Therefore, totaling services by time (for example, one-quarter hour for a medication check and one hour for 50 minutes of psychotherapy) toward a maximum allowable of 20 hours of service within a benefit year provides a better incentive for patients to obtain the most needed care.

Inclusion of Group and Family Therapies. Inclusion of these as covered treatments is based upon sound research into effective and efficient psychotherapies. We have been able to show insurers that these can be used to provide better care without increasing utilization. Rotating the identified patient among family members to obtain more than the allowed 20 hours of service per year is not permitted, and 60- to 90-minute group therapies are charged as one-half hour against the maximum of 20 hours per benefit year.

(continued on next page)

Example 8.1 (continued)

> ***Expanded Formulary.*** With good reason insurers fear the overusage of new, expensive medications. Because of our close working relationships with our capitation partners, they have been assured that our behavioral healthcare professionals will only prescribe these medications when less expensive medications have been ineffective. This trust has allowed the prescription benefit package to continue the inclusion of the new SSRI antidepressants and neuroleptics even when prescription costs are outside the capitation agreement.

meet clinical needs often is a sound strategy. The proposal should openly discuss quality features and options, and their relationship to cost. The assumptions behind a requested per member per month (PMPM) rate should be clearly articulated, including those related to expected utilization, start-up costs, administrative and overhead allotments, case management costs, and profit margin. Administrative and case management costs together typically amount to 20 to 25 percent of the PMPM, while 5 to 10 percent profit is considered acceptable. (See Chapter 12 for greater detail on writing the proposal.)

Case Retention

Marketing does not stop once a contract is signed. Capitation is a partnership. Frequent contact, joint problem solving, and rapid responsiveness continue between provider and payor for the length of the contract. A provider group, on a daily basis, must be perceived by the contractor as a resource for behavioral health services and business cooperation.

In a capitation agreement, the provider group has contracted to provide financial and data services, case management, and clinical care. Marketing involves selling, and continuing to sell, all three.

9

MODELS OF INTEGRATION BETWEEN HOSPITALS AND PROVIDER GROUPS

Robert Garcia, M.A.

In this era of healthcare transition, there are a number of organizational approaches to changing clinical programming and financial incentives for providers and inpatient facilities. Hospitals and practice groups are quickly learning that the future requires developing an organized, vertically integrated continuum of care that will succeed within capitation. This chapter discusses alternative organizational structures including: joint ventures, hospital-owned groups, contractual relationships, and special divisions within a hospital system—such as provider groups leasing hospital units.

During the last few years behavioral healthcare, as part of the overall continuum of medical services, has been affected in ways that may actually depict future directions for the rest of the healthcare industry. Payors have begun to appreciate that behavioral healthcare services do not operate in a vacuum. As benefit planners look at overall health issues for their enrollees, they are recognizing that behavioral health impacts on the general health status of their enrolled population. For many payors, relating physical and behavioral health in a way that ties the needs of the enrollee and his or her family together in a holistic manner has become an overt objective.

As primary care physicians or gatekeepers have begun to take greater control over the management of their patient populations, the need to access and to integrate the care of the mind and body has become essential, especially when primary care physicians are financially linked by capitation or other risk sharing to the medical and mental well-being of their patients. A referral to a behavioral healthcare professional can no longer be "lost" in the system. Requirements for formal referral notices, with requests for specific action and feedback reports, now tie the behavioral and medical practitioner together. Treatment of a patient's medical and psychiatric problems must be tightly coordinated.

In addition, national organizations have begun to develop and disseminate criteria regarding quality of care, which encourage providers to address the full continuum of care and the relationship of psychiatry to general medical care. HEDIS (Health Plan Employer Data Information Set, see Chapter 10) is an example of the quality criteria that providers must now address, including outcomes data, clinical indicators demonstrating the effectiveness of treatment, and process data on the progress of patients through treatment. Several for-profit behavioral health systems are attempting, with the assistance of some of the country's best academic programs, to develop outcomes evaluation processes demonstrating the effectiveness of the care provided under partial or full risk contracts. (See Chapter 19 and Appendix H.)

The effect of this scrutiny has been a realignment of the behavioral healthcare provider system. What was once a cottage industry of solo or small group practice providers today has become a regional and national care delivery system that organizes treatment between psychiatrists, psychologists, Master's-prepared therapists and hospitals in a manner that attempts to move the patient through a continuum of care using the least restrictive, least intensive level of intervention while maximizing clinical outcomes.

Hospital departments of psychiatry have ceased to be the locus of system development. No longer is the responsibility of care focused at the inpatient level. Instead, within capitated systems over 90 percent of the care

---

Robert Garcia, M.A., graduated from the University of Iowa in Hospital and Health Administration. He has served as Assistant Administrator of the University of New Mexico Hospital and with the New Mexico Department of Health and Environment, directing five mental health inpatient facilities. For 12 years Mr. Garcia has been an Administrative Director with Presbyterian Healthcare Services in Albuquerque, NM, most recently responsible for the Behavioral Health Network, including inpatient and outpatient behavioral healthcare and chemical dependency programs. In close collaboration with Mesa Mental Health, he has worked extensively with many managed care programs involving capitation. Mr. Garcia also has a background in emergency medical services systems, long-term hospitals, subacute units, hospital-based home care, and occupational medicine.

typically is provided at the outpatient level. Inpatient units that previously ran at 80 to 90 percent capacity and were accustomed to average lengths of stay of 30 days or more today are in decline. Only very chronic cases or those requiring acute stabilization before movement to a partial or outpatient level of care are now admitted to the inpatient setting.

The emphasis on the growth of inpatient care, driven for almost three decades by Medicare, Medicaid, and indemnity insurance coverage, has resolved into managed and organized care stressing a continuum of services structured for a "just in time" intervention. The financial risk of care is being transferred to the provider, who is in the best position to prescribe services from the continuum of care, when and where they are required. Inpatient services, previously the most publicly evident level of care, have largely become systems for evaluation and brief stabilization before referral to another level of care—which is usually not an inpatient unit.

This move to a new structure of delivering care has created new requirements for cooperation and collaboration between the various providers of healthcare. While competition is still evident in the marketplace, changing incentives, financial and otherwise, are bringing about these new market realities. The next section will discuss competition and alignment of incentives in a managed care marketplace.

ALIGNED INCENTIVES AND AVOIDING COMPETITION

The change in reimbursement from fee-for-service to capitation creates tremendous uncertainty in the provider community. Accepting risk, even with some aspect of a stop-loss arrangement, puts providers into a situation similar to that faced by insurance carriers: needing to assess the degree of risk and to actively evaluate the population to be served. A decision to embark on at-risk contracting challenges professionals' status quo. A capitated provider can no longer deal solely with individual referrals or one-on-one, patient-provider relationships. Instead the paradigm must now include managing populations of patients, often in the thousands. Instead of a patient selecting a provider, the payor now selects a care delivery system.

The term *integrated delivery system* was coined with this concept in mind. Under capitation, clinical decisions to a large degree are in the hands of the provider. So, too, are the financial implications of the provider's selection of one intervention over another. Under capitation, provider groups can no longer afford to treat every patient in a similar manner. Providers now must be well versed in a number of treatment options, some individualized, some group, and some not directly available through the provider group but instead purchased on an as-needed basis. Organizing care in a cost-effective manner in response to market forces must be the goal of any capitated provider.

In agreeing to accept risk, providers now must understand the cost/benefit implications of their treatment decisions. While many of the interventions to date have been evaluated on their clinical effectiveness, there are little data on their cost-effectiveness. However, the industry has made significant strides in this area. For example, within recent years large inpatient chemical dependency rehabilitation treatment services have virtually disappeared because alternative ambulatory programs have proven to be more cost-effective, without sacrificing good clinical outcomes.

Capitation realigns incentives for relationships between hospitals and provider groups. Since less hospital usage is strongly rewarded financially, services must shift to outpatient settings dominated by the provider group. It is imperative that any hospital-provider linkage take this trend into account. While some patients absolutely require inpatient services, the hospital is likely to see reduced usage of its traditional services and outpatient providers can be expected to find creative programs to circumvent hospital usage. Yet together, a hospital-provider relationship can be a formidable partnership in vertically integrating a care delivery system and presenting a powerful marketing entity to local and regional healthcare markets.

The next section discusses several organizational options for providers and hospitals to consider.

ORGANIZATIONAL OPTIONS

The development of integrated hospital-provider delivery systems in response to a maturing managed care environment requires a great deal of time, expertise, and, ultimately, capital. The legal ramifications can also be significant. Personal risk for providers can be overwhelming. There are, however, means by which risk may be shared with a hospital system, allowing a synergy between the parties that creates a stronger organization than could be created by either alone. Each organizational option has aspects that make it attractive under certain circumstances, but these are by no means the only options available.

Each option also requires a thorough legal review to insure that it is acceptable under state and federal laws. It is prudent to include reviews of regulations regarding fraud, abuse, and antitrust. In accepting financial risk through capitated arrangements for defined client populations, a review of state insurance rules and regulations is also necessary.

Joint Ventures.   One of the most common organizational structures is the joint venture. Hospitals have a history of creating joint ventures to capitalize a venture in which they have an interest. In this structure the two parties create a third organization. Both parties share in its creation, organizational governance, operation, and financing. In the formal joint business venture, one party, especially the hospital, must avoid the legal interpretation of having undue influence over the venture for its own benefit. It must also be clear that the venture is not designed primarily to funnel referrals between the sponsoring parties—that is, solely for one partner to bring referrals to the other. Hospitals in such a venture can use the newly created organization to their benefit but only at arm's length, that is, through transactions that a disinterested third party would consider to be reasonable business decisions.

The advantage of the joint venture is that it allows equal ownership and an equal voice in operation. The joint venture partners, however, must recognize that either party may dissolve the agreement pursuant to the specific terms of the incorporation contract. The strengths or assets that each brings to the venture may be different and complementary. The provider group can invest by bringing fixed assets and professional service commitments, as opposed to cash, while the hospital may bring cash and market recognition.

Careful decisions must be made as to the tax status of such a venture. There are specific requirements for for-profit and nonprofit corporations. Of special concern is the situation where the two partners are of different business types, for example a for-profit professional corporation (a provider group) and a nonprofit hospital system. Legal and tax implications for each partner will require careful consideration. In addition, any revenues above expenses in the joint venture must be clearly identified for reinvestment or distribution to the partners.

The joint venture corporation may be administratively attached to one of the sponsoring agencies, thus reducing some of the duplication of administrative overhead. The joint venture may engage in contracting for business, including capitated arrangements. Typically, the sponsoring agencies act as guarantors of the agency's debts and can provide additional capital as required.

Hospital-owned Groups.   There is an increasing trend for hospitals and, in some cases, payors and venture capital groups to acquire the practices of one or several providers. Revisions in state laws that previously prohibited corporate ownership of medical practices are now allowing this option to be selected by a growing number of provider organizations. In this manner, the hospital acquires the hard assets and the clinical service delivery potential of the provider group. By using the hospital's assets, the provider group may expand, relocate, or otherwise reconfigure provider services to meet marketplace demands.

Typically, the core clinicians in the group remain intact. Clinicians may remain in a legally separate professional corporation (P.C.) or professional association (P.A.). In this scenario, the hospital acquires the hard assets of the provider group practice and assumes the management of the group including employment of the nonclinical staff. The clinical P.C. or P.A. then contracts with the hospital to carry out the service delivery duties within the business. The hospital bears all or a majority of the financial risk, enters into contracts with payors, and provides the administrative infrastructure necessary to run the practice.

In order to meet current Medicare requirements, rates for reimbursement from the hospital-owned practice to the clinicians' P.C or P.A. must be set annually, and changed only if there is a significant alteration in the business volume. Typically, the payment rate for clinical service provision by the P.C. or P.A. is a fixed annual amount paid monthly regardless of volume or fluctuations. Renegotiation of these fees occurs each year depending on the profitability of the operations, the quality of the program, its efficiency, or other operational elements.

Fees for cooperative activities must be set to some reasonable standard. The Medical Group Management Association (see Appendix B) provides guidelines, which are often used as benchmarks because they provide information by specialty and by region. The fees become a business expense that both the hospital and the provider group must closely monitor, as these fees have direct bearing on the bottom line of the venture. The more successful the undertaking, the more financially advantageous the arrangement can be. However, these benchmarks generally are not sensitive to variations in volume. Much like capitation, they provide no incentive that more work will generate greater provider reimbursement. In fact, the lack of such an incentive results in a situation where the less hours worked the more "per-hour value" the fee has. The P.C. or P.A. and the hospital must develop financial adjustments for volume factors. Creating properly aligned incentives and measures of productivity for the provider group is one of the most difficult aspects of hospital-owned groups.

Contractual Relationships. Another commonly used organizational arrangement is outright collaborative contracting. Insurance companies are now issuing requests for proposals to which providers or groups of providers may respond with proposals involving more than one party, such as a hospital collaborator. Such collaboration between a hospital and provider group contractually links the two for the business in question, but does not require that other contracts or referrals be handled in the same manner. Contracts usually specify each party's degree of risk and expectations, typically with hold-harmless clauses. Basically, these clauses make each party responsible for its own actions and free the other party from any liability.

Provider Divisions within a Healthcare System. Recently a variation on the contractual theme has come into favor. In this arrangement a provider group actually leases the hospital's units and personnel. For a fixed monthly or annual fee, the lessor is then free to manage these assets in support of its mission. This allows the healthcare system to continue to include the service as part of its continuum, but the cost and risk to the hospital is fixed within the lease fees. The provider group may be able to acquire the lease at an attractive rate if the hospital system otherwise would have little or no use for the hospital programs by supporting and marketing them directly.

The onus of developing the market remains with the lessor. Depending on the conditions of the lease, the use of trade names, building and equipment upkeep, and so forth, can be borne by the lessee or the lessor. However, hospitals choosing to follow this approach may not be able to recover operational costs for unused portions of buildings or equipment not in the lease. This arrangement permits the party bearing the greatest degree of risk to structure programs in the manner that will best suit its needs. Again, reasonable business practices must prevail regarding lease fees and so forth. However, often the reality today is that the hospital may have only two choices, lease a mental health unit or close it and leave it empty.

As shown in this chapter, there are a number of organizational approaches to creating vertically integrated behavioral delivery systems that can succeed under capitation. Many providers, be they hospitals or professionals, are quickly learning that the future requires an organized, integrated approach to the provision of care. Coming to grips with the implications of integration and responding with the approach that best suits the demands of the marketplace are the art and science of the future in healthcare.

10

IMPLEMENTING TOTAL QUALITY MANAGEMENT

Bob Ericson, Ph.D.

Quality improvement programs will play an ever-increasing and critical role in capitated, managed behavioral healthcare delivery systems in the 1990s and beyond. Progressive businesses nationally are demanding that their vendors and partners implement total quality management programs. This focus has also come to healthcare, including behavioral health. The long-term viability of behavioral health services is dependent on the availability of quality data. It is anticipated that having a nationally awarded quality certification soon will be a prerequisite for obtaining capitation contracts. Through data-driven quality programs, provider report cards, and active participatory management (for example, continuous improvement teams), behavioral healthcare providers can demonstrate credibility, value, and a contribution to individuals, businesses, and the community.

B ehavioral healthcare and the quality movement have much in common. The general purpose of each is to use objective, statistical, action-oriented research methods to discover better ways to solve problems, in order to improve the quality of life. Both range in perspective and application from individual concerns to social, organizational, and systems issues.

Total quality management (TQM), also known as continuous quality improvement, is a set of beliefs, principles, values, attitudes, and tools which can help overcome problems facing the behavioral healthcare industry as a result of cost escalation in the absence of outcomes data. Quality management provides a vehicle for responding to challenges such as the questioning of the effectiveness of clinical practice. Quality management enables behavioral healthcare professionals to be accountable for the value of their services to the community. TQM can secure for behavioral healthcare a place in the changing healthcare system of the 1990s.

The Objective — Or, What's in It for Us?

In the current business and economic situation, the survival of many mental health clinicians and provider organizations is not assured. Clinicians who are not committed to participating in a large delivery system that requires and/or generates quality data will see a rapid shrinking in both referrals and financial rewards.

Beyond survival, clinicians as individuals or in groups must demonstrate that they are competitive. It has become imperative to be willing to subject one's therapeutic outcomes to comparisons with national benchmarking standards. Investing in computers and software to track patients' progress must now take precedence over traditional office capital investments. To be cost-effective, clinicians increasingly will need to cooperate with colleagues and other health professionals. Community services will become important adjuncts to therapy as a means of cutting costs, providing continuity, and preventing adverse events such as suicide or extended hospitalization.

TQM provides the philosophy, techniques, and experience to improve competitiveness and cost-effectiveness. Businesses can improve their competitiveness merely by focusing on customer satisfaction. An organization that strives for outstanding service is also a more viable organization than one focused on short-term profit. Professional and personal growth will be derived from learning through the successes and opportunities of improved outcomes.

Motivation and Impetus

The growth of the TQM movement in America as a response to challenges from Japanese industry has been well documented. Dobyns and Crawford-Mason (1991) present a comprehensive perspective about the need to em-

---

Bob Ericson, Ph.D., is Manager of Quality Management, Co-founder, and President of Mesa Mental Health in Albuquerque, NM. He was born and raised in Minnesota, where he completed his undergraduate studies. He completed his doctorate at New Mexico State University in 1978. Dr. Ericson was originally exposed to quality programs and concepts while serving as a pilot in the U.S. Air Force. He has received training at National Training Laboratories and taught graduate courses in consultation.

brace quality. American electronics and automotive industries have responded to the quality challenge by generating programs that have closed the quality gap significantly over the past two decades. American industry has embraced the quality concept so completely that demonstrated adherence to accepted quality standards is now commonly required before a contract proposal will be reviewed.

Quality-driven changes in the way healthcare is purchased have been supported by industry payors primarily because they recognize the value of quality programs in cutting costs and encouraging innovation. Large employers also recognize that a major reason for declining world market share and financial progress is skyrocketing healthcare costs. Like other healthcare providers, the behavioral healthcare industry is now being required by insurance payors to implement quality management programs. That is not necessarily bad, but as behavioral health professionals we must retool to remain viable.

The National Committee for Quality Assurance (NCQA, see Appendix B) exerts a great deal of influence in this regard, and its accreditation is highly valued. By the end of 1994, close to 50 percent of the over 500 managed care organizations in the nation had gone through an NCQA accreditation review. NCQA provides a report card based on indicators specified in the Health Plan Employer Data and Information Set 2.0 (HEDIS). NCQA currently evaluates programs in six major quality categories: quality management and improvement, utilization management, credentialing, members' rights and responsibilities, medical records, and preventive health services. Three new categories of standards have been proposed for inclusion in 1995: technology assessment, organizational quality assessment, and health management systems. Various publications, including standards and reviewer guidelines, are available through NCQA.

The Basis of TQM

The philosophy of TQM is really quite simple. It is a set of management tools that enable organizations to adapt to change, meet demands of the market, and continuously improve in both product and service. Every person who has a stake in the company's success, from the board president to the janitor to the most demanding and needy customer, has an opportunity to identify and fix problems. Empowering from top to bottom helps to create a commitment and a culture that ensures flexibility, adaptability, and survivability. Quality is a means, not an end. Continuous improvement builds trust, long-term profitability, and better service.

TQM principles are similarly straightforward. Although there are minor differences between leading quality consultants such as Juran (1989), Crosby (1984), Deming (1986), and Ishikawa (1985), a rich and consistent literature on quality management has emerged since World War II. Basic principles of TQM, which translate from the world of industry to behavioral healthcare, include the following:

keep customers (clients, patients) satisfied;
focus on the process, not just outcomes;
involve all employees in change and innovation;
make decisions that are supported by facts, not intuition;
prevent problems before they occur;
follow a vision and a plan;
build in feedback and corrective actions;
recognize and reward useful suggestions;
provide community improvement services;
constantly innovate both process and product; and
remember that reasonable financial performance sustains quality.

Bowles and Hammond (1991) have taken TQM literature, philosophy, and principles a step further than the tangibles of industrial production. They recognize the special issues and needs of service quality. Service is distinct because it is performance-based, heterogeneous, inseparable from consumption, and perishable. These factors present unique problems for adapting traditional quality measurements, especially for customer satisfaction.

The fundamental tools required to implement TQM are statistically based decision-making procedures (Scholtes, 1988). Compared to research settings, these statistical techniques are less sophisticated and precise. However, their power lies in their elegance and action orientation (Joint Commission on Accreditation of Healthcare Organizations, 1992). A simple list of quality tools includes:

cause-and-effect diagrams,
Pareto charts,
histograms,
scatter diagrams,
Shewhart control charts, and
flow charts.

Other tools include brainstorming, multivoting, force field analysis, surveys, story boards, and turtle diagrams. Any device that contributes to discovering, organizing, and analyzing data or facts can be considered a quality tool.

Getting the Program Started

Implementation of TQM involves several stages. Typically, senior corporate executives begin the process by making the decision to support a quality program. The key administrators in a clinical group should obtain training in TQM philosophy, principles, and tools. They may, if advisable and/or financially feasible, evaluate the need to contract with an outside quality consultant. Next they should develop and communicate a practice-wide policy regarding such a program, and develop a business purpose or vision statement for the group.

Quality programs must be viewed as part of the cost of doing business. Accordingly, the business must commit resources, including time, money, and personnel, to the project.

Time incorporates three different perspectives. First, the organization needs to decide how much time should be dedicated to continuous quality improvement on an ongoing, for example, weekly, basis. This decision may depend on current market situation or training needs. If market share is critically dependent on demonstrating a viable quality program, it may be necessary to commit the entire work force to a minimum amount of formal, just-in-time education. If a group is large or old enough to be bound by bureaucracy, a major effort may be necessary to remove the old hierarchy, which will probably require a serious time commitment. Small, new, and enthusiastic groups can get by with less time for training and move more quickly into running the program.

Two different approaches to time commitment may help to illustrate a range of possibilities. In the first example, a medical technology laboratory is stable in market share and work force. It has a five-year plan to develop TQM by incorporating no more than 10 percent of the work force at any one time for two hours a week on a generally voluntary basis in training and projects. Worker productivity and financial performance are minimally reduced and the assumption is that the participatory culture of TQM will grow to encompass the entire organization and become optimally effective within the proposed five-year time frame.

The second example is a behavioral health organization of 60 employees which is dynamic and rapidly increasing market share, challenging employees to adjust to constant growth with minimal entrenched bureaucracy. However, contractual requirements and management philosophy urge a major commitment to quality improvement. This organization requires all employees to train and work on quality projects for about four hours a week. The time frame for implementation is shorter, around two years for basic TQM procedures. Productivity and finances are immediately and significantly impacted. The investment is made to provide long-lasting dividends.

How long will it take to see the benefits of TQM? Most organizations, and several authorities, suggest that observable progress requires a minimum of two years, possibly three. Again, this depends on the problems to be overcome and the scope and loftiness of the goals to be achieved.

The third time perspective involves designating a key employee whose time is allocated to plan, develop, train, implement, monitor, and coordinate the program. If the TQM coordinator has other duties, these should not be so distracting as to interfere with smooth implementation of the plan. Ideally there should be a full-time position dedicated to TQM. If this is impractical, the minimum time during the first two years of developing the TQM program is 50 percent of the coordinator's work week. Less than that is likely to lead to an impotent program, which is not perceived internally or externally as genuinely supported by management or the board of directors.

The initial TQM program must include a training plan. Key management executives need the initial philosophical as well as hands-on orientation. A secondary group of work team leaders should receive training in the nuts and bolts of TQM, as well as in facilitation skills. This group of team leaders probably has the greatest day-to-day impact on job-site applications of TQM tools. Periodic work group and/or organization-wide training sessions are helpful to encourage and sustain the TQM culture. Through applied work groups, individual employees obtain practical learning experiences in solving organizational problems. Finally, if financial and network resources are available, sending individuals or small groups away for remote training or consultation can be a good investment.

It is virtually impossible, and certainly imprudent, for one individual to tackle a TQM program alone. Various teams should be established to spread the work load, facilitate empowerment, foster buy-in, and, in general, establish the foundation for participatory management.

Participatory management in various models and applications is critical to the success of TQM. As Kanter (1983) states, "Masters of change are also masters of the use of participation." She outlines the critical elements of participation in well-managed systems, including clear management structure, manageable tasks, accountability in time and relationships, standards of performance, training involving all stakeholders, visibility and reward mechanisms, and clear processes for the life of a participative group.

The first group that must be established in a TQM program is a committee or council whose job is to implement policy, to develop and implement the plan, and to create, empower, and support continuous improvement teams (CITs). Initially, the council must identify specific problems requiring the establishment of CITs. Problems can be selected from management, employee, or external customer suggestions. There should be a mix of issues ranging from short-term, practical issues such as upgrading the telephone system to strategic, continuous processes such as establishing standards of care. Some short-term problems should be selected to increase the probability of early successes, visibility, and rewards.

Next, the council must make intelligent decisions about dedicating resources to the various projects, particularly of time and money. A schedule of expected time lines for tasks creates momentum. Accountable budget line items should be identified for training and material start-up costs. Salaries for personnel that spend significant time on the project should also be included.

Any TQM program needs continuous assessment and feedback from its inception. Internal organizational evaluations can be conducted informally through interviews and questionnaires. However, management surveys are best handled by external, independent professionals whose main objective is to provide objective feedback in a constructive setting and manner. Other forms of evaluation include client satisfaction surveys and self-evaluations of the implementation schedule and training provided at various intervals.

BUILDING CONTINUOUS IMPROVEMENT TEAMS

After problems have been selected, resources committed, and an evaluation program put in place, it is time to charter CITs to execute specific projects. The chartering process involves specifying goals and expectations, time frames for completion, support procedures and resources, authority to make limited decisions, and permission to adjust work schedules to commit to the project.

If possible, training should be provided for all CIT members before the task formally begins. In some cases, particularly when there is employee turnover or additions in personnel, individuals will need to receive on-the-job training. CITs should be comprised of various internal customer groups in order to obtain the greatest cross-section of input and to avoid future coordination problems. For example, a group formed to revise the organization and content of client charts should have clinicians as well as the clerical staff who must pull, deliver, file, and store charts. Transcriptionists must be involved due to issues of timeliness and format. A team that does not include all relevant members of the system is bound to encounter problems requiring rework. Teams that are multidisciplinary will experience quicker success and greater satisfaction.

The quality council must monitor progress of the various CITs in order to provide support, if necessary, and to implement the solutions devised as well as providing rewards and recognition. Rather than providing oral reports, it is best to set up a written reporting procedure channeled through the TQM program coordinator, who in turn provides oral reports to the council. The coordinator can then anticipate problems to bring to the council in the form of recommendations, as well as information.

Written records of the overall TQM plan as well as a specific CIT's progress and accomplishments provide the documentation of the quality program that may be required by outside agencies such as NCQA. Records also provide an internal history to help guide future efforts. The format may vary but regular team notes should include discussion items, person(s) responsible, action to be taken, and time frame for completion.

Although CIT members should be trained, balanced in composition, and chartered with support and resources, they may not be able to complete their tasks without some external consultation and support. Participation in CITs can be frustrating and exhilarating. It is frustrating to deal with group process in which several participants are inexperienced and unfamiliar with the rules. The process can bog down due to inadequate leadership, power imbalances, or lack of knowledge and information. At these times further training or time investment by members of the quality council can be helpful to facilitate a transition back to a productive group process.

Rewards can be derived from having a tangible, productive impact on the organization. However, altruism has its limits in organizational life and must be supplemented by other rewards and recognitions. Continued enthusiasm is contingent upon recognizing and celebrating success, and on compensating contributors with financial rewards such as bonuses or other benefits. If possible, it is best to tie these financial incentives to an estimate of savings or revenues generated from the solution. T-shirts, parking spaces, dinners, entertainment tickets, and certificates may be part of a buffet-style recognition program. It is also important to be flexible, knowing that what is satisfying for a high-salaried employee may have little value for an hourly wage earner, and vice versa.

Once a CIT has completed its basic task, there is no more deflating experience than seeing its work ignored. To make a real contribution, the team must know that its product or recommendations have been implemented successfully. Results must transfer to daily business life. That is the job and mandate of the quality council and of management. Without it, the program is hollow and will not endure.

A final note on building and implementing team-generated products and recommendations is that the job may not be finished even though the team has disbanded. Participatory programs need constant renewal. One way to achieve this is to monitor and revise the product on an extended basis, probably for at least a year. This responsibility is best shared by the quality council and at least one member of the CIT.

SPECIFIC MENTAL HEALTH ISSUES

Behavioral health systems experience unique problems that provide targets of opportunity. Service delivery can be organized into three basic components: *structure, process,* and *outcome.* The structure of a behavioral health program includes written plans and records, assignment of authority and accountability, management coordination, provider contracts, employment agreements, credentialing procedures, and service complaint procedures.

Process components refer to the actual delivery of service to the client. The traditional components of behavioral health processes are utilization review and utilization management policies and procedures. A closely related component is chart or record review. Service delivery depends on client access to care, customer-friendly office hours, and a flexible, sophisticated telephone system.

Outcome measures provide the bottom line in behavioral health quality programs. Do you deliver the services that people want and need? Traditional outcome measures include client satisfaction questionnaires and grievance/complaint reports. More innovative, sophisticated, and potentially valuable outcome indicators are addressed in Chapter 19. The primary goal of outcomes research is to provide statistically sound and meaningful data on the effectiveness of clinical care. Without outcomes research there is no justification for claims of value-added service.

The Report Card.   A complementary approach to documenting and measuring quality is through specific indicators—valid and reliable quantitative measures of performance. These need not be highly sophisticated. For example, a valuable clinical indicator can be the total number of hospital re-admissions within a specified time following discharge. An indicator of patient access is exemplified by the average amount of time from the telephone's first ring until the call is answered by office staff. The percentage of subcontractor claims processed and paid within a certain predefined time period after receipt is an example of a business office indicator.

Indicators come in various types and forms—such as aggregate, continuous variable, and rate-based (Joint Commission on Accreditation of Healthcare Organizations, 1992). Of particular importance are sentinel event indicators—those that automatically trigger further investigation, for example, a client suicide. Indicators are also divided by their intended use: internal only or for external publication. Data on certain indicators will be kept entirely for internal quality improvement (such as percentage of third-party billings not requiring any reprocessing), while others are important to distribute for feedback to payors and contractors (for example, percentage of clients with a significant improvement in overall health status sustained one year after ending behavioral health treatment). It is the job of the quality council and management to set up, implement, and publish a full range of indicators which are continuously kept and actively used for continuous improvement.

Monitoring Continuous Improvement Efforts Through Reports. Quality is a means, not an end. TQM is a vehicle to the higher goal of relentlessly seeking to provide better service. An intelligent, forward-looking TQM plan builds in the need for constant evaluation and review through reporting. The plan should specify the frequency and the recipients of evaluative reports. Initially it is not uncommon nor unreasonable for a board of directors and major contractors to require quarterly reports on the progress of the quality program. After reasonable success in proving competence, annual reporting to external sources may be sufficient. By contrast, internal reporting to the quality council should remain quarterly. While this may seem onerous, a program designed with proper structure and resources will flourish with regular review.

Keep a perspective on your TQM program and the forces that drive it. Currently healthcare, and specifically behavioral health services, is being driven by cost, changing legislation, and the need to establish accountability. Bowles and Hammond (1991) have outlined stages and considerations in the hierarchy of quality programs. It is easy to be disheartened to see ourselves struggling with the lowest level of quality programs. However, as TQM in healthcare matures, behavioral health programs will demonstrate value in their services and be encouraged toward innovative programs. When value and innovation are integrated, we will have met the quality challenge.

REFERENCES

Bowles, J., & Hammond, J. (1991). *Beyond quality.* New York: Berkeley.

Crosby, P. B. (1984). *Quality without tears: The art of hassle-free management.* New York: McGraw-Hill.

Deming, W. E. (1986). *Out of the crisis.* (2nd Edition). Cambridge, MA: MIT Center for Advanced Engineering Study.

Dobyns, L., & Crawford-Mason, C. (1991). *Quality or else.* Boston: Houghton Mifflin.

Ishikawa, K. (1985) *What is total quality control? The Japanese way.* Translated by D. J. Lu. Englewood Cliffs, NJ: Prentice-Hall.

Joint Commission on Accreditation of Healthcare Organizations (1992). *The transition from QA to QI: Performance-based evaluation of mental health organizations.* Oakbrook Terrace: Author.

Juran, J. M. (1989). *Juran on leadership for quality: An executive handbook.* New York: The Free Press.

Kanter, R. M. (1983). *The change masters.* New York: Touchstone; p. 241.

Scholtes, P. R. (1988). *The team handbook: How to use teams to improve quality.* Madison, WI: Joiner.

DOING
CAPITATION

11

THE FINANCES OF CAPITATION

Neil Dickman, Ph.D.

Understanding the financial intricacies of capitation is crucial to successful at-risk contracting. This chapter presents some of the risks to consider, how to carefully define the benefit package being purchased, how to specify the population being served, and an array of caveats. The nuts and bolts involved in pricing a capitated contract bid are given, as are details to consider in examining the quantifiable aspects of capitation planning. Based on years of direct experience with several capitation contracts, Dr. Dickman then provides a carefully detailed example of pricing a capitation contract, including outpatient expenditures, hospital costs—both professional and per diem—overhead expenses, and profit margin.

The success of capitation as a reimbursement model for behavioral group practices is heavily linked to both quantifiable and nonquantifiable factors. The purpose of this chapter is to focus primarily on the most predictable aspects of capitation planning.

However, it is important to digress briefly to discuss some of the less tangible but equally important influences on successful at-risk contracting. The culture or shared vision of the behavioral healthcare group creates the cohesive glue that binds it. Establishing a successful group culture creates an environment where innovative new management and service technologies can be developed. An entrepreneurial spirit and strong management skills allow for the continued evaluation and retooling necessary to address the continually changing demands of the capitated environment. As capitation rates decline because of increasing competition and lower reimbursement for healthcare overall, the pressures on organizational unity will increase. Bringing all staff, both administrative and clinical, into the spirit of capitation through innovative compensation packages and team-oriented decision making will help focus the collective intelligence of the group on future problem solving. Given this proviso, there are some basic parameters that need to be considered when pricing a capitation proposal.

VOCABULARY OF RISK

A basic primer in the vocabulary of capitation is a necessary first step in understanding at-risk agreements. As discussed in some detail in Chapter 4, eleven categories of capitation risk are important to consider. These categories include direct risk, demand risk, utilization risk, beta risk, and price risk, plus six indirect risks: regulatory, insurance, liability, contract, infrastructure, and professional.

As much as possible, all of these risk types should be considered in negotiating a capitated agreement. As an illustration, the author's organization holds an exclusive capitated agreement with a large independent practice association (IPA) in Northern California. When the agreement was first negotiated, all of the IPA's contracted lives were concentrated in one focused geographical area. It was also agreed during the initial negotiations that patients would not travel more than a half hour to any outpatient facility. Not much more thought was given to this understanding because it seemed like an easy requirement to fulfill. Failing to anticipate the costs that would be incurred in creating the required geographic access, the organization agreed to the geographic access clause without linking it to increased compensation. Now, with nine outpatient clinics serving enrollees of this IPA, negotiating increases in the capitation rate to cover the cost of these new facilities has been difficult at best.

As a consequence of the number of variables involved in full at-risk contracting, some behavioral health groups that are new to the managed care marketplace might prefer to negotiate contracts that would protect them

Neil Dickman, Ph.D., is the Chief Executive Officer of Pacific Applied Psychology Associates, Inc. (P.A.P.A.). P.A.P.A. is a fully integrated behavioral health provider group in Berkeley, CA, which has specialized in managed care at-risk contracts since 1982, and currently has contracts for approximately 200,000 capitated lives. (See Chapter 24.) Dr. Dickman has dedicated his career to developing high-quality, efficient behavioral health delivery systems for underserved populations.

from full risk. The continuum of risk arrangements runs along the following path:

1. *Reduced Fee for Service.* Groups can offer a reduced fee for service. This is a typical preferred provider organization (PPO) and managed care organization (MCO) contracting formula.

2. *Per-episode Guarantee.* This attaches a stop-loss element to outpatient case referrals.

3. *Case Rate.* This is one basic charge for each referral no matter how long treatment lasts. It puts the provider group at risk for the length of treatment but protects the group from many of the other types of risk mentioned above.

4. *Risk Corridor/Risk Band Capitation.* This agreement protects the provider group from exceptionally high utilization resulting from referral rates and direct risk. The capitation rate per member per month typically rises and falls based on a system of preset variables, especially the utilization rate.

5. *Professional Fee Capitation.* The provider group is at risk for the professional fee portion of the costs, but not hospital daily charges.

6. *Full Capitation.* The provider group accepts one rate for all of the risk associated with managing a behavioral health benefit.

The next two sections speak directly to the specific parameters that must be considered in developing the pricing for a full capitated offer. These areas of understanding are critical to the success of the contract. It is highly recommended that they be addressed in a separate exhibit within the agreement between the behavioral health group and payor.

DEFINING THE BENEFIT

What services is the capitating group agreeing to provide, under what conditions and restrictions, and with how much flexibility? These are among the most relevant elements in pricing any capitated arrangement. What are the covered services and what are the exclusions to this coverage? These items should be discussed and clarified by both parties and then written as a separate exhibit to the contract. The discussion should include, but not be limited to:

1. *How is the coverage described in the enrollees' policy?* Does the description in the policy bear any resemblance to the description of the benefit being offered in marketing materials? Is there a broad

discrepancy? Will the payor agree to back you on strict enforcement of the benefit package? Negotiate consideration for a change in the reimbursement rate if benefits are added after signing the agreement.

2. *Is there a limitation on the length of outpatient treatment?* Is that limitation based on a restricted number of sessions, or is it based on clinical limitations like "crisis intervention only" or "medical necessity"? Or, as with many HMOs, is there language pertaining to both limitations? Is flexibility allowed in defining crisis intervention or medical necessity, or does the payor have its own standards? An understanding about the methodology for arbitration involving disagreements in application of clinical criteria should be established.

3. *Are there specific exclusions from the outpatient therapy benefit?* Some typical exclusions are:
   a. organic brain disorders,
   b. behavioral disorders,
   c. court-ordered treatment,
   d. learning disabilities, and
   e. biofeedback.

4. *Is there a limitation on the length of inpatient treatment?* A typical HMO limitation is 30 days per calendar year. Most insurance companies have a limit on hospital use. This restriction is usually defined in terms of either the number of days per calendar year or a lifetime benefit. Less often the benefit limit is described in terms of dollars used. Does a benefit exist for partial hospitalization? If not, can inpatient days be traded for partial days? The usual formula is two partial hospital days for one inpatient day.

5. *Is chemical dependency a covered benefit?* In California, where the author's company operates, many HMOs have found it difficult to administer a chemical dependency benefit and have not wanted to incur adverse selection. Consequently, there is no addiction coverage in 90 percent of the standard HMO benefit plans. Many HMOs offer a chemical dependency rider to the insurance package, but few companies have been willing to pay the extra premium.

If chemical dependency is offered as a benefit, it is important to establish its extent. Are both outpatient and inpatient chemical dependency treatment covered? If so, who decides the focus of treatment: the provider or the patient? Can the provider group contract with residential treatment centers or must all inpatient services be hospital-based? If detoxification is a covered benefit, is it considered a psychiatric or a medical cost? The author's group in its agreements has established detoxification as a medical cost, and the medical group pays for it. Rehabilitation is considered to be a psychiatric cost and is covered under the capitation agreement.

The following are some specific benefit coverage issues to be reviewed.

History-and-Physical Examinations.   When patients are admitted to a psychiatric facility they are routinely administered a medical examination, termed a History-and-Physical. In a professional fee-only capitated agreement, an understanding must be reached as to whether the cost of this exam is a professional fee or a facility charge.

Medical-Surgical Consultations.   One of the more overlooked areas of negotiation is whether the provider group is responsible for emergent psychiatric evaluations for patients hospitalized in a medical facility. If so, it is important to cost out and deliver timely medical-surgical consults.

Out-of-Area Coverage.   Full capitation almost always includes acceptance of financial responsibility for out-of-area treatment. This is both an outpatient and an inpatient issue. The provider group must plan for the ability to establish timely reimbursement and utilization review agreements with out-of-area providers.

Ambulance.   Transportation issues arise in several ways. Patients may be sent from a crisis unit to a hospital by ambulance, and interhospital transfers may also be necessary. Negotiating who is responsible for the costs of emergency transportation is an additional consideration.

In one of the author's HMO agreements, the insurance company began marketing a plan with unlimited outpatient treatment. Given the limited ability to apply utilization management to these cases, the author worked out an arrangement whereby the HMO paid on a reduced fee-for-service basis for all visits beyond six. This arrangement protected the group from a risk element that was beyond its control.

The list of possible benefits and exclusions is extensive and too numerous to completely cover in this chapter. The key is to clarify at the beginning of negotiation what services are to be the responsibility of the capitated provider group. Establish an agreement specifying that if the benefits are revised unilaterally, the contract rate structure can be reopened. Be sure to outline clearly the covered services, and the exclusions to those services, in a separate exhibit. Be sure to establish a mechanism for arbitration of patient complaints relating to administration and interpretation of the exclusions.

DEFINING THE POPULATION

Population risk dynamics are among the most unpredictable variants in capitation planning. The major protections afforded to a provider group are through increased volume of covered lives; risk is minimized as the population base increases. Often in new contract development, however, the population base begins at a relatively small level, maximizing individual risk factors. Some options for population risk limitation can be built into the contract language.

Referral risk is a chief concern. What happens in a fixed capitation agreement if significantly more referrals per thousand occur than predicted? This phenomenon can be caused by many different factors. All of the following have affected the author's group adversely at different times.

1. *Insufficient or Inaccurate Utilization Data.* Payors like HMOs, medical groups, and MCOs often have difficulty retrieving accurate historical data. Be very careful in predicting a capitation bid based on someone else's data.

2. *Shifts in Compensation Methodology of Referral Agents.* Primary care physicians (PCPs) are often the main source of HMO referrals. When PCPs have their compensation shifted from fee-for-service to capitation, their financial incentives change. Rather than treating mild mental health disorders themselves, PCPs begin referring most patients with behavioral and emotional problems to mental health treatment. Consequently, referral rates will increase substantially.

3. *Adverse Selection.* Several years ago a major contractor to the author's group took on two new large employer groups, a school system and a local correctional facility. Both of these new employer groups had referral rates significantly higher than predicted levels, and referral rates increased significantly. A contingency for such events would be a contract clause reopening pricing negotiations if utilization rises above a certain level.

4. *Special Needs Groups.* There are many types of special need population groups, whether based on language, race or ethnicity, age, or clinical syndrome. The author's group is based on a staff model, where financial stability depends on serving 80 percent of the outpatient referrals within the employed staff. When the provider group accepted risk for an employer group with a high percentage of Southeast Asian immigrants requiring a spectrum of different language capabilities, it resulted in an adverse increase in out-of-group referrals. Special groups or treatment situations must be given careful thought at the time of pricing a capitation bid.

Even the most thorough prior evaluation cannot completely protect the provider group from random adverse events. For example, two national news magazines recently published feature articles about Adult Attention Deficit Disorder. Within days, there was a flood of requests for evaluation and treatment of this disorder.

The best protection from the risks associated with adverse selection and special needs groups lies in the covered population size. These variables tend to even each other out as the law of averages takes effect with a large enough client pool. Populations of 10,000 to 20,000 are usually large enough to mitigate against a strong impact from adverse selection or special needs groups, especially if the population represents a broad spectrum geographically and among several employer groups.

Risk bands or risk corridors are contractual methods of affording protection from unanticipated utilization. As discussed earlier, the risk corridor is a means of agreeing on expected utilization between the two parties. A utilization rate range is set in which the capitation level remains firm. If the referral rate exceeds that range, then the capitation rate rises according to a preset formula. Some contractors will insist on the same preset formula for decreasing the capitation rate for a lower referral rate. In new contract agreements some form of utilization rate risk protection is essential because of the many variables in prediction discussed earlier.

One final tip: sometimes contracts are lost. Be sure to anticipate this possibility. Draw up distinct terms for all post-termination services, including reimbursement requirements. Fee-for-service arrangements are best for handling post-termination services, since there is no longer any incentive to be at risk.

PRICING THE CONTRACT

How to structure the pricing of services is to a large extent dependent on whether a staff or network provider model is utilized. This structural issue is primary in setting a capitation rate because labor is the largest line item cost. How one chooses to manage professional service costs is fundamental to the success of the capitation.

There are many benefits and deficiencies in both models. Currently this is a debated issue in the behavioral healthcare provider community. A full discussion of the pros and cons of the different systems falls outside the scope of this chapter. (See Chapter 15.) For ease of illustration the following examples of pricing a capitation bid are based on a network service delivery model. The basic principles and final cost figures are similar with a staff model. Complicating factors for the purposes of illustration include professional and nonprofessional staff payroll costs and hospital per diem rates, which vary widely by group and region.

The rate-setting parameters that are critical to any capitation pricing agreement are: outpatient and inpatient utilization rates, average inpatient length of stay, and average number of outpatient treatment sessions per episode of care. Utilization statistics can vary considerably depending on many of the variables discussed earlier.

Outpatient Utilization. The range of utilization for outpatient services can be quite wide. The previous history of the population and the benefit structure have much to do with this. For HMO subscribers, where the outpatient benefit is relatively limited, highly efficient provider groups can effectively employ brief therapy strategies (often including an array of group therapies with group visits counting as one-half or one-third of a traditional individual psychotherapy session). Look for the average outpatient treatment episode to run four to six traditional sessions in length. In such settings the service utilization rate (often referred to as the penetration rate) tends to be 3 to 4.5 percent of enrollees accessing mental health treatment, resulting in 120 to 220 visits per thousand enrollees. For broader MCO benefits, look for 170 to 300 visits per thousand.

Inpatient Utilization. Rates can range between 13 and 30 days of inpatient treatment per thousand enrollees, with two to three enrollees per thousand requiring hospital care.

Pricing Illustration

Figures 11.1 to 11.9 provide examples of pricing a full-risk bid. The utilization and cost figures quoted should not be used as hard numbers, but as guidelines. Greater efficiency in service delivery, especially in hospital facility and professional costs, could significantly lower the cost of this bid. Again, it is important to have statistics and data unique to one's payor, region, and provider group.

In pricing, it is most important to predict and negotiate the areas of risk described in this chapter. Whenever possible, add at least 10 percent for profit and to cover unexpected or unpredicted risk contingencies.

In conclusion, properly predicted capitation rates afford an opportunity for behavioral health groups to maximize profit through effective case and fiscal management. Efficient, high-quality care and business functions are the keys to successful at-risk contracting.

Figure 11.1 Assumptions in Pricing Illustration

- The capitated population is 100,000 enrollees.

- Mental health outpatient and inpatient benefits are covered, but not substance abuse/chemical dependency benefits.

- The benefit structure is a typical HMO plan with up to 20 outpatient visits and 30 inpatient days per year, with each partial hospital day counted as .5 inpatient day.

- Consultations in medical and surgical facilities are not to be capitated.

- History-and-physical examinations, hospital laboratory costs, and pharmacy charges are not to be capitated.

Figure 11.2 Hospital Professional Services

UTILIZATION:

25 days per 1,000 lives:	2,500 days
Average length of stay (ALOS)*:	8 days
Average number of admissions/year (2,500/8):	312 admissions

PHYSICIAN COSTS:

312 initial visits at $120:	$37,440
2,188 daily follow-up visits at $90:	$196,920
Total physician costs per year:	$234,360

PSYCHOLOGIST COSTS:

Psychological testing of 7% of admits:	22 patients
Average cost of testing:	$500
Total testing costs per year:	$11,000
Total hospital professional costs per year:	$245,360

*ALOS = 6.5 days for adults, 12.5 for children and adolescents (children and adolescents account for 25 percent of admissions).

Figure 11.3 Outpatient Professional Services

UTILIZATION:

Enrollees accessing care (3.5%):	3,500 patients
Average 4 visits per patient:	14,000 visits

PROFESSIONAL COSTS BY DISCIPLINE:

	M.D	Ph.D.	LCSW/MFCC
Percentage of all visits	20%	40%	40%
Total visits per year	2,800	5,600	5,600
Initial visit fee	$120	$90	$90
Follow-up visit fee (3/tx episode)	$70	$70	$70
Average co-payment collected/visit*	$18	$18	$18
Average cost per visit**	$64.50	$57	$57
Total costs per discipline***:	$180,600	$319,200	$319,200

Total outpatient professional costs per year: $819,000

  * Average patient co-payment due of $20 with 90% collection rate
 ** (Initial fee + (3 x follow-up fee) – (4 x co-payment collected)) / 4
*** For each discipline: Total visits per year x average cost per visit

---

Figure 11.4 Professional Services Per Member Per Month (PMPM) Rate

---

Inpatient professional costs per year:	$245,360
Outpatient professional costs per year:	$819,000
Total professional costs per year:	$1,064,360
Professional services capitation charge*:	$0.89 PMPM
Plus profit/contingency of 10%:	$0.09 PMPM
Total professional fee capitation bid:	$0.98 PMPM

* Formula: Annual costs / 12 months / Total capitated lives = PMPM.

Figure 11.5 Hospital Facility Costs

Hospital days per 1,000 capitated lives:	25
Total hospital days:	2,500
Cost per hospital day*:	$365
Total hospital facility costs per year:	$912,500

* Assumes $480 inpatient and $250 partial hospital per diems, with 50% of total hospital days in inpatient and 50% in partial hospitalization.

Figure 11.6 Hospital Facility Per Member Per Month (PMPM) Rate

Total hospital facility costs per year:	$912,500
Facility capitation charge*:	$0.76 PMPM
Plus profit/contingency at 10%:	$0.08 PMPM
Total facility capitation bid:	$0.84 PMPM

* Formula: Annual costs / 12 months / Total capitated lives = PMPM.

Figure 11.7 Annual Overhead Costs

STAFF COSTS:

Intake and Triage staff (1.0 FTE):	$36,000
Physician for UR (4 hours/week at $100):	$19,200
Ph.D. for UR (6 hours/week at $70):	$25,200
Office Manager (1.0 FTE):	$48,000
Clerical (1.0 FTE):	$24,000
Data and claims processing (1.0 FTE):	$36,000
Misc. payroll costs (primarily benefits):	$40,800
Total payroll costs per year:	$229,200

OTHER COSTS:

Practice management pro rata allotment:	$90,000
Total equipment, supplies, rent per year:	$90,000
Quality management (includes outcomes research):	$15,000
Total other costs per year:	$185,000
Total overhead costs per year:	$424,200

Figure 11.8 Overhead Per Member Per Month (PMPM) Rate

Total overhead costs per year:	$424,200
Overhead capitation rate*:	$0.35 PMPM
Plus profit/contingency at 10%:	$0.04 PMPM
Total overhead capitation bid:	$0.39 PMPM

* Formula: Annual costs / 12 months / Total capitated lives = PMPM.

Figure 11.9 Full Service Per Member Per Month (PMPM) Rate

Total capitation costs per year (without profit/contingency @ 10%):	$2,652,560
Professional services PMPM:	$0.98
Facility services PMPM:	$0.84
Overhead services PMPM:	$0.39
Full service PMPM:	$2.21

12

WRITING THE PROPOSAL

Steven Sehr, M.D.

This chapter introduces the reader to the process of responding to requests for proposals (RFPs) to deliver and manage capitated clinical services, and describes the necessary contents of successful proposals. It looks at the hard and soft aspects of writing these proposals, and identifies the competencies that a healthcare system must master before attempting to compete in the capitation marketplace. Technical information to be included in an RFP includes a description of the provider organization, a definition of the benefit structure, an outline of the management information system, a description of the provider network, complaint resolution procedures, and responses to quality management requirements. Also discussed is how to project confidence in your organization and its capabilities to payors.

Previous chapters have described how a capitated delivery system should look, feel, and perform to be successful. However, no matter how effective a delivery system is at providing high-quality, cost-effective services, successful contract acquisition depends on convincing purchasers that the organization is prepared for the task. The process of selling the merits of a clinical and management delivery system involves responding to requests for proposals (RFPs).

Purchasers generate these requests as a means of gathering information about, and assessing the capabilities of, competing delivery systems—in anticipation of eventually selecting a provider. Responding to these requests involves enormous effort, since the information requested is becoming ever more comprehensive. Beyond general information about an organization, purchasers are becoming more sophisticated in their demands for information about quality of care and services.

DESCRIBING YOUR ORGANIZATION

RFPs ask for information about the organization responding to the request. This information usually includes the age and experience of the bidding organization, the stability and experience of its leaders, and the stability of the organization in the community. The successful organization uses this opportunity to display its current skills in managing a delivery system. If this is the organization's first contract, it is an opportunity to identify the practice group or network as a stable provider entity willing to act in a forward-thinking manner. The educational level, experience, and stability of the organization's leadership can project the know-how and confidence to manage a capitated population. Do not underestimate the importance of these qualifications in the initial sections of the proposal.

Clinical Services

All RFPs contain questions about an organization's clinical delivery system. These questions help the organization describe the scope and depth of clinical services provided. The RFP will ask for information on *how* the system delivers clinical services. Such issues as access and intake for new clients, emergency response, clinical standards, and outcomes protocols help differentiate the proposal from others.

Intake and access are very important issues for purchasers, especially those shopping for quality services. Purchasers want to be assured that their members will have easy, quick, and effective access to services when needed. How do members contact the organization when they need services? Are the delivery sites convenient enough to ensure easy access? Are clients taken through an intake process and, if so, how long does this

Steven Sehr, M.D., is the Executive Director of Mesa Mental Health, a large multispecialty behavioral health group practice in Albuquerque, NM. He has served in this position since 1991, having been Mesa's Medical Director since 1988. In addition he is Program Medical Director for the Behavioral Health Network of Presbyterian Healthcare Services in Albuquerque. He has been writing capitation proposals and negotiating capitated contracts since 1987. Dr. Sehr is a graduate of the University of New Mexico School of Medicine and is Board Certified in Adult and in Child and Adolescent Psychiatry.

process take from initial contact to the beginning of treatment? What will clients do in an emergency? These questions must be answered in detail.

Besides the structure of the delivery system, many questions in the RFP will ask about the *scope of services* covered under the proposal. Here the issue of covered services usually is clearly outlined. Many RFPs, especially those designed by consultants, specify benefit structure in the request, making it difficult to differentiate an organization from others based on services provided. Some smaller, more progressive purchasers will ask the respondent to create the benefit package, providing more opportunity to be innovative and to clearly differentiate the provider's product from other proposals. Services such as employee assistance, prevention activities, and medical-surgical consultations can then be offered as part of the proposal. These services obviously affect the total capitation rate, due to increased costs, but they may also add value to the product. (See Chapter 11 for an explanation of how benefit coverage and exclusions greatly affect the capitation rate.) Even when the benefit package has been thoroughly defined, it is permissible to offer additional services which are clearly described and priced separately from the defined benefit structure.

THE BENEFITS PACKAGE

Without advocating any one specific benefit philosophy, the following are the key issues in evaluating a benefit structure. The most important issue is *covered services*. In a behavioral health capitation contract, the list of covered services must be as precise as possible. Covered services generally include such things as psychotherapy, medication management, inpatient professional and facility services, and similar services. Medical-surgical consultations, emergency room visits, biofeedback and chronic pain management, employee assistance services, medication costs, inpatient ancillary fees (such as fees for taking a medical history, performing physical exams, and administering laboratory tests), and treatment for organic illnesses (for example, neuro-psychological testing) are examples of services that must be addressed explicitly in the proposal. These are frequent areas of negotiation in contracting for services.

It is important to clarify the issue of noncovered diagnoses, commonly known as *exclusions*. Health maintenance organizations (HMOs) often use benefit exclusions as a way to reduce their exposure for patients with chronic conditions. Their benefit structure often excludes personality disorders and certain behavioral problems—since these clients have been identified as very high utilizers of services, and the efficacy of brief, acute treatments are questionable. Marital problems as a focus of treatment are also often excluded because these are not perceived as a health issue. Currently some purchasers are moving away from benefit designs that feature clinical exclusions, as enlightened purchasers understand that wellness requires providing behavioral health treatment to everyone in their population.

Who pays is probably the next crucial issue in the benefit structure. Deductibles, co-payments, and maximum out-of-pocket expenses need to be identified to determine the capitation rate. These specifics not only affect the cost to the individual client and payor, but can have dramatic effects on the population's utilization rates. In general, the higher the expense to the client, the lower the utilization rates, especially for clients whose needs are not acute. However, high costs to the client ultimately may result in more crisis and hospital services. In pricing it is also important to consider the likely rate of client co-payment collections. Outpatient co-payments can often be collected at 90 percent or better while hospital co-payments may fall below 50 percent in what can actually be collected. (See Chapter 11.)

The quantity of services covered also dramatically affects utilization and, therefore, capitation rates. The number of allowed outpatient visits, inpatient days, and other available services strongly determines risk exposure in a situation of maximal utilization.

Finally, the *covered population* or geographic area of responsibility must be clearly identified. Is the organization at-risk for out-of-area emergencies and services or does the purchaser accept this responsibility? Is there any coverage for out-of-area services? When bidding on a point-of-service plan with out-of-network benefits, who is responsible for the cost of out-of-network activities? Clarify a plan for these issues in the proposal.

Managing Information and Reporting

In bidding on a capitation contract, it is most important to identify how utilization will be monitored, and how providers and facilities will be paid. To do this requires a management information system (MIS). Describe the MIS and provide samples of its reporting capabilities. Do not try to enter into capitation without these capabilities! Few purchasers today will choose a provider without an MIS clearly defined and in place.

An adequate MIS system will adjudicate claims from network providers and facilities, collect utilization review information, and track overall utilization patterns in the covered populations. The capability to maintain and provide data on precertification and utilization approvals for continued services must also be demonstrated. If the delivery system is carefully tracked, the costs of providing these services can be regularly monitored, thus eliminating financial surprises. (See Chapter 16.)

Paying claims requires a system that can process and track all aspects of insurance protocols, including co-payments, deductibles, out-of-pocket amounts, and co-insurance. Demonstrate capabilities in these areas in detail by either describing the system or providing sample forms as attachments to the proposal.

Describing the Network

In a capitation arrangement, the contract group becomes responsible for managing the clinical providers. Even in a staff- or a blended staff/network-model provider panel, the organization controlling the contract is responsible for ensuring that providers are competent to perform the identified services. The contracted agency takes on the legal responsibility to health plan members of ensuring that the providers are appropriately screened and credentialed.

The credentialing process can be integrated with the existing purchaser's policies, or it can be managed directly by the contracting organization. If the contracting organization manages the process, a systematic mechanism for credentialing providers is necessary. (See Appendix D.) Be prepared to describe the process and attach key documents from the credentialing plan. The details of credentialing are beyond the scope of this chapter, but in general the mechanisms must verify training and degrees, licensure, subsequent experience and supervision, prior adverse incidents, and malpractice coverage of providers.

The purchaser is likely to ask for the provider mix within the delivery system. Provider mix constitutes not only the mix of training levels (that is, physicians, behavioral healthcare professionals, and so forth) but also their specialty orientation (such as child, geriatric, or addiction treatment). The purchaser wishes to be assured that the provider group is capable of providing comprehensive services to its members. In addition to the clinical mix, if the contract covers a large geographic area, the geographic distribution of the provider panel should be included.

After describing the network from the perspective of clinical personnel, most RFPs ask for a definition of the relationship and rules between the contracting organization and the network of providers—both professionals and facilities. Issues such as balance billing, payment structures, financial protection of the client, and hold-harmless clauses must be described in a proposal. In addition, the purchaser will be interested in any mandated quality activities in which providers must participate. Are they required to undergo routine quality screens or to participate in peer review or outcomes studies? Are there mandates for ease of client access, communication with the primary care physician, or other service-related issues? The more effectively these quality issues are articulated, the more effectively the system will be differentiated from others.

Complaint Resolution

Being responsible for the management of the member population also requires being responsible for resolving any complaints or disputes that arise in the service network. Such complaints can arise from access or clinical issues, are generated from support staff activities, or may be related to utilization management decisions. The organization needs to articulate a clear and standardized process to collect, research, and resolve member and provider complaints. In addition, a clearly stated procedure to resolve disputes involving utilization review decisions is absolutely mandatory. Who reviews them? What is the appeals mechanism? Describe the process and perhaps attach a copy of written procedures.

Quality Management

In the past, quality management was a buzzword that confused providers and purchasers alike. However, in the last few years the term has come to mean very specific activities and criteria that providers can no longer ignore. It has become increasingly difficult to even offer a proposal without the thorough understanding and implementation of a comprehensive quality management plan.

This chapter cannot fully elucidate the nuances of quality management. (See Chapter 10.) However, the reader must be aware of two key current quality management structures that are instrumental in setting purchaser expectations. These structures are the National Committee for Quality Assurance (NCQA) and its quality measurement program, the Health Plan Employer Data Information Set 2.0 (HEDIS; see Appendix B). NCQA accreditation, based upon HEDIS performance measurements, is creating a new standard by which provider organizational performance can be measured and compared.

NCQA is a national certification organization for HMOs, much like the Joint Commission on Accreditation of Healthcare Organizations (JCAHO) for health facilities. NCQA's primary activity is to define purchasers' expectations relating to the structure and scope of an organization's quality management activities and, subsequently, to accredit organizations that meet these requirements. NCQA generally surveys HMOs, but can survey any large delivery system if requested to do so. As the capitated provider for a purchaser that may be accredited or will seek accreditation, the contracted group will be asked to become a "delegated quality activity," requiring it to work toward meeting applicable NCQA requirements. The areas addressed by NCQA are quality improvement, utilization management, credentialing, member rights and responsibilities, prevention services, and medical records. An NCQA surveyor will be interested in an organization's policies, procedures, management structures, and other activities that support accreditation objectives.

HEDIS is a set of clinical criteria developed by a consortium of large national purchasers in an effort to understand clinical quality and compare different provider organizations. In the HEDIS data set, criteria for childhood immunization rates, mammography rates, and cesarean section rates, for example, are set forth. In behavioral healthcare the current focus is on recidivism rates, outpatient follow-up after inpatient stays, and overall utilization rates for mental healthcare and addiction treatment services. Although HEDIS was not meant to be the end point for describing clinical quality, it is a document that has set expectations for the data that purchasers today are generally requesting from bidders. HEDIS also requests information about an organization's financial stability and member satisfaction.

Address NCQA and HEDIS readiness in the capitation proposal. If you do not have these activities in place, it is vital to discuss plans for making the organization knowledgeable about these expectations, and to include either current quality statistics or a plan to develop them. Do not be afraid to state that the organization is not currently capable of providing these data. Almost every other bidder is in a similar situation. However, to successfully compete in today's capitation marketplace it is crucial to demonstrate knowledge and commitment to pursuing these goals.

THE SOFTER ASPECTS OF WRITING THE PROPOSAL

Having introduced the technical contents of an RFP, we now must discuss the less concrete aspects of writing the proposal. These will have as much to do with its success as the technical contents. When responding to an RFP, it is necessary to be knowledgeable about the purchasing organization, including the purchaser's population, service expectations, and culture. By understanding these issues, it is possible to target a proposal toward the purchaser's expectations. (See Chapters 7 and 8.) Investigate the purchaser's other relationships. What are the qualities it seeks in a contractor? Are there issues in the RFP that require special attention because they are so important to the purchaser? Is the purchaser using a benefits consultant?

If the answer is yes, do the same research on the consulting firm, since it, too, will have personal interests and biases.

Be honest. Describe the organization carefully and accurately. Never mislead the purchaser into thinking you have a capability that you may never be able to provide. Misleading the purchaser will haunt you forever, whether you are awarded the contract or not. There is no quicker way to discredit an organization than to lie in a proposal.

This is not to say that responses should not be structured in ways that highlight an organization's strengths and minimize its current weaknesses. Expound on those areas of the proposal that differentiate services from competitors' and demonstrate the organization's strengths. Minimize the organization's weaknesses by bringing as little attention as possible to those issues that may need further development. Most of all, be confident in describing your capabilities. Be proud of what the organization can offer to the purchaser and express that pride in the proposal.

Finally, keep abreast of current RFPs, especially those originating from large, national employers. Even if you do not intend to bid on these requests, their contents can help in developing an organization that is ready to compete successfully for capitation contracts. Generally, large purchasers set the stage for systemwide expectations. Many of the requirements found in the RFPs of large corporations seen as leaders in employee benefits likely will trickle down to smaller local purchasers. Stay ahead of the curve by being knowledgeable about what capitated organizations will be required to provide in the future.

CONCLUSION

The process of responding to an RFP is only one aspect of successfully competing in a capitated environment. To obtain contracts effectively, an organization must be skilled at responding to RFPs. However, in order for your organization to be recognized in the RFP process, purchasers must know that it exists and is capable of responding to their requests. Therefore, the aggressive marketing of an organization, as discussed in Chapter 8, is a prerequisite for competing in the RFP arena. Community awareness of an organization's capabilities and skills, along with some experience, will generate requests to which it is possible to respond. Stay in touch with the community's expectations and needs, especially regarding behavioral health services. Most businesses in a community have similar concerns about costs and quality of behavioral healthcare services. Be aware of these concerns and be prepared to respond with unique and creative solutions.

13

THE CAPITATION CONTRACT

Harry Pollack, Attorney-at-Law

The contract is a manual for the provision of and payment for services. It must be carefully drafted, read, and renegotiated. This chapter provides legal advice on how to make certain that the contract language and provisions are accurate, complete, and fair. Negotiating the provisions, due diligence investigations, provisions to insist upon or avoid, termination, and dispute resolution are discussed, with direct advice. This chapter is essential reading for groups with existing contracts or those just entering the at-risk arena.

The capitation contract does what most contracts do: it defines each party's responsibilities under the agreement. What will be the responsibilities of the capitating provider group? What will be the responsibilities of the payor? In this sense, the contract is a manual. The provider group and the payor collectively have certain responsibilities to patients, employers, government, and society. Make sure that the contract presents these responsibilities accurately; make sure it is complete.

HOW IMPORTANT IS IT? THE CONTRACTING PROCESS

Responsibilities and Risk Allocation. The capitation contract, like all contracts, also allocates risk regarding possible future events. This risk allocation is separate from the economic risks assumed in a capitation contract. (See Chapter 4.) The risks are not easy to find in the contract; there will not be a section with the heading: *"Warning: These Are Major Risks to You, the Provider. Please Read Carefully!"* Instead, the risks will be woven into the fabric of the contract language.

For example, indemnity provisions and direct insurance provisions allocate risk. Similar, but more difficult to recognize as involving risk, are provisions defining the scope of services. A typical provision will obligate the practice group to provide or arrange for all "covered behavioral health outpatient services." Does this include specialists? Is there a limit on the obligation to pay specialists? These questions should be specifically addressed in the contract.

Every provision of the contract relates to money. This is obvious in provisions stating the capitation rate (per member per month) and in other places that include a dollar sign. It is less obvious, but equally important, in other provisions. One common example is the section defining reporting requirements. If the capitating group can meet those requirements with current equipment and staff, then the cost will be minimal. If not, the provider practice may need more or different equipment, software, and/or staff—with obvious additional costs.

The Contract Language Negotiation Process.   What happens after a proposal has been accepted and the provider group and payor have shaken hands, agreeing to a capitation contract? A few days later the contract arrives in the mail. It is 35 pages long and full of obtuse legal language. The numbers orally agreed upon are contained in Exhibit E. Thumb through the contract, sign it, and send it back, right?

In fact, further review is still required. Step back a few days. At the time of shaking hands, the provider group should ask the payor to send the proposed contract to the group and its attorney concurrently. The group meets with its attorney, preferably even before the draft contract arrives, to discuss the expected and necessary language of the contract.

The draft contract as initially received will be one-sided. *Do not sign it as is.* If there is any doubt about the unfairness of the contract as sent, look in three places. Compare the section defining the provider's duties with the section defining the payor's duties. Be suspicious if the list of provider's duties is four pages long and the list of the payor's duties is a half page.

Harry Pollack, Attorney-at-Law, a partner in Cheasty, Davis and Pollack, has represented Pacific Applied Psychology Associates in Berkeley, CA, (see Chapter 25) in capitated and other agreements since its founding in 1982. Mr. Pollack also represents other behavioral healthcare providers as well as group pediatric and dental practices. In addition, he practices in real estate and business transactions and litigation. Beyond his law practice, he is a principal in Conservation Partners, Inc., a real estate brokerage which arranges land transactions for preservation and conservation.

Next, compare the section defining what constitutes a default or breach of contract by the practice group with the parallel provisions defining the payor's default or breach. Finally, compare the length of the remedies sections of the contract: what are the contracting group's rights if the payor defaults, compared with the payor's rights if the provider defaults? One goal of negotiating is to make such provisions of similar length.

But will a large multistate insurance corporation negotiate the language of its form contract? Won't the insurer insist that it be signed without changes? No! The insurer will negotiate and make changes because it understands the form contract was only submitted to establish a bargaining position. The payor wants to do business with *you*, not someone else.

There are several reasons to negotiate changes:

1. Some of the provisions in the form contract will be unacceptable.

2. The form contract may not accurately reflect the discussions held with marketing staff with whom oral agreements were made. The marketing staff may not have communicated the complete contents of these discussions to the operations staff or the attorney who drafted the contract.

3. The negotiations are an early step in a long-term relationship. The pattern of the future relationship is being set, in part, by negotiations over contract language. Do not start by accepting things that should be unacceptable. You might even learn that what was accepted in discussions with marketing staff is quite differently structured in the contract. There are times when the best choice is to not sign the contract.

4. During negotiations learning occurs about how business will be transacted with the payor. Negotiating details of the contract should lead to discussions about the day-to-day, nitty-gritty details of the future business relationship. Be sure to consult with operations people during negotiations, to understand how obligations in the contract will affect operations. It is important to partially shape the provision with the payor to fit with the clinical group's daily operations.

5. Negotiating helps providers to better understand the risks being assumed. Finding out what provisions the payor is unwilling to change will imply the level of risk for the provider with regard to these provisions. Even if the original language is accepted, the risk will be better understood and consequently better anticipated.

There are several things which *must* be done with the contract after negotiating, but before signing:

1. Examine the contract language extremely carefully. Read every word. Determine what is understood and what is not understood. Reread the parts that seem understood. Are you sure? Read the definitions section carefully. Costs and risks are often contained in the definitions. Do not assume that the meaning of a term (such as "emergency" or "medically necessary") in the definitions is the same as later in the contract.

2. Make sure the contract includes all of the promises and representations made during the negotiations. During negotiations, the payor probably described its procedures, what it expects from the provider group, and what it will do for the provider. For example, the payor may have described how enrollment data will be communicated. The decision to enter into a contract is made, in part, with reliance on the description of these procedures. If a procedure is not described adequately in the contract, add it as you understand it.

Investigate the Other Party. Perform *due diligence*. At some time prior to signing a contract, the provider group must investigate the other party. Why? Won't a good contract negotiated by a qualified attorney protect the provider? No, it will not! A contract is only a piece of paper. It describes how the parties are obligated to act. People and organizations do not always act in a manner consistent with the obligations of a contract. (That is why attorneys and psychotherapists stay busy.) Only sign the contract when you are reasonably confident that the payor will actually fulfill the obligations as written.

Begin investigating the payor when starting the exploration of a possible contract, and continue throughout the contract negotiations. In fact, assessment of the negotiation process is part of the practice group's due diligence investigation. This due diligence investigation should seek answers to numerous questions, including the following:

1. Is the payor capable of delivering what it promises?
2. Does the payor have a history and reputation for following through?
3. Can the payor be trusted?
4. What kind of entity will be executing the contract? Is it a subsidiary of a larger company? If so, does this change any expectations about the relationship?
5. Does the payor have the financial strength to perform?

6. Is the payor's service philosophy consistent with yours?
7. What are the payor's utilization review procedures?
8. Does the draft contract accurately reflect the promises made?
9. Are its promises of performance real and enforceable?
10. Are you respected and treated well in the negotiating process?
11. Are telephone calls promptly returned?
12. Is the payor responsive to provider concerns and willing to accommodate reasonable requests?

Due diligence requires talking to people who have had recent, direct experience with the payor's utilization review procedures. A thorough investigation should include speaking with other providers who do business with the payor and with the payor's operations personnel, as well as examining certain financial records. Of course, the payor will be performing its own due diligence investigation. It may want to see your financial records. Release such information only after receiving a signed confidentiality agreement.

Contract Provisions.   The "standard clause" is a myth. Do not let any payor insist that its contract is just the standard contract with standard clauses. There is no such document. There are standard topics covered in most capitation contracts, but each topic can be handled in a variety of ways. The questions to ask for each clause are: What does it mean? How does it affect the ability to provide services? What risks are involved? How will it affect operations? How will it affect profitability?

Some of the standard topics included in a capitation contract and some thoughts on each topic are set forth below.

1. *Definitions.* At the beginning of every capitation contract is the definitions section. Understanding definitions is critical to understanding the meaning of the contract. Do not assume knowledge of what the terms mean. The use of terms outside of the contract may be different than the definitions inside the contract. The purpose of the definitions section is to define the terms for purposes of this contract. General understanding of a term is irrelevant if it is defined differently in the contract. Read the definitions carefully. Some important definitions include:
   A. "Covered services." Make sure that the definition of covered services is in this contract, not in some other contract over which the provider group has no control. For example, the covered services section should define the maximum number of visits providers are obligated to provide. Covered services should not be defined

as the number of visits contained in a contract between the payor and an employer—since that contract can be modified without the approval of the provider group.

B. "Medically necessary services." An acceptable definition includes services that are "appropriate and necessary for the diagnosis and treatment of a diagnosable medical condition (such as Axis I diagnoses in DSM-IV)."

C. "Ensure." Beware of certain words like *ensure*. Do not ensure anything. For example, do not agree to ensure that subcontracted psychotherapists will comply with the terms of the capitation contract. However, it is acceptable to agree to a provision that your written subcontracts with network psychotherapists will include that they shall comply with the terms of the capitation contract.

D. "Eligible members." How are these defined? Insist upon the right to audit the payor's records to confirm that it has properly reported the correct number of members.

E. "Co-payments." All contracts allow providers to collect co-payments from the patient and prohibit all other collections from the patient. The dollar amount of the co-payment should be defined in the contract. Do not give the payor the right to unilaterally change this amount. The co-payment and the capitation rate are a package. Reduce co-payments and the capitation rate should increase.

2. *Provider's Obligations.*

A. The basic obligation is to provide covered services to eligible members. Sometimes the obligation includes paying for covered services performed by others in an emergency or out of the provider's service area. Analyze the risks relating to this carefully, and have the provisions carefully defined in writing.

B. Performance standards: The contract may set performance standards. For example, it may limit the waiting period for evaluation and/or treatment, set the days and hours of operation, define unacceptable performance standards, and mandate office locations. Make sure these are realistic and that they can be met. Do not agree to comply with standards that are not explicitly defined in the contract. Do not allow the payor the authority to unilaterally amend the standards or set new standards during the term of the contract.

C. Right to subcontract (assign obligations): Provider groups, even if they initially intend to use their own staff completely, must have the right to hire subcontractors to perform covered services. Write in provisions that permit broad discretion to do so as long as the subcontractors meet the standards set forth in the capitation contract. This requires having a written contract with each subcontractor. The terms of the subcontract must mirror the terms of the capitation contract.

D. Medical records: Make sure that the obligation to provide the payor with medical records does not conflict with:

   i. professional obligations to keep medical records confidential, and

   ii. obligations under state medical records laws. For example, California has several sets of laws that restrict disclosure of medical records, including Psychotherapist-Patient Privilege, Confidentiality of Medical Information Act, Knox-Keene Act disclosures to HMOs, and certain behavioral health disabilities acts. The capitation contract language for medical record disclosure must be very carefully drafted.

E. Management reports and records. Do not agree to provide information beyond your ability. Both the quantity and format must be realistic. The payor must not be able to unilaterally demand information in a way that would require major changes to the provider's information and operating systems.

3. *Payor's Obligations.*

A. Obligation to pay:

   i. The payor's obligation to pay must be specific and unconditional. Some payors try to make payment to the provider group contingent upon the payor's receipt of money from a third party (for example, an employer). This is not acceptable.

   ii. The payor should pay for contracted services in advance, with reconciliation for changes in enrollment in subsequent (but not-too-distant) months. There should be a deadline for payment and a penalty with interest if the payment is late. Failure to pay should be grounds to terminate the contract.

   iii. In addition to the minimum capitation payment, negotiate for additional payments from shared risk pools and/or from savings realized by the payor from the provider's excellent treatment and management. Be creative about how to measure these and obtain compensation for them.

B. Obligations regarding authorization: The payor should be obliged to provide for timely and accurate data and communication. If it errs, the costs and risks should be borne by the payor, not the provider. For example, the payor should indemnify the provider if the provider refuses coverage based on the payor's erroneous member list.

C. Marketing obligations: The payor will be marketing itself. Make sure that the provider group is prominently mentioned in brochures and other forms of advertising. However, do not give *carte blanche* for use of your name, trade name, or trademark. Providers should not agree to limit their own marketing.

4. *Term of the Contract.* A five-year contract that can be terminated with 90-days' notice without cause is not a five-year contract; it is a 90-day contract. Treat it as such. With regard to termination, the rights to terminate the contract should be spelled out clearly, without the possibility of leaving providers overextended (such as with long-term leases and employee commitments) on short notice. All contracts permit termination for *cause.* Cause should be defined as serious, unremediated provider defaults. Written notice and a reasonable opportunity to remedy problems are essential provisions. Do not agree to give the payor the right to terminate the contract when the payor unilaterally determines that the provider group has breached the contract. If the payor asserts that the contract has been breached and the provider failed to remedy the breach after notice, then the provider group should have the right to impartial arbitration prior to termination becoming effective. When the contract terminates, some of the patients will want to continue service with the provider group. The contract should include the amount and method of compensation for those continuing service.

5. *Miscellaneous.*

A. Covenants not to compete: These are a bad idea unless the provider group is guaranteed a sufficiently large number of lives under the capitation contract to forego other business. If it becomes absolutely necessary to agree not to compete, then there should be clear limits: limit the geographic area and define the nature of the competing business. (For example, is the treatment of private and insurance indemnity patients allowed?)

B. Dispute resolution: Every contract must contain a dispute resolution section. It is important to define clearly how conflicts will be resolved.

   i. Arbitration is faster and less expensive than litigation. Some judges make wild decisions; so do some arbitrators. Since there generally is no appeal from an arbitrator's decision, arbitration carries more risk. Overall, however, arbitration is still better.

   ii. The site of arbitration or litigation should be the state and county of the provider group's principal place of business. National payors will want arbitration to be conducted in their

home state and county so that if providers require legal remedies they must try to do so a long way from home. Do not
agree to this.

C. Indemnification: Be careful. There is big risk hidden in these
clauses. Draft narrowly and carefully. There is no "standard" indemnification clause.

D. Knox-Keene regulations: The Knox-Keene Act is a California
statute regulating healthcare service plans. Although the definition of "healthcare service plans" is quite broad, it has not yet
been extended to include behavioral healthcare providers entering into capitated contracts, and so is not covered here.

14

NEGOTIATING THE CONTRACT

Timothy Schultz, M.B.A.

Pricing, quality, bonus payments, and renegotiation are all fundamental issues in negotiating a capitation contract. This chapter discusses negotiating the per member per month rate, based on patient access, benefit design, and anticipated utilization, as well as negotiating data reporting requirements and planning ahead with performance guarantees and risk corridors. Clarifying the quality indicators, whether clinical, administrative, or satisfaction, is described, with an emphasis on specifying tolerance levels for each quality indicator.

This chapter reviews the fundamental business issues to address in negotiating a capitated contract with the payor, including pricing, quality, bonus payments, and renegotiating the contract. Other contract issues such as contract term, liability/indemnification, and legal jurisdiction have been covered in Chapter 13. The context of this discussion also omits specific negotiating strategies. Undertaking a capitation agreement is a very serious matter and in all cases provider organizations should utilize an attorney with experience in this field throughout the negotiations.

PRICING

Three areas must be addressed in pricing assumptions: anticipated utilization, cost per unit of service, and administrative services, including reporting requirements.

Anticipated Utilization. This is highly dependent on the type of product being offered by the payor, as well as the demographic characteristics of the covered population. In order for a payor to negotiate a capitated agreement with a provider, that payor must be at risk for the services to be delivered. While point-of-service plans, exclusive provider organization plans, and large employers occasionally may capitate providers, the most common capitation arrangements occur with health maintenance organizations (HMOs). This chapter assumes that the capitation agreement is with an HMO, although the principles could be applied to the other agreements as well.

Three critical factors to consider in assessing anticipated utilization with the HMO plan are: the patient access method to be employed by the HMO, benefit plan design, and transition of care. There are two access models used by HMOs, direct access and gatekeeper. In the direct access model, the member may contact the provider organization directly, without prior authorization from the primary care physician. This model tends to yield more patients accessing behavioral health benefits, since there are no barriers to access and the primary care physician is less likely to provide behavioral health services him- or herself. In the gatekeeper model, the member must obtain authorization from the primary care physician prior to contacting the provider organization for services. This model tends to yield fewer patients accessing behavioral health benefits. In negotiating the agreement, it is critical that the access model be specified so that pricing assumptions are accurate.

Benefit Plan Design. The design will impact on both expected utilization and the average amount paid per unit of service. The benefit design dictates what levels of care are covered, as well as the maximum number of service units and co-payments for each level of care. (See also Chapters 11 and 12.) Covered levels of care have an obvious impact on forecasting utilization. For example, some HMO plans provide no coverage for inpatient psychiatric care, which means that the provider organization does not include inpatient care in its pricing assumptions.

Timothy Schultz, M.B.A., is Vice President for Provider Services with OPTIONS Mental Health, Inc., a managed behavioral healthcare organization based in Norfolk, VA, which manages behavioral health benefits for over two million lives. In this capacity he is responsible for provider quality profiling and the development of relationships with group practices and healthcare systems. Mr. Schultz has consulted with several mental healthcare groups and systems around the country in the development of integrated service systems, as well as with group practices in Southern California, where he implemented systems to effectively manage at-risk arrangements.

Co-payments will also impact on utilization, as higher co-payments tend to discourage use of services. For example a plan with a $10 co-payment for outpatient visits would be expected to have higher outpatient utilization than a plan with a $50 co-payment. The plan with a $50 co-payment may, however, have greater use of emergency services. In addition, the co-payment will impact on the expected cost per unit. For example, if the provider organization's average allowed amount per service is $75, and the outpatient co-payment is $10, the actual cost to the organization would be $65 per unit, while a $50 co-payment would yield a $25 per-unit cost. Provider organizations unfamiliar with pricing capitated agreements may consider using an actuary to assist in developing their utilization assumptions.

Once the access model and benefit plan design(s) are identified, a utilization model should be developed. For each level of care, this utilization model should take into account:

- the anticipated number of patients accessing care,
- the average number of units of service provided per patient,
- the price per unit of service, and
- the co-payment.

See Chapter 11 for sample pricing charts. In ideal circumstances, the provider will have the payor's historical utilization statistics available prior to bidding. However, in practice the payor often either does not have this information available, or is not willing to share the information during the bidding process. If historical utilization data are not provided, the provider organization is faced with making a business decision about whether to bid at all and, if it bids, what utilization assumptions to make. One way of covering this risk is to indicate the member penetration assumptions made in the utilization model. In other words, specify what proportion of the members are anticipated to access their benefits over the course of the year and indicate that the pricing is based on that assumption — so that substantial variations from the assumption may result in pricing changes. While this does not guarantee obtaining higher fees in the event of higher member penetration, it at least provides an opening to discuss such an adjustment.

In cases where the payor has multiple benefit plan designs, it is beneficial to negotiate a rate for each plan. This provides a self-adjusting mechanism in total payments to the organization to reflect changes in enrollment between plans. Some payors may require a fixed capitation fee across all plans, in which case it is necessary to estimate relative enrollment among the available plans and arrive at a blended fee. In such cases, the provider organization should specify the general distribution of enrollment on which the assumptions are made, and indicate that material deviations from the specified distribution require price adjustments. Again, this does not guarantee that the fees will be adjusted, but it provides an opportunity for the discussion to occur.

Transition of Care.   This addresses how patients who were in treatment prior to the contract effective date will be managed. The author's experience with transition of care in HMO plans is that the transition benefit usually is limited. It is not uncommon to allow patients to continue seeing their existing provider for a maximum of 30 days or four sessions following the new contract effective date, after which time services are only paid if rendered by the new provider organization. In negotiating the price, specific fees for managing the transition, as well the claims cost for nonnetwork providers during the transition, should be considered.

Another factor to include explicitly in negotiating the contract price relates to the reporting requirements of the payor. To the extent that the provider organization is required to provide reports in addition to standard encounter data (that is, HCFA 1500 forms for professional fees and UB82s for facility fees), it is reasonable to define the scope of the reporting requirements and include pricing for the level of reporting specified in the agreement. To the extent that additional reports are required by the payor in the future, the agreement should indicate that the payor will cover the reasonable cost of producing such reports.

In addition to these factors, the actual price a provider organization is able to negotiate will be highly dependent on competitive pressures in the marketplace. In talking to providers around the country, the author has seen the pricing for a basic HMO product vary by as much as 500 percent, with the lowest prices found in markets with the highest HMO market share. Knowing the competition, how it designs and prices its services, and its sales approaches is critical to ensuring that the provider organization negotiates the best possible price.

QUALITY

Quality is often claimed by providers, but frequently not supported by hard data. In negotiating an agreement, quality parameters need to be identified as clearly as pricing. Quality can be defined in terms of quality indicators (clinical and administrative), patient satisfaction, and provider satisfaction. (See Chapter 10.)

Quality Indicators.   Such indicators serve as benchmarks which, if met, infer quality on the balance of the system. Clinical indicators may include application of clinical criteria, relapse/recidivism rates, appeals, and adverse incidents ("Industry Analysis," 1994). Application of clinical indicators requires the provider organization to make available its clinical process criteria and guidelines to the vendor, and to ensure that these are applied consistently. They may include an external audit of cases to ensure compliance. Relapse/recidivism rates indicate the percentage of patients re-admitted to outpatient or inpatient care within specified time frames. Appeals relate to the number of utilization or clinical decision appeals made by patients, families, and providers, and the ratio to the number of covered members. Adverse incidents are the occurrence of suicide attempts or other situations where patients harm themselves or others.

Administrative Indicators. These may include patient and provider access, customer service, provider network access, and claims payment ("Industry Analysis," 1994). Patient and provider access measures may include the number of telephone rings before answering, call abandonment rates, call hold rates, telephone access to clinicians for clinical inquiries, and the time frame for initial appointment scheduling. Customer service measures include the turnaround time for response to telephonic and written inquiries. Provider network access measures include network turnover, geographic proximity to covered members, and adequate distribution of provider specialties for the covered population. Claims payment measures include the accuracy of claims payment, both in terms of coding and pricing, and claims turnaround time.

Contracts are likely to indicate specific levels of tolerance for each quality indicator. It is important that office systems be able to capture and report data on each of these indicators, and that the cost of doing so is taken into account when pricing the agreement.

In addition to these quality indicators, payors may require demonstrated minimum patient satisfaction levels. While defining quality can be elusive, satisfaction appears to be a significant factor to patients in choosing their healthcare, and thus critical to payors ("Health-care Report Cards," 1994).

PERFORMANCE GUARANTEES AND RISK CORRIDORS

Performance guarantees are frequently built into the capitation contract based on the organization's achievement of specified levels of quality indicators. For example, if the contract requires 95 percent of calls to be answered within three rings, and the organization fails to achieve that level of performance, a portion of the capitation fee may be forfeited. Typically, the amount of the performance guarantee approximates the provider organization's anticipated profit for the contract.

Risk corridors (also called risk bands) may also be negotiated. The provider organization would be responsible only for a portion of the services to be delivered, such as professional fees. A typical risk corridor establishes utilization and/or cost targets for the care not capitated, such as facility fees, and provides bonuses or penalties for savings or extra expenses incurred. The contract may establish a target amount for facility fees, and share the savings or extra costs above or below that target, up to a maximum percentage of the capitation fee.

For example, an agreement may apportion 50 percent of savings or extra cost of target facility fees to the provider organization, up to a maximum of 30 percent of the capitation fee. A risk corridor may also be negotiated as a stop-loss provision. For example, it may be agreed that individual cases exceeding a specified dollar limit (using fee-for-service equivalents) are to be paid on a fee-for-service basis or that if the population utilization rate rises beyond a certain level an additional per member per month amount is added. These provisions become less necessary when the number of covered lives is greater. The author's experience is that 15,000 or more covered lives in a contract provide a sufficient pool to cover the risk and forgo stop-loss provisions.

RENEGOTIATING FOR RENEWALS

Renegotiation for renewal begins during the original negotiation of the contract. When the agreement covers multiple years, escalator clauses may be built into the agreement tying fee increases to premium increases, inflation, or some other mutually agreeable index. When the term of the agreement expires, pricing negotiations are likely to begin again, with the same factors listed above needing to be addressed. The main difference at renegotiation is that the provider organization knows precisely what the utilization has been and what, if any, additional savings may be achieved.

The provider organization has the ability during renegotiation to demonstrate the impact it made on service delivery. It can demonstrate the member penetration (the proportion of covered members accessing service), actual utilization data along the continuum of care, patient satisfaction, provider satisfaction, and outcomes data. However, as in the original negotiation, the provider organization still must respond to competitive pricing pressures, and be aware that the payor is likely to attempt to use the above data to extract price concessions, particularly if the provider has been successful in lowering costs. While being the incumbent has definite advantages in renegotiation, provider organizations should not rely on these advantages to enable them to obtain rates superior to the competition.

REFERENCES

Industry analysis: What performance standards are used to evaluate managed behavioral health plans? (1994, March). *Open Minds* 7(12).

Health-care report cards are getting low grades from some focus groups. (1994, May 19). *The Wall Street Journal.*

15

CREATING THE CLINICAL NETWORK

Paul A. Buongiorno, M.D.
Richard C. Baither, Ph.D.

Offering accessibility, assigning patients to appropriate levels of service, becoming multidisciplinary, credentialing providers, creating specialty services, and establishing intake systems are all tasks to be undertaken in setting up an effective network of employed and subcontracted clinicians to provide clinical services within a full capitation contract. Drs. Buongiorno and Baither provide direct practical advice on how to accomplish these tasks, as well as warnings regarding some difficulties encountered in the process.

In creating a clinical network to provide capitated behavioral health services, the first task is to define the requirements. While most of the requirements will be dictated by the capitation contract, health plan, or managed care company, there are several key areas to address.

First is to serve all age groups and clinical conditions. It is essential to provide all levels of service, including outpatient, structured outpatient, acute inpatient, partial hospital, and residential care. If providing these services cannot be done under one roof, they can be obtained by contract from existing provider programs. (See Appendix C.) Staffing requirements generally are set at one full-time equivalent provider per 3,000 enrollees (that is, the population served). The blending of provider disciplines will be discussed below.

Second, consider the accessibility of services. Generally, benchmarks for access only permit drive times of less than 30 minutes to outpatient care and less than 45 minutes for inpatient care in metropolitan areas. When providing services in rural areas, longer drive times may be permitted. Emergency care must be provided seven days a week, 24 hours a day, with a usual response time of less than 30 minutes to telephone calls and one hour for on-site response.

Individual provider characteristics are another important issue. Clinicians must be able to work independently as well as with a team, complying with group policies, procedures, and protocols. It is essential that they treat patients with courtesy and respect. While providers with all types of theoretical approaches and expertise are needed, the predominant requirement is for those with a brief therapy perspective. Finally, it is necessary to select a handful of providers to function as quality managers. They will perform all of the utilization review, case management, and outcomes management for the group.

BECOMING TRULY MULTIDISCIPLINARY

Before credentialing providers, consider the philosophical approach of the network. The goal should be to establish a truly multidisciplinary, or even interdisciplinary, system. To be more specific, the overall goal for all

Paul A. Buongiorno, M.D., is a graduate of Georgetown University School of Medicine in Washington, DC, where he currently is clinical assistant professor of psychiatry. He is the founder and Medical Director of the Chronic Pain Program at Fair Oaks Hospital. Dr. Buongiorno is also President and Chief Executive Officer of The Northern Virginia Psychiatric Group in Fairfax, VA, and Medical Director of Integrated Behavioral Care, a preferred provider organization in northern Virginia. Additionally, he serves as President of Adult Behavioral Care, Inc., which specializes in geriatric psychiatry. Dr. Buongiorno is a consultant for, and has played an integral part in implementing managed care at, American PsychManagement (now Value Behavioral Health).

Richard C. Baither, Ph.D., is a clinical psychologist with the Northern Virginia Psychiatric Group in Fairfax, VA. He serves as a team leader, Capitation Contract Manager, and member of the management team, along with his involvement in planning and implementing the practice's managed care product line. Dr. Baither has been a peer reviewer and Director of Outpatient Case Management for American PsychManagement (now Value Behavioral Health). Currently he consults with Integrated Behavioral Care, a regional managed healthcare company serving the Baltimore, MD-Washington, DC, area, where he is the Director of Outpatient Case Management and a member of the Credential and Quality Improvement Committees.

providers credentialed by the network must be quality patient care, with a vision to improve care—based on outcomes data, not merely emotional responses or educational biases. This means that, despite varied training and theoretical bases for treatment, providers must be willing and able to learn each others' language and ultimately develop a common language to describe problems and clinical situations.

Teamwork and leadership are absolutely necessary, yet often are the most difficult to accomplish. The leader is not automatically the one with the most prestigious degree. There is no place for posturing or pride in this scenario. All providers must be on an equal footing, with varying talents and abilities, all of which demand respect. Individual strengths and weakness must be noted and dealt with appropriately. Some of the most innovative treatment options are developed by individuals with exceptional talent, vision, and purpose.

CREDENTIALING PROVIDERS

There are two key elements in credentialing: *criteria* for membership in the network and *qualifications* for granting privileges to practice. Policies and procedures should outline both of these elements as well as disciplinary options and processes, termination mechanisms, and appeals procedures. Membership qualifications must also consider each provider's ethical standing in the community as well as licensure and discipline. It is important to have a balanced network including behavioral healthcare professionals and clinical nurse specialists.

Privilege-to-practice criteria are more extensive. (See Appendix D.) The following list outlines only the minimum areas that need to be evaluated:

- education and training,
- licensing status,
- areas of competence,
- health status,
- references, and
- malpractice history.

To obtain this type of information, it is important to review a variety of sources, including the provider's application, primary verification (with insurance, training, and state agencies), references, quality assurance information, and national data banks. Research any discrepancies in an application either through a personal interview or a request for more information.

After credentialing staff, whether in-house staff or subcontracted providers working in their own offices, a vigorous program of education and monitoring must be adopted to maintain quality of care. First, educate providers about policies and procedures, including both clinical and administrative routines. Since individual and group provider performance is such an integral part of the network process, it is also important to educate and counsel individual staff about their performance. There are many sources of information about staff performance, including customer and patient complaints, peer and office staff feedback/complaints, quality assurance monitors, and annual performance reports about utilization management. Offer feedback as soon as possible in negative situations and involve clinical managers in the process. Staff who do not respond appropriately to education and counseling should be dropped from the network.

Recredential all staff every two years. For this process, use a complete renewal of the initial application, with attention to citizenship and to areas of clinical competence that are now driven by absolute numbers of procedures performed (for example, electro-convulsive therapy or inpatient utilization). In reviewing performance data, it is possible to derive significant information internally. However, it is also important to develop procedures to coordinate and summarize that information for recredentialing staff.

INTAKE PROCEDURES AND POLICIES FOR NEW PATIENTS

The network must provide around-the-clock emergency coverage. Staff must respond to emergency calls within 30 minutes and be able to see these patients the same day. A telephone triage can be done in 20 minutes, with feedback to the health plan or managed care company. In order to accomplish this, the network must establish one intake team per 150,000 enrollees. Each team should include one physician and two nonphysicians dedicated to seeing only new patients. The nonphysicians gather clinical and historical information for the physician, who verifies diagnoses and prescribes treatment. Medication evaluation can be done during the intake process to avoid costly and unnecessary delays that may result in hospitalization.

The nonphysicians then implement the prescribed treatment by referring to the appropriate provider or program, selecting the least intensive treatment setting. The nonphysicians, in conjunction with the intake physician, inform the primary care physician, employee assistance program, or other managed care referral source about the prescribed treatment recommendations. Finally, they prepare a written evaluation for the treating provider.

It is our experience that having a standard intake evaluation form facilitates this process and promotes consistency and quality assurance monitoring. An appointment scheduling module on the information system also facilitates the smooth transition from the intake team to treating providers. Routine appointments should be seen within 24 hours. We have found that patients who have been offered an appointment within 24 hours as a rule do not accept an appointment for five days due to their own scheduling commitments.

Having an intake team ensures that new patients will be referred to the appropriate provider for their problem. This process establishes a basis for clinical quality in the assignment of new patients. The intake team must be very familiar with each provider and clinical resource within the network. The team should also monitor available therapy time to minimize backlog and the inability to place new patients. Provider shortages must be reported to managers for planning and hiring purposes.

New evaluations must be focused and directive in order to deal with the emergent nature of the problem and to comply with time targets requested by the health plan. At times an evaluation is done only to ascertain where the most appropriate level of care will be (that is, inpatient versus partial hospital). A more comprehensive evaluation is then conducted at a later date.

SPECIALTY SERVICES AND SUBCONTRACTING

Until there is an ongoing and critical demand for a specific service (for example, eating disorders treatment or addiction treatment rehabilitation), the prudent policy is to subcontract for specialized services on an as-needed basis. Develop affiliate relationships with other providers on a fee-for-service or fixed-fee basis. It is important to establish sufficient economic motives to be certain that the network's goals and objectives are met. In implementing a capitation contract, deficits in the network service delivery will become apparent, for example, inadequate numbers of female therapists or therapists who serve children. The need for a specific program such as structured outpatient addiction treatment may also arise.

Fill these unmet needs by developing linkages with alternative delivery systems (for example, more subcontracted outpatient providers, hospitals, partial programs, structured outpatient addiction treatment programs, residential programs, or day treatment programs). It is best to share the risk with these programs. This can be accomplished through subcapitation of specific services, per-diem rates, or case rates. Negotiating per diems or services and cost items clearly is necessary to avoid economic losses for the capitated provider or the dissatisfaction of clients resulting from misunderstanding the covered benefit. For hospital programs, an example of an all-inclusive per diem would be one that covers: room and board, nursing care, lab tests, routine radiology exams, medications, and ancillary charges.

Prevent overutilization, unnecessary services, and extraordinary lengths of stay through utilization review and case management, especially for all subcontracted programs and services. Case management often requires obtaining copies of initial evaluations, discharge summaries, or other records for hospitalized patients. These requests often cause the medical records department grave concerns about confidentiality issues. Early education about how the confidentiality of data will be protected and about the purposes of case management will prevent misunderstandings. In almost all cases patients have signed a release of information form allowing the payment source access to clinical data. The release extends to capitated providers on contract to the payment source.

SUMMARY

In developing a network of providers, strive for reasonable access to care, variety in services offered, and clinicians with whom you enjoy working. Focus energy, money, and time on the initial selection of excellent providers, not on trying to change or remove a problem provider later. Maintaining a quality network is a process that requires careful and on-going planning, care, and attention. The heart of any healthcare organization lies in the clinical staff who provide the care.

16

DESIGNING THE COMPUTER SYSTEM

Gayle L. Zieman, Ph.D.

The management of at-risk contracts is financially and clinically complex. An array of current data analyses are essential. Without a refined and easy-to-use computer system, the prognosis for success within any capitation arrangement is poor. The necessary features, costs, and methods for purchasing, developing, and installing an effective information system are frequently under-recognized by provider groups and clinics. A sound grasp of computer requirements and possibilities is crucial for success. This chapter provides practical information for selecting and evaluating computer systems to administer capitation contracts.

Several recent articles have advised practitioners to retool their practices for capitation (Pollock, 1993; Scroggins & Brayer, 1993). Such retooling includes the need for savvy management information systems (MIS) to provide the necessary data for succeeding in capitation arrangements (Coke, 1993; Moran, 1993). But almost nothing has been written about how to locate and evaluate a capitation MIS (Zieman, 1993).

Until the early 1990s, developing a computer system in-house for capitation management was the only means available. Today there are several MIS choices available for groups entering into direct, at-risk relationships with insurers and employers. Capitation systems generally track preauthorizations, allow direct access to enrollment files, adjudicate subcontractor claims, produce form letters to primary care physicians and patients, allow for concurrent utilization review, profile provider and patient patterns, and manage the financial accounting of capitation dollars. Systems currently in development will expand the horizons of MIS for capitation management to include outcomes data management, complaint tracking, provider credentialing, and more powerful custom report generation.

To Create, Lease, or Purchase?

Many practices and clinics in the 1980s and early 1990s created their own capitation MIS. These providers learned quickly that software development is extremely time and energy demanding. Writing software for one's own MIS requires sophisticated knowledge of efficient computer programming, as well as thorough understanding of the intricacies of integrating clinical data with advanced financial accounting. The process of writing, debugging, documenting, and constantly enhancing an MIS is a major, and ongoing, challenge. The time and cost required for custom software development almost always exceeds projections.

Today, programming their own capitation MIS is a wise choice only for those groups not requiring a full-featured system. A single contract for a small capitated population (30,000 enrollees or less) or a subcapitation arrangement for the management of a segment within a larger contract are the two cases in which programming one's own system remains viable and cost-effective. The powerful relational database programs available today for personal computers make excellent vehicles for the custom construction of MIS packages. A minimum of four months should be allotted to write, debug, install, and fully test a small customized system.

Leasing MIS services can be practical in some cases, especially for subcapitation. Typically data management services are leased from the insurer or employer sponsoring a capitation contract. Using the computer system of a contractor, however, has two distinct drawbacks. First, regardless of security arrangements (passwords, and so on) the contractor, for system management reasons, will always have access to the capitation data. The contractor will know exactly what services were provided by whom and at

In 1988 Gayle Zieman had 60 days to develop a computer system that could handle the daily information needs of a capitation contract for 30,000 enrollees. Severely stretching the limits of a spreadsheet, he created a system that calculated co-payments for various inpatient and outpatient benefit plans, produced detailed statements paying subcontracted providers, and tracked utilization by provider and CPT code. In 1989 he wrote a sophisticated relational database program to manage capitated behavioral healthcare contracts. By 1992 he had turned to tracking the development of computer systems to . manage at-risk contracts and was modifying health maintenance organization software to administer capitation. Today he monitors the development of capitation computer systems and has coauthored software for the analysis of outcomes data.

what cost. It is hard to successfully renegotiate or extend a capitation contract when the contractor knows more about your data than you do.

Second, it is almost impossible, again for data security reasons, to acquire additional capitation contracts with other payors if one's data processing occurs on the computer of a competitor. Seldom will a capitation source agree to allow its data to reside on the computer system of another similar business. In the future it may become possible to lease computer services from third-party processors of healthcare data. To date, the author knows of no healthcare data management company that is willing to process data from capitating groups. As a rule, healthcare data companies use large mainframe computers and find capitation data-processing needs too small to be cost-effective.

The wise choice for the vast majority of group practices and clinics involved in at-risk contracting is to purchase a full-featured computer system from an established vendor of healthcare systems. (See Appendix F.) Several such systems are now ready for purchase and installation, several existing systems are being updated, and new systems are on the way.

SHOPPING FOR THE RIGHT MIS

Evaluating and purchasing an MIS for capitation is an involved process. Capitation systems vary greatly in features and capabilities. Available choices must be investigated thoroughly to prevent the purchase of a system which fails to meet the complex business and clinical needs of capitation management, or which will become inadequate as enrollments grow, volume of data accumulates, or the number of contracts increases.

In reviewing software systems there are several rules to follow. First, the search team must be multidisciplinary—representing clinical, utilization review, financial, accounting, MIS, and clerical expertise. The inclusion of clerical staff is important to evaluate user friendliness. Especially important to day-to-day use are: the layout of the data entry screens, the use of menus to reduce reliance upon rote memory and paper lists, the number of steps involved in moving between operations, and the ease of report generation. Any system that is difficult for clerical staff will forever remain inefficient and troublesome.

Second, the system should be carefully previewed. Most software vendors will happily provide demonstration disks or demonstrate their system via modem. A third important step is to carefully assess the financial integrity and business stability of the vendor. Establishing that the vendor is a sound, enduring company that stands behind its product is essential before signing a purchase agreement. Additionally, customers from the installed client base for the program should be queried. Get references. Calling or visiting existing users can be an invaluable step in evaluating a software package for capitation.

An MIS specialist should also review the system to judge how efficiently it is programmed (this will greatly affect speed as the system fills with data), the likelihood that it will remain viable and supported by the vendor for several years, and its capabilities for integration with other computerized office functions such as accounts payable and accounts receivable.

The search for an MIS should conclude with a full, face-to-face demonstration that includes a thorough review of the manuals documenting how to use the system and a demonstration of the training that would accompany the installation. The hands-on demonstration should employ a data set large enough to simulate daily functioning—almost any system will look speedy if it contains only a few hundred records.

A wisely purchased computer system can be expected to remain in use for four to six years before becoming antiquated, and much longer if the vendor aggressively updates and enhances the system.

GENERAL SYSTEM REQUIREMENTS

Software packages, even those as complex as required for capitation management, can run with speed, agility, and high user friendliness on a local access network (LAN) of desk-top computers. Clinics or provider networks with large capitated populations (150,000 to 200,000 or more covered lives) may need to consider a wide area network (WAN) with a minicomputer server (such as Digital VAX, Data General Avion, IBM RS600) connecting geographically distant offices.

Except for the management of very small capitation contracts, a multi-user network is necessary. (See Figure 16.1.) In the author's experience, a single office clerk can handle the routine data management and claims adjudication tasks for a behavioral-health-only contract covering up to 70,000 lives. However, even for capitated populations of less than 70,000, a network is still needed to connect preauthorization, utilization review, and accounting functions into an integrated system.

Recent software and hardware advances now allow for open architecture, making it possible for programs to run across multiple types of computers and operating systems (such as MS-DOS, Mac-OS, or UNIX). It is preferable to select an open system if this choice is available. A capitation MIS that operates on a variety of platforms can greatly enhance connectivity to other applications and may reduce the need to install new hardware.

The ability to import and export records to a standard medical office billing program (accounts receivable) and to general accounting software

Figure 16.1 Capitation System Requirements

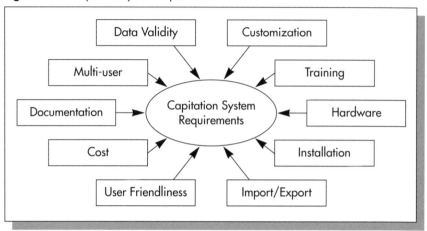

is very important. Processing data for clinical services delivered by providers within a practice or clinic (non-subcontractors) is greatly enhanced both in efficiency and in error reduction when electronic claims submissions and payments occur between the capitation MIS and the accounts receivable system. The ability to accept electronic claims submissions from subcontracted facilities and providers is also highly desirable. Except in the management of a single small capitation contract—where the double entry of receipts and payables from capitation is not excessive— easy, efficient communication with a general accounting system is helpful. Some capitation systems come programmed to interact with specific accounting software packages.

COST AND INSTALLATION

The basic capitation software package for a group practice or clinic costs between $25,000 and $40,000. Training and installation costs are usually included. Customization costs can add from $3,000 to $20,000 (custom programming typically is charged at $80 to $130 per hour). Most users will need customization to set up the details of importing and exporting data with insurers and the peculiarities of the insurance benefit plans under capitation, such as co-payment structures and riders. In addition, most systems have a maintenance or licensing fee billed monthly or annually. These fees allow the user access to ongoing technical support and to future enhancements added by the vendor. Prior to the purchase, a contract should be agreed upon with the vendor specifying the details of base cost, installation, customization, and how future technical support and upgrades will be handled. Detailed specifications for the custom work should be developed and agreed to before programming begins. From time to time, such as when a new capitation contract is added, a return to the vendor for custom programming is necessary for most practices and clinics.

Costs for hardware and network software vary greatly. The hardware for a stand-alone, single-user system may cost as little as $2,000 while a multi-user LAN with several terminals may run 10 times that amount. The installation of a minicomputer WAN can be expected to cost $15,000 to $35,000.

Thus, the total expense for a capitation MIS will range from $30,000 to $100,000. Ongoing expenditures of several thousand dollars a year for maintenance, licensing, and future customization must be expected. With the exception of a very small and simple capitation system, in-house MIS development is not cost-effective. Given the extensive time necessary to program even a simple capitation MIS, and the cost of a skilled programmer (usually $20 to $40 per hour), the total for development will generally exceed the cost of purchasing an existing system.

Installation requires a minimum of two months from signing the purchase agreement. This time is needed to complete training, finish even minimal customization, and get the system operational on-site. Programming your own capitation MIS, even a simple, no-frills system, will take many months, with several additional months needed to create adequate manuals and debug the entire system.

SPECIFIC SYSTEM FEATURES

A fully operational MIS for capitation management must have integrated modules for each of the following functions. (See Figure 16.2.)

Enrollment/Eligibility. Using online connectivity or data importation via modem or physical media (tape drive, floppy disks, optical disk), the system should maintain up-to-date enrollment data. Eligibility should be checked during other functions, such as preauthorization of services and adjudication of claims. Reports should be available that track enrollees nearing their maximum allowables or the end of their effective date. Management of small capitation contracts may be handled with manual enrollment and eligibility checking from paper printouts provided by the insurer, but accuracy as well as speed dictate that a full-featured system should have enrollment information readily available.

Preauthorization/Precertification. Outpatient preauthorizations and facility precertifications must be easily entered, with the reporting capability to

Figure 16.2 Capitation Contract Administration

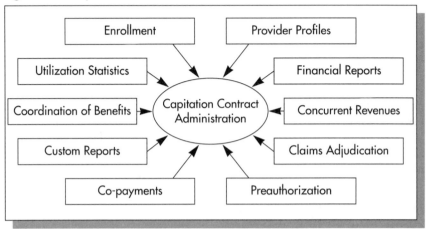

track authorized services by provider, CPT code, and setting (such as inpatient, intensive outpatient, and so on). All authorizations should include a treatment plan complete with five axis diagnoses, risk factors, estimated length of treatment/stay, and fields for ad-hoc comments. Integration with provider and facility files is necessary to verify that services have been authorized only for providers or facilities credentialed to provide those services. Preauthorized service entries should generate accumulated financial liability reports of services authorized, but not paid.

Utilization Review. A crucial feature in any capitation package is the tracking of services provided and authorized. The system should be designed for concurrent review as a follow-up to preauthorization and precertification. On a daily or weekly basis, lists of patients or providers with expiring authorizations should be available for contact. A complete audit trail of concurrent approvals and denials must be maintained, with changes in diagnoses and treatment plans carefully documented, as well as free-form comment fields for utilization review staff to document information about each contact. Inpatient and outpatient utilization reports and statistics must be available for individual enrollees and by employer, diagnosis, and provider. Excellent utilization reports are critical in sound capitation contract management.

Co-payments, Stop Losses, and Amounts Due. Almost every benefit plan has a complex set of rules governing the division of charges and payments for different services into discounts, disallowances, patient co-payments, and allowed amounts. Stop-loss amounts are also frequently applicable based upon the total co-payments paid or the total charged fees accumulated by an enrollee or subscriber. Across the many benefit plans of one or several capitation contracts a sound capitation MIS must flawlessly and adeptly calculate co-payments, stop losses, disallowances, and discounts under the most complex of circumstances. These may include clinicians from different disciplines providing multiple services on one day, first outpatient and then inpatient, where differentiating between the applicable mental healthcare and addiction treatment benefit structures is required. Accumulated co-payments for individual subscribers and groups of enrollees must also be available for reporting to insurers, which are required by law in many cases to monitor comparisons between co-payments charged and premiums collected.

Claims Adjudication.   Service claims submitted by the group or clinic's providers or by subcontractors and facilities must be easily processed, posted, and paid. Claims not matching with preauthorizations or claims for noncovered services must be accurately denied. The capitation MIS must also check for possible duplicate claims. Once a claim has been adjudicated, a very readable Explanation of Benefits (EOB) statement must be automatically generated to each provider, including clear descriptions for any denials. (See Appendix G.) The capitation program must print checks for the subcontractors and export payment details to the general accounting system. A thorough weekly or monthly report of claims accepted and denied by enrollee, provider, and contract is another necessary feature of the system. Throughout the claims adjudication process, the coordination of benefits with other insurers is necessary. If another insurer is primary for a claim, the system should automatically pend payment until the primary insurer has paid. If another insurer is secondary, then the system should label the co-payments and discounts applied as to be billed to the secondary insurer.

Provider, Facility, and Payor Profiles.   To complement utilization statistics, provider profiles analyzing the referral and treatment patterns of individual providers and subsets of providers are very useful. These reports allow for comparisons between providers and facilities on length of treatment, charges, acceptance of new patients, and specialty referrals. These analyses are valuable in making decisions about provider recredentialing. Profiles of utilization or payment patterns by insurers, benefit plans, or employers can also be quite useful.

Financial Reports.   To fully administer direct, at-risk contracts the capitation MIS must work closely with an accounting general ledger. Monthly capitation revenues based on the per member per month rate must be entered for comparison with the outstanding liabilities incurred as well as the claims adjudicated. A monthly profit and loss report must be available by benefit plan within each contract, by contract, and across contracts. (See Appendix G.) Printing subcontractor 1099 tax forms should also be available within the system or through communication with a general accounting system.

User-created Reports.   While any viable system will have a plethora of standard reports, each user will have numerous unique information needs requiring fast, on-the-spot data analysis and reporting. An online custom report generator allows flexibility in data management without custom programming. With very little training, users should be able to search, sort, combine, and print data across multiple files, for example the mean cost of treatment for all patients with a specific diagnosis, employed by a particular company, who had a certain treatment during a set time period. The report generator should allow for the calculation of basic descriptive statistics on the data and be able to format the report into an attractive, functional printout. A powerful custom report generator can be an indispensable tool.

Utilities.   Any viable system will include security features (for example, password protection), which allow users different levels of access—view data only, enter data, modify data, or source code access. Full-featured systems will also have sophisticated data validity checks, for example, recognizing that July 4 is an unlikely date for a patient to have attended a partial hospital program.

A capitation MIS may include many helpful add-on features, such as the ability to monitor specialist referrals, compile initial patient contact statistics, track patient/enrollee complaints, and connect with an appointment scheduling module. Integration with word processing and mail merge capabilities is also useful for the production of form letters to enrollees and providers. A desirable feature that improves processing speed is the archiving of old data. Archival records remain accessible, but are not routinely loaded. The ability to easily export data to spreadsheets and outcomes databases is another handy utility. Future capitation packages will likely provide for automated provider credentialing and modules for tracking outcomes data.

SOURCES OF CAPITATION SYSTEMS

Since the late 1980s several software companies have taken an interest in capitation management. A list of known vendors is offered in Appendix F.

It is expected that the options for behavioral health group practices and clinics involved with at-risk contracts will dramatically increase over the next several years, an event likely to drive down the cost of capitation systems.

REFERENCES

Coke, J. (1993) Government reforms, market needs and the role of information technologies. **Behavioral Healthcare** *Tomorrow* 2(5): 21–26.

Moran, G. F. (1993) Rate restructuring in managed care contracts demands detailed information. *Medical Group Management Journal* 40(4): 9–10, 13.

Pollock, W. M. (1993) Succeeding under capitation. *Medical Group Management Journal* 40(4): 6–7.

Scroggins, E. S., & Brayer, K. A. (1993) How to approach managed care contracting in the 1990's. *Medical Group Management Journal* 40(2): 70–74.

Zieman, G. L. (1993) Information systems and capitation contracting. **Behavioral Healthcare** *Tomorrow* 2(1): 40–43.

17

UTILIZATION MANAGEMENT: SOME PRACTICAL ADVICE

Kathryn Hemker Bobbitt, Ph.D.

In the past it was observed that "managed care is utilization review" (Becker, 1990). A new conceptualization of utilization review includes utilization management (UM), which ranges from determining whether a specific intervention is appropriate for a given client to looking at overall utilization patterns for an entire system. Whether micro- or macroscopic, UM enables managed care agencies and capitated providers to cut down on inappropriate use of expensive services, to develop programming that addresses the needs of their member populations, and to demonstrate to customers enhanced efficiency and quality of care. This chapter focuses on practical advice for situations commonly encountered by at-risk managed care and provider organizations in providing UM, both internally and externally.

Utilization review (UR), a concept associated with inspection, restriction of services, and administrative barriers to care, hardly appears to be consistent with the spirit of enhancing the quality of clinical care to the populations we serve. UR is often seen as a necessary evil in the world of managed care—the "cop" that watches over providers to make sure that they, and their patients, do not abuse the system.

Chapter 1 of this book describes the long evolution of prepaid health plans and "managed care." As one of the key tools of managed care, UR, too, has evolved beyond the obstructionist mentality that dominated our field in earlier decades. The efficient management of the healthcare dollar is a given in this competitive market; management of care and customer service concerns have become increasingly important values in reviewing utilization of services, managing cases, and constructing benefits. As a result, the mission of UR has broadened to embrace concepts of quality and creative implementation of programming, in addition to ensuring that services are provided within specified insurance or benefit design parameters.

Utilization management (UM) has, in many respects, replaced the more passive, inspection-oriented concept of utilization review.

In an ideal managed care world, each provider conducts his or her own UM. Therapists are sensitive to their patients' average length of stay, and strive to make their therapy more innovative and efficient. They understand benefit structures and exclusions and work with patients to consider alternative arrangements when services are not covered by insurance. Agencies as a whole systematically observe their patient populations, working together to develop programming that handles recurring types of problems in novel ways. Hospitals (especially those working under episode-of-care payment arrangements) have mechanisms for reviewing the quality of care and feedback loops to the insurance company to document appropriateness of treatment and recidivism. Crisis workers understand the importance of assigning patients to the proper level of care, and financial incentives are consistent with this goal.

Therapists, however, are just beginning to recognize their role in gathering data and educating patients on insurance benefits, in addition to providing primary care. Many still believe that these functions are best left outside of the clinical office. Even some managed care agencies are just in the nascent stages of defining themselves as interdependent systems managing the same patient population—as opposed to groups of independent practitioners, each struggling to care for its own caseload. Financial incentives with hospitals often remain misaligned, so that independent UM becomes an antagonistic battle to shorten stays while the hospital strives to lengthen them. The real world of clinical care is changing. As experts in the nexus of clinical care, data collection, and system analysis, UM staff can help new and maturing managed care agencies and capitated behavioral delivery systems to enact these broader changes.

Kathryn Hemker Bobbitt, Ph.D., earned her B.A. in History from Yale University in New Haven, CT, in 1984, and her Ph.D. in Clinical Psychology from Washington University in St. Louis, MO, in 1989. The following year she was appointed Human Values Fellow, and worked with Professor Emerita Jane Loevinger on the Ego Development Project at Washington University. Ms. Bobbitt subsequently moved to Colorado, where she practiced as Senior Psychologist and Assistant Center Director for Biodyne, Inc., a leading managed behavioral healthcare provider. Her current position is Utilization Management Coordinator with Mesa Mental Health in Albuquerque, NM.

BASIC STRATEGIES OF UTILIZATION MANAGEMENT

While there is no doubt a broad range of opinion about the best techniques to use in UM, several basic principles are recognized by most agencies as being critical to success:

- Everyone in the agency needs to understand the importance of UM. As mentioned above, UM cannot be performed by an isolated office behind closed doors, furtively auditing charts. Therapists must feel that UM is a resource to them in managing their client load. Administrative staff must understand patients' benefit plan designs to give accurate information to clients and to interact knowledgeably with insurance companies, providers, and facilities. The UM department must work closely with intake and crisis intervention staff to ensure that policies regarding coverage and risk management are implemented consistently. Education and communication within the agency are the broad goals of UM.

- Whenever possible, review of care should be provided by a similarly credentialed professional or accredited utilization review personnel. Individuals with little formal training in behavioral healthcare are poorly equipped to render opinions about the most appropriate treatment, and will have a difficult time interacting with other professionals regarding alternative options. Alternatively, accrediting boards are now certifying professionals in UR and UM.

- The most important question is what, not where. UM staff can easily be drawn into heated debates with facilities and providers about where treatment needs to occur. Should it be rendered in inpatient, partial hospital, or outpatient treatment settings? These questions are often premature. Inpatient and partial hospital units are places, not treatments. It is always helpful to go back to the primary question of what the patient needs. What intervention is going to happen in the hospital that would be of help? In behavioral healthcare, many creative and clinically appropriate alternatives exist to the highly restrictive setting of the inpatient unit.

- Official policies and procedures drive repetitive functions. All work must be documented. UM cannot be an inconsistent affair. Cases must be subjected to the same basic questions, decisions must be made and communicated in a timely fashion, and customers must know the procedures involved in an appeal or grievance. Standards for each of these functions should be set and regularly reviewed. Considerable guidance in developing UM policies and procedures can be found in the National Committee for Quality Assurance (NCQA) standards ("Review Guidelines," 1993). Compliance with standards set by the agency must be documented. As in the clinical domain, "work not documented is work not done."

• Positive provider relations are invaluable. Therapists who provide services for managed care companies and capitated provider entities frequently feel as if they are making professional compromises in order for their business to remain viable. Engaging therapists in the conjoint mission of providing high-quality services more efficiently within a capitated system builds a trusting, task-oriented relationship. Utilization managers frequently encounter providers who, misunderstanding the role, reassure the UM person that they will aid in presenting distorted or incorrect clinical data to insurance companies, "so it will be covered." It is this very attitude, probably sparked in the past by the real need to misrepresent data, that leads to inflated costs for everyone. Such an attitude must be changed by encouraging truth and by offering ourselves as resources. For example, routinely giving providers feedback on their length of treatment can be very educative, benefitting both the clinician and the UM department.

• Managing risk, enhancing clinical efficiency, and administering insurance policy or benefit design parameters must be concurrent concerns. Embracing the concepts of UR and case management, UM must effectively manage high-risk patients, suggest more efficient clinical interventions where possible, and arbitrate denials of services. A perfect balance between quality, efficiency, and customer satisfaction is rarely achieved, but it serves as a more sensitive model than choosing one end product at the expense of another. Managed care agencies, with their limited resources, may focus their energies on one domain—for example, eliminating unnecessary hospitalizations. Within that task, however, the need to offer alternative treatments and to maximize the customer's satisfaction with the outcome take on equal importance.

Matching Services, Needs, and Benefits

How do UM staff begin to implement the seemingly conflicting agendas of the managed care agency or capitated delivery system that contracts with affiliated providers? Simply put, the UM process begins with an assessment of the patient's needs. A thorough assessment, detailing the patient's diagnosis, recommended treatment plan, and history of treatment, is the bedrock on which subsequent utilization decisions are made. The primary diagnosis may or may not reflect a problem that is covered by the patient's insurance or the benefit plan for which the capitated entity is at risk (a marital problem, for example). The treatment plan may or may not call for a type of intervention that is covered (marital therapy, for example). The history of treatment may or may not suggest the likelihood of a successful outcome with another treatment episode. At a case-by-case level, the role of UM then becomes one of matching the right patient with the right services.

PATIENT NEEDS AND BENEFITS

One of the first questions answered by an assessment of the patient is whether the services he or she needs are covered by the insurance plan. If not, the patient may wish to consider other alternatives that will be less costly to him or her, such as a sliding scale arrangement with another agency or community resources. Many insurance companies and managed care plans base eligibility for coverage on the concept of *medical necessity*. Medically necessary services are often defined as services that:

- are adequate and essential for the evaluation and/or treatment of a condition as defined in DSM-IV;
- generate a reasonable expectation of change from the intervention;
- are consistent with the symptoms, diagnosis, and treatment and in keeping with generally accepted standards of care; and
- are provided in the least restrictive setting necessary.

Although these criteria would seem to define the type of intervention more than the patient treated, in practice the initial assessment reveals whether the first two criteria are met—whether the patient has a behavioral health diagnosis that can benefit from a behavioral health intervention. If so, it becomes the job of the agency to recommend a treatment intervention that is appropriate and provided in the least restrictive setting possible (see below).

The management of patients with chronic conditions (those for which intervention is not likely to "generate a reasonable expectation of change") can be a difficult business, given that most commercial insurance accounts do cover hospitalization for acute exacerbations of a chronic condition. Utilization managers frequently find themselves in the paradoxical position of denying services for patients with chronic problems on an outpatient basis, only to admit the same patient later when the lack of outpatient support has precipitated a crisis.

Capitation contracts must establish explicit criteria for inclusion or exclusion of the severely mentally ill. Subsequently, a consistent, documented philosophy regarding such inherent contradictions in eligibility and coverage will protect the agency from claims of unfairness and enhance the effective management of high-risk cases. The utilization manager may, for example, enact a policy of systematically identifying patients at high risk for more intensive services, and elect to override the exclusion in those rare instances.

An alternative approach is to manage exclusions universally, such that all services, including inpatient care, are excluded for individuals with conditions excluded by the policy. In a helpful chapter on this topic, Theodor Bonstedt, M.D. (1992) suggests using the following criteria in defining patients as *chronic:*

- number/duration of hospitalizations (four or more psychiatric hospitalizations in the previous four years, or 90 days of hospitalization in two successive years within the previous five);
- degree of disability (receives disability benefits for a behavioral health condition);
- lack of cooperation (documented noncompliance); and
- independent second opinion supporting the evaluation of the patient as chronic.

Providers are often under the mistaken impression that the treatment of personality disorders constitutes non-medically necessary services in that there is no reasonable expectation of improvement with psychotherapy. Utilization managers often receive initial assessments from providers that give a primary diagnosis of adjustment disorder, but clinically paint a picture of a borderline or dependent personality. Treatment plans that focus on helping such patients strengthen coping mechanisms and achieve stabilization are clinically appropriate, supported by research in the field, and are straightforward to authorize. In contrast, a treatment plan aimed at actually resolving the Borderline Personality Disorder will need to be discussed with the provider and revised.

Frequently other exclusions exist to the medical necessity criterion. Specific conditions, such as learning disabilities, marital problems, or mental retardation, may be excluded. Certain forms of therapy, such as psychoanalysis, may not be covered. Court-ordered treatment in the absence of medical necessity is nearly always excluded. In the author's group, if after a telephone assessment it is believed that the requested services may not be covered, the person is often referred to other community resources. If the person insists that the services ought to be covered by insurance, an initial face-to-face evaluation is offered, and the assessor is alerted that a question exists as to whether the patient meets criteria for coverage.

Managing exclusions of specific modalities of therapy poses an equally delicate problem. Some insurers still specifically exclude marital and family therapy. Attempting to provide services to, for example, extremely young children with legitimate psychiatric syndromes without the use of family therapy is clinically questionable, if not unethical. Once again, utilization managers must document a philosophy of care that addresses such difficulties. Marital therapy may be provided, for example, in cases where one spouse has a psychiatric diagnosis and conjoint meetings are the clinical intervention of choice. In contrast, marital therapy that is aimed solely at improving marital relations in the absence of medically necessary conditions may be excluded.

Some providers joke that "everyone meets the criteria for an adjustment disorder." Given the frequency of that diagnosis on initial assessment forms, this would indeed appear to be the case. Managed care agencies and at-risk providers must implement a more conservative stance with this diagnosis. When clinical data do not support that the patient displays "marked distress that is in excess of what would be expected given the nature of the stressor, or marked impairment in social, occupational, or academic functioning" (DSM-IV, 1994), ask for more supporting data or a revision of the diagnosis.

Patients who have behavioral health benefits, but not addiction treatment benefits, also pose problems in the interpretation of exclusions. There are few substance abuse addicts who do not have some concurrent, bona fide behavioral health problems in conjunction with their addictive disorder. In such cases behavioral healthcare services can be authorized, provided that the patient produces evidence that he or she is seeking treatment elsewhere for substance abuse. If the patient stops compliance with the addiction treatment and the behavioral health problem appears directly related to the addiction problem, further mental health services may be denied.

Finally, the client who has benefits but clearly is not motivated for treatment poses a common challenge for managed care plans and capitated provider entities. This client frequently asks emphatically for help, but fails to show up for appointments, does not follow through on recommendations, or simply seems to use therapy as an opportunity to complain—without generating any solutions to problems. While there are many sound clinical interventions for this type of client, ultimately the utilization manager must ask: When have we done enough to assess this client's motivation for treatment? This is especially tricky when lack of motivation is a key symptom of the client's illness, as in addiction. In these instances, formal behavioral contracting is essential. Clients must be informed of the treatment plan, expectations regarding their participation, and consequences for nonparticipation. The contract should be signed by the therapist and the client.

In sum, the interpretation and management of insurance parameters requires flexibility, creativity, and a problem-solving orientation. If services are to be denied, the utilization manager must constantly ask on what objective basis was this decision made, what alternative services might be covered, and how can the patient obtain the needed care elsewhere? Rigidly denying coverage, with no clearly documented rationale and no other options specified, leaves the agency vulnerable to legal action, and leaves customers angry and dissatisfied.

PATIENT NEEDS AND SERVICES

Individuals who review utilization of medical services presume that an observable process occurs during treatment, involving a measurable change in the patient's condition. By observing and recording this process, the person reviewing the treatment can make determinations regarding what intervention is most suitable for a patient's set of symptoms, whether that intervention is having any effect, and when the intervention has succeeded such that it can be terminated.

A further assumption is that patient self-reports regarding progress and symptoms are not, in themselves, reliable for the purpose of review. In many medical disciplines, independent tests exist to verify a patient's report; X-rays, CAT scans, blood tests, and even the measurement of body temperature and heart rate can explain and verify a patient's description of his or her experience.

These assumptions become insurmountably complex in the realm of psychotherapy. There are over 100 different psychotherapy modalities, each with distinct and often conflicting interventions, each recommending different lengths of stay for various disorders, and many with passionate adherents but no research base whatsoever to prove or disprove claims of effectiveness (Garfield, 1980). To make the picture even more complicated, most psychotherapies are grounded (as they must be) in the inherent veracity of first-person statements. While professional psychology has struggled to create a scientific model, there have been no simple solutions to the fact that in psychotherapy what generally changes is the person's experience of him- or herself and the world—something to which a third party has, by definition, no direct access.

As a result, the managed care movement has imposed a perspective on the provision of healthcare services that is ill-suited, even inimical, to the traditions and values of psychotherapy. Of 803 articles on "utilization review" produced by a computer search of medical literature since 1985, only 31 (four percent) addressed behavioral health specifically, as opposed to medical care. Review strategies for the vast majority of cases that we encounter every day as reviewers in behavioral health—"problems in living" involving marital conflict, family discord, chronic unhappiness, interpersonal stylistic difficulties, and other experiences that can be understood only phenomenologically—have yet to be scientifically validated.

Given this confusing picture, several strategies are invaluable in the process of determining the appropriate service for a particular client.

- *Second Opinions.* Consensual validation by professionals with specialized training is an extremely compelling device in the process of differential diagnosis and recommended treatment. Second opinions may be obtained from staff members, in addition to peer consultation and supervision, to fulfill this function. If two internal opinions contradict each other, a third opinion from a clinician outside of the agency may be sought. Such re-assessment demonstrates the agency's good-faith attempt to genuinely determine what the patient needs, and bolsters the patient's belief that the agency is working on his or her behalf to be fair and impartial.

- *Appeals.* Similarly, it is important to demonstrate to patients that denials are subject to appeal and review. Rather than argue with patients about whether decisions are justified, it is more helpful to adopt the role of helping them learn how they can have the decision reviewed. This can immediately defuse antagonism.

- *Research.* Scarce though it may be, solid clinical literature on treatment can justify a course of action and lend legitimacy to decisions that may appear to be financially motivated. For instance, it has been helpful to relate to patients that some studies show no increase in future sobriety for long-term inpatient addiction treatment versus outpatient rehabilitation; or that inpatient services may actually make some conduct problems worse. Utilization managers need to keep abreast of current research, and disseminate information to providers to help drive the evolution of community standards for various disorders.

- *The "Equal Alternatives" Solution.* For better or worse, this has been the strategy that insurance companies and capitated provider entities have relied upon most heavily in constructing benefits for patients. If two (or a hundred) possible interventions exist, with no independent means of selecting one over another, the less expensive alternative is used. Thus, where clinical data cannot drive a decision, other concerns, such as finances, can prioritize treatment options. Patients may angrily accuse the agency of "just choosing the cheaper way." In such an equal alternatives scenario this is, unapologetically, true.

STRUCTURE AND FUNCTION

Documentation.   For routine outpatient therapy cases, utilization management should document the following:

- diagnosis;
- precipitant for this episode of care;
- history of previous treatment, including outcome;
- history of any previous high-risk incidents, such as hospitalizations or self-injurious acts;
- recommended treatment plan, including modality and type of therapy indicated, in addition to recommended length of stay;
- symptoms that will be the primary focus of treatment; and
- an operationalized estimate of the severity of targeted symptoms.

Agencies may wish to collect additional information as needed, but it is wise to keep forms as brief as possible.

For hospitalizations, ask facilities to submit within 72 hours copies of the psychiatric evaluation, history and physical, and other supporting documentation as needed. Cases may be provisionally denied at the time of admission, but a formal denial is not generated until these documents are reviewed by two UM staff members. A tracking sheet is kept on each patient, reflecting when documentation was requested, when it was received, and when a decision was made. This enables tracking of compliance with UM policies and procedures. Also record every contact with the facility, including the relevant clinical information given, the recommended treatment plan, and the number of days authorized. Hospital stays generally are reviewed at least every three days, depending on the acuity and complexity of the case.

Providers, and hospitals in particular, frequently interpret the denial of services to mean that they must discontinue treatment. It is important to keep the role of the UM process absolutely clear when this occurs. The decision about whether to continue or discontinue treatment is up to the provider. If a disagreement exists about whether treatment is being provided in the least restrictive setting possible, the utilization manager can provisionally deny treatment and encourage the facility to submit an appeal. Should the facility argue vehemently that a more restrictive setting is needed, but discharge the patient when it learns that services have been provisionally denied, clear grounds exist for suspicion regarding the original request.

Statistics.   Discussion of documentation of cases leads naturally to the mention of data management and analysis. It is on this level that the UM department can provide critical information about system needs, goals, and achievements. The following data are commonly tracked:

- penetration rate (number of new episodes of care per year, expressed as a percentage of the total managed care population);
- hospital days per thousand enrollees;
- re-admission rate (number of patients re-admitted in a benefit year for treatment of the same condition);
- average length of stay in outpatient treatment (often analyzed by provider and by diagnosis);
- percentage of patient population managed within a *brief therapy* model (less than five sessions, for example);
- percentage of patient population requiring long-term therapy model (more than 20 sessions, for example); and
- percentage of patients managed in group therapy.

Agencies that are starting up in the managed care business will want to carefully consider data management systems able to render this information readily. (See Chapter 16.)

THE BOTTOM LINE

As this chapter has made clear, the "bottom line" is no longer the bottom line. Utilization management impacts on, and is impacted by, many areas of the agency's functioning—not just financial performance, but also intake and assessment, risk management, therapy, and clinical programming. As a result, a key challenge for UM staff is to define and focus the mission and philosophy of the department, especially as it intersects with the vision of the agency as a whole. No longer "cops," we are becoming true systems therapists, with new paradigms yet to come.

REFERENCES

Becker, R. J. (1990). Managed care is utilization review. *American Journal of Hospital Pharmacy* 47(10): 2274–6.

Bonstedt, T. (1992). Managing psychiatric exclusions. In J. Feldman & R. Fitzpatrick (Eds.). *Managed mental healthcare: Administrative and clinical issues.* Washington: American Psychiatric Press; pp. 69–82.

Diagnostic and statistical manual of mental disorders (4th Ed.) (DSM-IV). (1994). Washington: American Psychiatric Association; p. 623.

Garfield, S. (1980). *Psychotherapy: An eclectic approach.* New York: John Wiley and Sons; p. 225.

Review guidelines for the accreditation of managed care organizations. (1993). Washington: National Committee for Quality Assurance.

SPECIAL TOPICS

18

GRAPPLING WITH ETHICAL ISSUES

Randall C. Wyatt, Ph.D.

Discussions of ethical practice and managed behavioral healthcare often focus exclusively on the perspective of the provider, consumer, or payor. Each domain demands unique ethical solutions for its concerns, but only an approach acknowledging all three domains can hope to reach a balanced resolution. In the provision of quality and cost-effective services, a new set of ethics is required to deal with population-based treatment, timely access to services, treatment closure, time-limited therapy, psychiatric exclusions, treatment guidelines, and confidentiality. Dr. Wyatt offers practical advice for handling these ethical issues and proposes 12 principles for ethical managed care practice.

D iscussions of managed behavioral healthcare practice and ethics often center around threats to confidentiality, loss of professional autonomy, refusal by insurance to reimburse for services, and informed consent. Rarely is a distinction made between managed care as provided by capitated group practices and fee-for-service arrangements provided by indemnity insurers or managed care organizations (MCOs). The primary focus of this chapter will be on the ethical dilemmas facing behavioral group practices and clinics working under prepaid or capitation contracts, while highlighting comparisons with indemnity and MCO fee-for-service ethical issues where relevant.

It is important to clarify what domains of ethics are to be considered. Three ethical domains will be explored: clinicians' ethics, managed care insurance contract ethics, and the personal ethics of clients.

Balancing the ethical *triumvirate* of managed care assumes that these three participants have relatively equal authority. Equal authority means that none of the parties can act without the implicit cooperation of the others. Insurers need members and providers. Clients seeking behavioral health services need providers and insurance benefits (or another method of coverage). Providers need clients and insurers (or payors). Juxtaposing, clarifying, and resolving the various ethical concerns of this triumvirate call for a delicate balance of ethical, financial, and contractual strategies. Only by stepping out of single-domain ethical approaches is it possible to grapple with the ambiguous reality facing clinicians, payors, and clients every day.

CAPITATED/PREPAID AND FEE-FOR-SERVICE VALUES COMPARED

Comparing prepaid and fee-for-service approaches and values rarely results in clarity about what is ethical or unethical. Instead, each model has its ethical advantages and disadvantages. The following discussion of utilization review issues and models of service delivery (individual versus population-based) highlights the ethical dilemmas facing capitated and fee-for-service practices.

The motivations to provide and limit services differ widely when comparing prepaid arrangements and indemnity or MCO fee-for-service arrangements. Fee-for-service clinicians are financially and professionally rewarded for treating clients for longer periods of time, thereby risking overutilization of limited provider resources and possibly overtreatment. The greater the demand for services, the more the fee-for-service clinician is financially rewarded. In contrast, capitated MCOs and practitioners are financially rewarded for reducing utilization and for treating a greater number of clients for briefer periods of time. The capitated group practice is financially better off, at least in the short run, if its services are utilized at

Randall C. Wyatt, Ph.D., is the Clinical Director of Pacific Applied Psychology Associates, a behavioral group practice in Northern California. He directs quality assurance, outcomes projects, and professional staff development. Dr. Wyatt is an adjunct faculty member at the California School of Professional Psychology, Alameda, where he teaches "Intensive Clinical Case Seminar" and "Managed Mental Health Care and Brief Therapy." He has published articles on counter-transference reactions to managed care demands and on models of mental illness. His current professional interests include psychotherapy outcomes, innovative uses of psychoeducation, and supervision and training in time-effective treatment.

a lower rate. Thus, the risk in fee-for-service arrangements is overtreatment and overutilization; the risk for capitated arrangements is undertreatment and underutilization. Both reimbursement approaches have benefits and liabilities which become more evident when examining the concept of treating the population versus treating the individual.

Traditional, private practice, fee-for-service clinicians have focused on treating individuals and their families, with little overt consideration of how focusing on only a few clients might affect the community at large—in other words, high individual client cost, few clients treated, only select clients treated, and long waiting lists. Group practices with capitated contracts, much like community behavioral health centers, seek to treat an agreed-upon population, thereby focusing on treating more individuals, rather than on clients needing intensive long-term services. In other words, individuals and their families receive behavioral health services but the services are limited to crisis interventions and brief treatments, so that more members of the population can receive treatment within the limited financial resources available for that population.

The shift toward population-based treatment models that value the prudent use of resources creates ethical concerns for clinicians who are required to manage length, cost, and quality of services. Moreover, the needs of the population at large hold little weight for a clinician sitting with a severely depressed client who has exhausted his or her twenty-session behavioral health benefit. A suffering client commands more immediate attention than a theoretical population. Indeed, most behavioral health-care providers have been trained to focus on the individual model of service and may have little training in managing time limits and brief interventions. Thus, clinicians may struggle with feelings of anger toward managed care or their own organization, or else experience guilt about denying further treatment. Other clinicians may overidentify with managed care limitations and blame clients for seeking additional treatment (Wyatt, 1993a; 1993b). Such experiences, if left unexamined, can lead to clinical errors and to potentially unethical actions.

The capitated group practice or clinic is required to balance the needs of the individual seeking treatment with the needs of the entire capitated population. In the short run, refusing to treat patients or cutting off treatment is an effective cost-containment measure. The short-sighted capitated practice focuses on crisis intervention and symptom reduction without providing services to increase coping abilities (Herron, et al., 1994). Such practices result in the problems associated with underutilization, as noted above. Ultimately, refusal of appropriate care is detrimental to the capitated group practice because of decreased client satisfaction, decreased reputation for quality, clinician unrest, increased hospitalization, adverse events (such as patient suicides), and strained ethical practice. Indeed, capitated practices in business for the long term are motivated to provide services that are both ethical and efficient. Groups dedicated to treating a population are also motivated to help people in crisis become stabilized and equipped to face new crises. Thus, the pressures and ethical dilemmas facing capitated group practices and clinics—and their clinicians—are unique among service providers.

THE DOUBLE-EDGED SWORD OF MANAGED CARE PSYCHIATRIC EXCLUSIONS

Commercial benefit plans include psychiatric exclusions because without them 20 percent of the population may use up 80 percent of behavioral healthcare resources. The typical managed care insurance policy defines psychiatric exclusions as psychiatric conditions that are chronic in nature, not likely to respond to short-term treatment, or not meeting the crisis limitation requirement of the benefit plan. Psychiatric exclusions financially benefit the capitated behavioral health group by excusing it from any obligation to treat chronically ill patients or clients seeking long-term growth therapy. Thus, psychiatric exclusions make it possible for capitated practices to limit their financial risk, since these clients would soon drain limited financial resources. It should be noted that private, fee-for-service clinicians use the opposite form of exclusion, excluding patients who cannot afford to pay the indemnity insurance deductible or the self-pay fee. Also, indemnity insurance plans often include lifetime maximum benefits, which amount to an exclusion from treatment for those with chronic disorders.

Despite the short-term cost savings of psychiatric exclusions, in the long term they do not hold down overall health costs to insurance companies or to society as a whole. Excluding patients with severe behavioral illnesses from treatment merely pushes clients toward county or state hospitalization, decompensation, drug abuse, hopelessness, and social and community unrest.

If capitated behavioral health groups were to reduce limitations and provide liberal access to necessary services (that is, available treatment for chronically ill and growth therapy clients), then the capitation rate would have to be increased to reflect this shifting focus of treatment. However, at this time in the United States both prepaid and MCO fee-for-service models are working under limited financial resources and, therefore, must make difficult decisions about allocation and distribution of clinical care.

One point regarding psychiatric exclusions must be emphasized: ethical clinical practice may not require individual private practice clinicians to treat each individual who seeks treatment. However, an at-risk capitation contract legally requires the provider group to treat every individual who is eligible to receive a covered benefit. In capitated group practices, contract law is at work. First, the insurer and the member make a contract for what benefits are covered and not covered. Providers enter the picture only after the deal has been made. Clinicians then sign contracts with the health maintenance organization (HMO), MCO, medical group, group practice, or employee assistance program (EAP). The group practice and its clinicians have agreed to honor the insurance benefit's coverage in addition to their own professional ethical code. The group practice and its clinicians must continually balance these tensions while searching for creative ethical solutions and compromises.

Another method of limiting or excluding psychiatric benefits is the ambiguous use of benefit criteria. Managed care benefit packages often include treatment language requiring treatment for "crisis intervention only," "medical necessity," or "problems amenable to brief therapy." Who are the arbiters of these terms, which originated not from academia or clinical practice but from insurance companies? What are the reliable definitions of these terms across providers in actual practice? Similarly, there are disagreements among behavioral health professionals about what problems are amenable to brief interventions.

Another complication arises when the ambiguity of psychiatric diagnosis comes into play. For example, a client in a personal crisis, such as a marital break-up, may not meet the criteria for a psychiatric diagnosis. Another client may have a psychiatric diagnosis, such as dysthymia, but not be in crisis. Regardless of their clinical orientation, the group practice and its clinicians must interpret the benefit language and decide who receives services: both, one, or neither.

The group practice concerned with long-term viability takes a population-based approach to the care of patients who need help but may be excluded from coverage, with a focus on time-sensitive interventions. Refusing to treat a client based on strict exclusionary methods will save short-term behavioral health resources but will burden the medical and behavioral healthcare system in the long term. A long-term, population-based focus is an excellent example of how a capitated group practice can combine ethically and financially viable solutions.

The subjectivity of decisions about medical necessity, psychiatric diagnosis, and criteria for crisis intervention ensures variance across providers, insurance executives, claims examiners, and even clients. Group practices and utilization review panels should develop consistent and clear policies about psychiatric inclusions and exclusions. Such policies should be understandable by clinicians and utilization review panels, as well as by clients. When there is a disagreement between these parties there should be a standing, neutral appeals panel to arbitrate disagreements and seek creative solutions.

The Changing Meaning of Informed Consent

Standard informed consent in private behavioral healthcare practice includes informing clients of the limits of confidentiality, professional licensure status, financial obligations, and so forth. In managed care, informed consent becomes much more complicated. First, clients typically believe they are paying their therapist for services rendered through their co-payments, while their insurance merely covers the rest of the expense. In capitated arrangements, however, co-payments are a small source of revenue, and in reality providers are financially incentivized to reduce, rather then lengthen, the treatment.

Thus, a difficult dilemma presents itself: to what extent should clinicians working under capitated contracts inform their clients of their financial arrangements? In order to be forthright, do clinicians explain the terms under which they are providing treatment, including financial incentives, restrictions on referral, and criteria for treatment? Or do they guard such information, thereby avoiding the awkward role of explaining capitation and risking the confusion, anger, or bewilderment of clients?

This issue is rarely discussed. Thus, there appear to be no standards of ethical or unethical clinical/financial practices. Historically, however, clinicians have not discussed with clients their professional salaries, financial arrangements with insurance companies, or partnerships in group practices. In general, it appears that clinicians may not be obliged to discuss the details of capitated financial contracts with their clients, since involved discussions with inquiring clients may interfere with the therapeutic relationship while doing little to appease persistent questions.

However, client questions about criteria for treatment should be discussed openly and in a style suited to the client. The managed care clinician should explain benefits and policies in a straightforward manner. Clinician judgment, tailored to each individual client, should be used to discern what form such conversations take (Wyatt, 1993a; 1993b).

Confidentiality Revisited

Confidentiality is an endangered species in behavioral healthcare practice, as in other aspects of our lives. Credit card companies know our hobbies, interests, and purchasing patterns. Law enforcement agencies have our fingerprints. Behavioral health practitioners are often required to break confidentiality for reasonable suspicion of child abuse, elder abuse, spousal abuse, or danger to self, others, and property, as well as in many legal cases where behavioral health issues are being disputed. Managed care limits to confidentiality are among the many erosions of privacy and confidentiality in today's culture.

Some MCOs have limited protection for patient confidentiality, so that client records, diagnoses, history, and family issues may be considered in order to determine financial responsibility. Most clients are not fully aware of the amount and the nature of the information that is released by their clinician to MCOs and, if they were, some would surely feel embarrassed, angry, or bewildered.

Despite the information available to MCOs and internal utilization review supervisors, misuse of this information appears to be uncommon. MCOs and group practices typically have strict confidentiality requirements which protect release of sensitive client information to nonauthorized personnel and the population at large. Thus, the central issue may revolve around not how many people are aware of a client's confidential information, but how closely and respectfully those who have such access guard that information.

Figure 18.1 provides a synopsis of confidentiality limitations in different clinical settings. The farther down the list, the more limited is confidentiality, that is, the more information must be released by the clinician about the client's life in order to obtain reimbursement or to meet the requirements of the insurance contract.

Precautions can be taken to guard privacy and increase client acceptance and comfort. For example, capitated group practices may limit reports of confidential information to descriptions of symptoms, diagnosis, and a brief treatment plan. Also, many capitated group practices have internal utilization review procedures which fall under professional supervision and consultation where confidentiality is closely monitored. Finding a balance between providing enough information for appropriate utilization management but not enough personal information to injure the fragile safety of the therapeutic relationship must be continually kept in mind. Managed care confidentiality is an evolving area of concern; the essential balance between maintaining client privacy while acknowledging the payor's need to know has yet to be fully achieved.

Figure 18.1 Confidentiality in Different Settings

CLINICAL PRACTICE FEE ARRANGEMENT	STATUS OF CONFIDENTIAL INFORMATION
Fee-for-service—no insurance:	Information shared between clinician and client.
Fee-for-service—indemnity insurance:	Information shared between client and clinician. Clinician provides client's psychiatric diagnosis and dates and types of services to obtain insurance reimbursement.
Prepaid Provider or Capitated Group Practice:	Information shared between client and clinician. Clinician provides client's psychiatric diagnosis and dates and types of services for internal record keeping. Clinician presents selected clients for administrative and clinical review through supervision, peer review, or on-site internal utilization review procedures.
Managed Care Organization Fee-for-service:	Information shared between client and clinician. Clinician provides client's psychiatric diagnosis, and dates and types of services to external case managers to obtain insurance reimbursement. Clinician also provides extensive evaluation and history of client with treatment plan as part of request for initial and ongoing treatment authorization. If clinician disputes treatment authorization, appeals panel becomes involved.

Access to Appropriate Care

"A mental health manager also must decide whether to emphasize access to a department for new patients or depth of treatment for the patients already there."
(FELDMAN, 1992)

A common critique of capitated group practices and clinics is that they inhibit access to services through long waiting lists. In response to this criticism, many managed care groups and clinics have developed methods of responding quickly to psychiatric emergencies and crisis calls, and of providing timely access to initial appointments. It is now considered standard practice to measure the timeliness of first appointments. (Note that fee-for-service providers, with their focus on the individual, historically have had long waiting lists without adequate referral systems for overflow clients. However, capitated groups practices, by definition, seek to provide access to the entire targeted population; timeliness is a central concern.)

Unfortunately, making certain that initial appointments are readily available has caused other problems. For example, one common method has been to require clinicians to allot a fixed number of intake appointments for new clients each week, regardless of whether they have openings in their schedules. Consequently, clinicians must shuffle their schedules, see clients two, three, or four weeks after the first appointment, precipitously terminate clients, do phone check-ups, or prematurely refer clients to groups or medication maintenance treatment. Often clinicians in this situation are implicitly pressured to engage in such practices regardless of the clinical appropriateness for their clients. The quality of treatment is sure to suffer. To address this problem, group practices and clinics are now beginning to measure client satisfaction with follow-up appointments and the outcomes of the clinical care provided.

Alternatives to consider when attempting to provide timely appointments include developing a consistent internal philosophy that values time-sensitive and time-effective techniques (Budman & Gurman, 1988). Active supervision of caseloads is also extremely helpful in identifying difficult cases and developing creative approaches to more effectively manage time and treatment. If a clear treatment philosophy is in place and access to appointments falls beyond predefined time limits, then it becomes clear when to hire new staff, refer out to network providers or community clinicians, reorganize the clinical staff to better manage treatment plans, or renegotiate the capitation contract.

How to provide timely first appointments, timely follow-up appointments, quality treatment and referral, and efficient treatment while maintaining financial and ethical viability certainly poses a quandary for capitated group practices and clinics. Lest managed care treatment access be viewed out of context, it should be remembered that in traditional private practice settings waiting lists are considered a sign of the clinician's excellent reputation as well as clinical and business acumen. Thus, capitated group practices and clinics are actually breaking new ground (following the lead of community mental health clinics in the 1970s) by attempting to provide the most timely access and follow-up services ever available to large populations.

Fixed Session Limits versus Time-Effective Therapy

Managing the length of clinical treatment is a crucial part of balancing quality and cost containment for a capitated group practice. Two basic approaches are used to address this issue. The fixed session limit method consists of clinicians informing their clients that they have, for example, six sessions. Treatment extensions must meet strict criteria such as high suicide risk. The length of treatment under such policies is likely to be about six visits, with little variation. An alternative method consists of practicing time-effective psychotherapy (Budman, 1990). Using the time-effective therapy model results in wide variance (that is, one to twenty sessions) in the length of treatment, since the clinician is tailoring the treatment to the unique state of the client. Neither of these practices is inherently unethical, but each has benefits and costs.

While appealing in its simplicity, the fixed session model does little to make prudent use of resources or stretch the creativity of the clinician. This policy does not address the insurance benefit issue in a straightforward manner and results in a distortion of the managed care contract. It also obfuscates the opportunity for the clinician and client to creatively make the best use of time and resources by arbitrarily setting the session limit.

Certainly the time-effective model requires creativity and savvy on the part of the provider, who must be both clinician and timekeeper. It is crucial that capitated group practices and clinics aspiring to provide time-effective services invest in the time and training necessary to provide clinically effective and ethical management of time and resources. To do otherwise is to court idiosyncratic treatment, overly subjective session limits, and inconsistency across clinicians; in essence a hodgepodge of widely variant clinical and administrative decisions regarding the length and form of treatment.

Ethical Treatment Closure versus Patient Abandonment

Treatment closure in managed care practices occurs frequently due to the briefer nature of treatment. The term closure is preferred to the more final word termination since many capitated group practices use intermittent brief therapy over the client's life span, wherein the client may gain closure on multiple episodes of treatment (Cummings, 1990). The clinician must handle closure in a manner that is compatible with the client's insurance benefit and sensitive to the unique clinical issues facing this client.

Patient abandonment occurs when the client's benefit is no longer operative due to various causes (such as loss of insurance benefit due to job change or exhaustion of insurance benefits), all of which may result in the clinician inappropriately terminating treatment without proper closure or referral. Such precipitous closure of treatment may have an adverse impact on the client's functional status. In such cases, therapists must guide clients to consider ending therapy, converting to self-pay, transferring to a low-fee therapy clinic, being referred to community resources, making fewer visits over the next several months, or receiving emotional support to ease separation issues. Appropriate discussion of these options can clarify the client's direction in an ethical manner while continuing to uphold the insurance, HMO, or EAP contract of the capitated group practice.

According to the code of ethics of the clinical professions, abruptly stopping treatment with a client in severe distress is considered gross patient abandonment. Even if the clinician is following the policies of the organization, and even if the clinician has correctly assessed the client's status with regard to the insurance benefit, it is the clinician's professional and ethical duty to make arrangements for an appropriate closure to treatment, even if that results in a financial loss for the clinician and the organization. Additionally, this ethical practice must be carried out regardless of whether the clinician is working for an MCO or capitated group practice or under fee-for-service indemnity arrangements where the client has reached a lifetime maximum benefit. In practice, the clinician can avoid patient abandonment in several ways, such as seeing the client for an additional one to three sessions at the co-payment rate or following the client on an intermittent basis until appropriate connection is made to a more affordable provider.

Ethical Use of Treatment Guidelines and Protocols

The use of clinical practice guidelines is becoming more prevalent, particularly in managed care-driven practices. MCOs have used practice guidelines as a mechanism to allow or disallow treatment authorizations. Capitated group practices, among others, are using practice guidelines to increase consistency and quality among providers. The guidelines can also be used as a resource and reference guide for clinicians regarding clinical case management.

While all of the above uses are ethical, clinicians continue to fear mandatory treatment protocols. Clinicians may be pressured to use mandatory protocols when they believe another mode of treatment would be more effective. What, then, is the ethical course of action?

Ethically, clinicians should voice and document their concerns and their professional opinions to the appropriate case manager, utilization review committee, or supervisor. They may be faced with either betraying the policies of their organization or going forward with an intervention that they believe is not in the best interests of the client. Informing clients of alternative treatment options, whether within or outside of their insurance benefits, may be the best way out of this ethical impasse. Another option is to transfer the case to a clinician who can perform the most appropriate services.

Clinicians should begin a dialogue with MCOs or their group practices to develop procedures to address instances when clinician judgment and practice guidelines differ. Those in leadership roles can facilitate flexible use of guidelines. Clinical practice guidelines should inform and augment, rather than control or restrict, creative clinical evaluations and therapeutic interventions.

Appreciation of Ambiguity and Irony

Once clients who were hesitant to embark on a course of long-term therapy were seen as resistant (Feldman, 1992). Now clients in managed care settings are seen as resistant when they actively insist on long-term therapy. Similarly, a client leaving treatment after eight sessions traditionally was viewed as a treatment drop-out. Today, eight sessions of focused brief therapy is often viewed as an efficient and effective way of helping the client.

The changing nature of healthcare and the myriad of financial, ethical, and clinical trends may make today's standards different from those of the past. Thus, it is incumbent on the clinician to forgo impulsive judgments of clients or colleagues who advocate for ideas and practices that do not fit into today's managed care practices. The ethical group practice clinician or manager learns to appreciate ambiguity.

Proposed Ethical Principles for Behavioral Group Practices and Clinicians in Managed Care Settings

Professional associations are beginning to incorporate the changes in behavioral healthcare into revisions of their ethical codes and guidelines. New laws regarding managed care practices will affect insurers, providers, and, ultimately, clients. In Figure 18.2, 12 ethical principles are proposed as a step toward developing ethical guidelines for clinicians, group practices, and clinics involved in managed care and capitated fee arrangements. The principles have been presented with an eye toward simplicity and parsimony; complexity and expansiveness likely will follow in the near future.

Figure 18.2 Proposed Ethical Principles for Behavioral Group Practices and Clinicians in Managed Care Settings

1. Clinicians strive to uphold the ethical guidelines of their professional associations and licensing agency.

2. Clinicians and practice managers endeavor to fulfill the letter and spirit of managed care contracts and benefit plans to which they have agreed.

3. Clinicians strive to relate and interact with clients and potential clients in a manner that takes into account the client's clinical and ethical expectations, needs, and circumstances, as well as financial, emotional, and interpersonal resources.

4. When faced with conflicting loyalties between the ethical needs of the clinician, client, and insurer (or payor), the clinician attempts to carefully address, negotiate, and/or resolve the needs of all parties in a forthright and equitable manner.

5. Clinicians and managed care group practices seek to provide accessible and timely behavioral health services, attempting to reduce all unnecessary gatekeeping and other onerous procedures, which unnecessarily restrict timely access and sound clinical care.

6. Behavioral health administrators and managers seek to inform clinicians, as well as be informed by clinicians, regarding how to provide quality services within given benefit structures.

7. Detailed financial questions by clients about managed care financial issues and capitation arrangements are referred to an appropriate benefits manager or other personnel within the group practice, medical group, or insurance company.

8. The clinician explains benefits, policies, and treatments in straightforward English, avoiding jargon whenever possible.

9. Clinical practice guidelines and protocols inform and guide rather than control or restrict creative clinical evaluations and therapeutic interventions.

10. Clinicians make every effort to avoid patient abandonment and to provide for ethical treatment closure and appropriate referral for all clients.

11. Group practices and clinicians attempt to manage clinical treatment with a focus on time-effective treatment models and clinical/administrative supervision, rather than by the use of restrictive or punitive methods to obtain clinician compliance.

12. Clinicians and administrative executives seek to appreciate the ambiguity and the continually changing nature of behavioral healthcare practice, which affect ethical considerations.

SUMMARY AND CONCLUSION

Neither fee-for-service, MCO, nor capitated group practice approaches to behavioral healthcare avoid all ethical pitfalls. Fee for service did little to encourage prevention, outreach, integration with other health services, or quality control. MCOs risk loss of client confidentiality, use of restrictive psychiatric exclusions and gatekeepers, patient abandonment, loss of sound clinical judgment, and inconsistent and subjective case management. Groups and clinics working under capitation contracts have their own share of potential difficulties, including undertreatment, variable quality control, provider financial risk, decreased client confidentiality, and exclusions from treatment.

No longer can ethical issues be resolved by narrowly examining a single domain of the ethical triumvirate of contemporary clinical practice. The need to balance the ethical demands of the consumer, insurer, and clinician becomes ever more pressing as managed care and capitation arrangements increase. Only an approach that acknowledges all three domains can hope to truly resolve these conflicts. Striving to balance the triumvirate will move us toward a higher quality of clinical services while making maximum use of available resources. Capitated group practices and clinics are in a unique position to clarify these questions and to develop creative and balanced solutions.

REFERENCES

Budman, S. H., & Gurman A. S. (1988). *Theory and practice of brief psychotherapy*. New York: Guilford.

Budman, S. H. (1990). The myth of termination in brief therapy: Or, it ain't over till it's over. In J. K. Zeig and S. G. Gilligan (Eds.). *Brief therapy: Myths, methods, and metaphors*. New York: Brunner/Mazel; pp. 206–218.

Cummings, N. (1990). Brief intermittent psychotherapy throughout the life cycle. In J. K. Zeig and S. G. Gilligan (Eds.). *Brief therapy: Myths, methods, and metaphors*. New York: Brunner/Mazel; pp. 169–184.

Feldman, J. L. (1992). The managed care setting and the patient-therapist relationship. In J. L. Feldman and R. J. Fitzpatrick (Eds.). *Managed mental healthcare: Administrative and clinical issues*. Washington: American Psychiatric Press; pp. 219–230.

Herron, W. G., Javier, R. A., Primavera, L. H., & Shultz, C. L. (1994). The cost of psychotherapy. *Professional Psychology: Research and Practice* 25: 106–110.

Wyatt, R. (1993a) Countertransference reactions to managed care demands: Part 1. *California Psychological Association Briefings: Managed Care*, p. 13.

Wyatt, R. (1993b) Countertransference reactions to managed care demands: Part 2. *California Psychological Association Briefings: Managed Care*, p. 14–15.

19

DESIGNING OUTCOMES STUDIES

Teresa L. Kramer, Ph.D.

This chapter systematically outlines and describes the steps for establishing an outcomes management program within a capitated group practice or clinic. Consideration is given to financial resources, patient rights and convenience, staff availability, and ongoing quality improvement activities. The objectives of an outcomes research program, considerations in developing the methodology and selecting the instrumentation, and the processes of data collection and analysis are discussed. Numerous references to assessment instruments are also provided.

Influenced by the escalating costs of healthcare, many employers, managed care companies, and third-party insurers are, at the very least, carefully monitoring the costs and benefits of mental health treatments and, at the other end of the continuum, restricting the amount, kind, and service delivery of such treatments. New requirements for assessing the efficacy and efficiency of psychotherapy and psychopharmacology have emerged, resulting in the integration of outcomes management research into routine clinical practice. Such research evaluates changes in patient satisfaction, symptoms, and/or functioning over time to determine the success (or failure) of various psychological or psychiatric interventions.

Numerous large companies have already embarked on the tasks of measuring symptom levels in patients, comparing such symptoms to those of other patients linked to large data bases, and monitoring the short-term effects of treatment—whether that treatment includes hospitalization, outpatient psychotherapy, or medications. Symptom and functional improvement is also measured against costs, for example, the cost of individual versus group psychotherapy treatment, duration of hospitalization, and so forth. More and more, patient care is guided by the clinical and utilization data provided to practitioners. The development of outcomes research reflects a trend on the part of employers and managed care companies to demand that practitioners comply with utilization procedures and be accountable for treatment outcomes.

Outcomes research predates managed care. Most published outcomes studies historically were conducted to demonstrate the efficacy of a particular treatment. The purpose of outcomes management today is to monitor and improve the specific care provided by a particular practice, agency, or delivery system. Most of the historical studies were conducted in academic settings, with randomization of subjects, comparisons across equivalent groups, and rigorous methodologies—which are prohibitive in a more clinical environment.

OBJECTIVES OF AN OUTCOMES RESEARCH PROGRAM

The key to establishing a productive, efficient, and worthwhile outcomes management program (the word program is used to emphasize the ongoing, integrative nature of this endeavor) lies in obtaining an appropriate budget and identifying the desired objectives to be accomplished—before deciding upon instruments, methodology, statistical analyses, computer software, or staff development.

As mentioned previously, many insurers or employers have mandated the implementation of outcomes research as part of a total mental health package, especially in capitation. Thus, a practice may wish to demonstrate cost-benefit ratios, efficacy in treatment, and cost containment in utilization. However, there may be other objectives to consider for a research program, to the practice's benefit:

Teresa L. Kramer, Ph.D., is a clinical psychologist and assistant professor in the Department of Psychiatry at the University of Cincinnati College of Medicine, Cincinnati, OH. She currently serves as Director of Research and Coordinator of Child and Adolescent Services at University Psychiatric Services, a capitated managed care outpatient practice affiliated with the Department of Psychiatry. She graduated from the University of Cincinnati, completing her internship and post-doctoral fellowships, respectively, at the Medical University of South Carolina in Charleston and Wright State University in Dayton, OH. She has been on the faculty of the University of Cincinnati since 1990.

1. An outcomes research program may provide objective data about patient satisfaction or progress, to be incorporated into an overall marketing plan or to gain additional knowledge for future planning and quality management. For example, a practice manager may want to know which clinicians are most effective in treating patients, in order to maximize the practice's network of providers.

2. A practice manager may want to know which clinical programs show the highest patient improvement rates, in which case a study may be designed to compare patient progress across one or more treatment sites or programs.

3. A practice manager may be primarily interested in documenting the effects of various office procedures or staff on patient satisfaction, with the outcome being modification of certain procedures if problems are identified.

4. An outcomes research program, if carefully designed, can also include clinicians in such a way as to assist them in treatment review and planning. Through periodic follow-ups clinicians can learn how well a patient is faring as a result of the treatment they initiated and then alter interventions accordingly. Such data are critical for clinicians to decide which modalities are essential in the treatment of a given patient, which are useful adjuncts, and which are ineffective (Mirin & Namerow, 1991).

5. Outcomes data also provide a framework for studying the longitudinal course of patients, particularly those with a chronic mental illness whose symptom status invariably will be different from patients with more acute disorders.

While these are just a few objectives to consider, the goal is to develop a cohesive and consistent outcomes management program that meets payor requirements, improves the quality of care provided for patients, and ensures that the practice remains competitive within the mental health industry.

INITIAL PLANNING STAGES

Internal Development versus Outside Contracting.   In designing an outcomes management program, clinicians and practice managers have three options: contracting externally with a company to conduct all aspects of the research program, internally developing their own outcomes management program, or combining these options by developing their own program but hiring an outside consultant when certain aspects of the program extend beyond their expertise.

When hiring an external company, the workload is shifted outside the practice, thus containing the amount of time and energy required by existing staff for this endeavor. Most consulting companies of this nature already possess the instruments, software, and computer programming for easy data collection, entry, and analysis. These companies also prepare written summaries comparing practice data to those of other practices similar in patient size, financial assets, and so on. There are several disadvantages of contracting with such companies. Such arrangements limit a practice's ability to customize assessment measures to meet specific practice needs. Longitudinal research may become very expensive. Also, the company's access to patient data may infringe on confidentiality as well as dictate the type and extent of data analyses the practice is able to perform independently.

On the other hand, developing a research program internally is time-consuming and labor-intensive. Most smaller practices do not have the staff willing and available to devote extra effort to developing such a program, much less the expertise needed to do so. Practices most likely to succeed at such an endeavor assign a specific person and/or a part-time consultant to lead an interdisciplinary outcomes team in establishing the program's objectives, developing a budget for start-up and ongoing costs, and adhering to a mutually agreed-upon timetable for designing and implementing the program (typically about one year from conception to implementation). Practices that include clinicians in the planning stages will be more likely to overcome clinical resistance—which may arise from the fears of being monitored and evaluated through outcomes research.

Finally, an outcomes management program can be developed and implemented internally, with the assistance of consultants who may be responsible for developing assessment instruments, writing computer programs for data entry and/or analysis, and generating summary reports from the data to distribute to clinicians, staff and/or managed care companies. This third option will allow practices to retain some control over the research process, while designating some of the more labor-intensive or technical aspects of the program to others.

Regardless of which option is selected, having some basic knowledge of available instruments, methodologies, and data analyses will facilitate initial planning phases. Basically, assessment in outcomes research can be segregated into two categories: (1) that which focuses primarily on patient attributes; and (2) that which focuses primarily on treatment effects. (See Figure 19.1.) Evaluations of patients can range from simply administering satisfaction surveys to projects involving assessments of a number of patient variables over time. Evaluations of treatment effects encompass the various

Figure 19.1 Decision Tree for Developing Outcomes Management Program

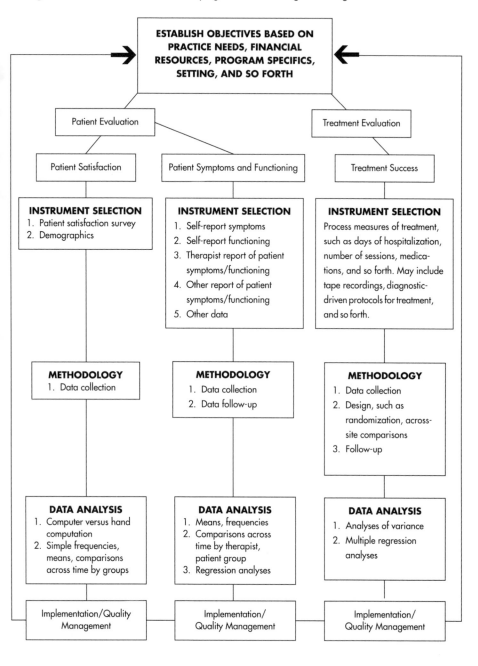

components of the treatment intervention in order to demonstrate whether differential effects exist. In most studies, both patient and treatment variables are measured, although emphases may vary. (See Appendix H.)

Patient Satisfaction Surveys

Sampling Methodology.   Patient satisfaction surveys, which are usually the simplest in that they can be administered quickly within a short time frame, demonstrate how patients perceive the treatment they have received from a number of persons affiliated with the practice—therapists, office staff, and/or billing services personnel. There are several choices in planning the methodology for a satisfaction survey. Usually, such surveys are administered periodically (every six months to a year) to all patients currently in treatment; however, special efforts can be made to contact those individuals who, for whatever reasons, have ended treatment.

It is also feasible to administer the survey on an ongoing basis by selecting every fifth or tenth new patient to complete a beginning services questionnaire or by requesting that current patients complete ongoing services questionnaires every six to ten sessions. As the surveys are administered over time, trends in satisfaction rates can be monitored for quality management purposes. (For an excellent description of a prototypical satisfaction study in a medical setting, see Rubin, et al., 1993.) Satisfaction surveys can also be administered by telephone. In this case, patients would be randomly selected for interviews, due to the high costs involved in interviewing everyone.

Survey Content.   The most widely used written survey is the Client Satisfaction Questionnaire (CSQ, Attkisson, et al., 1982). Its authors have established normative data as well as reliability and validity criteria for this instrument, permitting some comparisons with other patients in a mental healthcare setting. Like most satisfaction surveys, the CSQ contains items assessing the patient's perceptions of the amount and kind of treatment received, of clinicians' competency and availability, of symptom improvement since treatment began, and of support staff cooperation and efficiency. Other categories of service questions can also be included, such as (1) billing procedures, (2) office convenience and comfort, (3) insurance coverage, (4) emergency support, and (5) explanation of treatment procedures, goals, and so forth. In this author's practice, supplemental items have been added to the CSQ so that analyses can be performed regarding differences in satisfaction rates among various insurance groups or socioeconomic or cultural backgrounds; among patients seeking individual, group, or family therapy; and among patients being seen at different sites.

Advantages and Disadvantages. There are several advantages to administering satisfaction surveys. First, office staff or practitioners can distribute surveys from their offices when patients present for treatment, circumventing the costs of postage and enhancing follow-up rates, which usually range from 20 to 40 percent when mailed. Although telephone interviews also avoid postage costs, the additional staff time invested in this process almost always costs more. Second, the information gathered provides a "report card" of the practice's performance in several areas, particularly over time when service changes may occur as a result of practice expansion, relocation, or staff turnover. Finally, the survey is an excellent way for practices to experiment with designing and implementing a patient study before deciding to embark on a more comprehensive outcomes research program.

There are several disadvantages to using surveys. First, they do not provide any data regarding the symptomatic progress of patients, which is of primary interest in managed care and also for continuous quality improvement to therapeutic processes. Second, most patients respond favorably to items in a satisfaction questionnaire, to appear socially desirable and to avoid offending their therapists. Therefore, the range of responses is minimal, which can limit the meaningfulness of the data. Finally, because of the low follow-up rates, it is often difficult to discern whether the few poor responses obtained actually reflect the opinions of a larger group of dissatisfied patients who either left treatment or were still in treatment but did not take the time to respond to the survey.

Patient Assessment

There is considerable controversy in the field about which specific aspects of the patient's mental health should be assessed in more comprehensive studies of outcomes (Azar, 1994). In medical outcomes research where diagnostic-related groups (DRGs) are most commonly used to differentiate patient groups, assessment is confined to the primary symptoms constituting the diagnosis, with some report of functioning. However, in mental health outcomes research, patient variables may include primary symptoms, comorbid symptoms, functioning levels (such as physical, social, or emotional), and demographics. Unfortunately, there is no consensus yet on which instruments should be included in an assessment battery.

There is some agreement about the general areas to assess (patient functioning, global symptomatology, and diagnostic-related symptoms) and the fact that instruments should be standardized, with reliability and validity data available. However, other issues need to be considered in selecting the most appropriate patient assessment instruments. These include whether to use questionnaires available in the public domain or proprietary questionnaires, whether to select questionnaires that can be scored manually or to invest in optical scanning technology, and whether to develop software programs for generating individual and/or aggregate reports or to rely on an outside company to do so. (See Appendix I for a list of resources regarding these issues.)

Generally, outcomes studies focus on one of two areas of patient improvement: (1) global symptomatology, in which a variety of symptom clusters (such as anxiety, depression, somatization, obsessive-compulsive tendencies, and so forth) are assessed; or (2) diagnostic-related symptomatology in which the presence of a "tracer" condition (Smith, 1993), for example, major depression, is established and specific symptoms of that condition are monitored. In each case, there is usually some measure of general patient functioning as well.

Measures of Patient Functioning. Most researchers agree that any patient evaluation must include a description of the patient's functioning in various domains including social, familial, and vocational. The SF-36 (Ware & Sherbourne, 1991), which measures health and physical functioning, and the PES (Ihilebich & Gleser, 1982), which measures vocational, familial, and interpersonal functioning, are two instruments used for these purposes, although there are certainly others.

Measures of the Patient's Global Symptoms. A global assessment of symptomatology provides an overview of the patient's condition. The Brief Symptom Inventory (BSI, Derogatis, 1985) is one example of an instrument that measures nine domains of symptoms, such as depression, anxiety, and psychoticism. Another instrument recently introduced into the field and currently being used in several locations is the BASIS-32, a brief self-report inventory which assesses five domains: relation to self and others, daily living skills, depression and anxiety, impulsive and addictive behaviors, and psychosis (Eisen, Dill, & Grob, 1994).

Specific Diagnostic Measures. Researchers have also recommended diagnostic-specific assessment measures to be administered in a battery or separately for groups of patients meeting criteria for *DSM-IV* (1994) disorders, such as major depression, generalized anxiety, or substance abuse. This approach is consistent with that established by the medical field to create condition-specific surveys (such as for arthritis, heart disease, and so forth), which will eventually contribute to the development of condition-specific treatment guidelines.

For example, G. Richard Smith, M.D., and colleagues at the Center for Mental Healthcare Research have developed outcome modules for several diagnostic groups, including panic disorder, major depression, and alcohol abuse. These self-report questionnaires in combination with a brief form completed by the practitioner allow for ongoing monitoring of a patient's progress in treatment with regard to his or her primary symptoms. In addition, the Health Outcomes Institute in Bloomington, MN, is developing an Outcomes Management System (OMS) consisting of general and condition-specific surveys, along with the software needed for data entry and analysis. There are also diagnostic-specific instruments published in the literature and/or available through private companies (such as the Beck Depression Inventory, Beck, et al., 1961; and the Michigan Alcohol Screening Test, Selzer, et al., 1975).

As an alternative to, or in conjunction with, self-report inventories is the clinical assessment of diagnostic criteria using structured or semi-structured interviews, such as the Structured Clinical Interview for *DSM-III-R* (Spitzer & Williams, 1990). However, most practices or agencies do not have the personnel available to conduct such in-depth evaluations, which also require reliability and validity checks. In addition, patients do not participate as willingly in studies that are time-consuming and do not appear to pertain to their circumstances, given the overinclusive nature of the interview.

Global versus Diagnostic-Specific Measures.   The decision of whether to include diagnostic-specific instruments is predicated on the objectives of the practice's research program. The advantages are that information is generated on groups of patients with diagnostic homogeneity, which permits more in-depth cost-benefit analyses of specific clinical interventions, allows for more careful monitoring of patient treatment by various practitioners, and creates a very distinct database from which future research can evolve. Unfortunately, few reliable and valid diagnostic-related instruments or interviews currently exist. In addition, by using such procedures, practices, hospitals, and agencies limit themselves to assessment of one or two groups of patients, which may not satisfy insurers, employers, or internal quality improvement needs.

Other Assessment Variables.   Finally, other questions may be included in a battery of tests to assess additional variables. These include: patient demographics, information regarding prior and/or concurrent medical or psychiatric treatment, and history of trauma. Other patient characteristics

affecting symptom progress, such as interpersonal relatedness, self esteem/
identity problems, and availability and use of social supports, may also be
desirable based on the objectives of the program. Because prior research
has shown that all of these variables can affect outcome, it is important to
select one or two as mediating variables worthy of specific assessment. Assessments may also include data from the patient's family members, therapist, or, in the case of children, school teachers and counselors. For
example, the PES has a therapist rating form. Outcome research studies
might also incorporate the Global Assessment Scale (Endicott, et al., 1976)
and Axis I and II diagnoses.

Treatment Assessment

Treatment Variables.   Another component to outcomes research is the
assessment of treatment. Most insurers and mental health groups seeking
to understand their own treatment outcomes will want minimal data
related to the interventions provided, such as the number and frequency
of psychotherapy sessions, psychopharmacological interventions, identity
and discipline of the practitioner, length of stay for partial versus inpatient
hospitalization, or a combination of the above variables. However, more
complex outcomes research studies rely heavily on a more inclusive
description of the treatment in which the following variables are clearly operationalized: type of psychotherapy provided (for example, psychodynamic, cognitive-behavioral, family systems, brief problem focused);
process of psychotherapy (for example, practitioner and patient attitudes,
practitioner and patient alliance, practitioner empathy, patient resistance);
and/or the inclusion of supplemental treatments (for example, support
groups, psychopharmacology). Other critical data relating to treatment are
costs and utilization of other medical interventions during and after mental
healthcare.

   When treatment effect is the primary focus of the research program,
then patients should be randomized, that is, referred in a random manner
to the various treatment conditions, such as inpatient versus partial hospitalization. This, of course, can be extremely difficult in practice settings
where high-quality standards in treatment must be maintained, where it is
unethical as well as impractical to establish alternative treatments or waiting
lists, and where the patient is often unwilling to participate in one type of
intervention over another. However, without this component, it is virtually
impossible to know whether changes in patient symptoms or functioning
levels are a result of the actual treatment or some other unknown factor.

Data Collection and Analysis

Data Collection. The most difficult aspect of outcomes research is the process of collecting the data from patients, especially during the follow-up period. A number of methods have been attempted to facilitate patient participation: (1) therapist involvement, (2) distribution of surveys in the office versus home mailings, (3) follow-up postcards and/or telephone calls to remind patients to return surveys, (4) telephone follow-up interviewing, and (5) incentives to increase participation, such as small payments, offers for magazine subscriptions, and so forth. In the end, the most successful methods are those that encourage participation from both the patient and clinician from the outset. Clinicians should be consulted in the initial planning stages regarding what information is most important for them to know about the therapeutic process. Patients should be informed that the study represents standard clinical practice and, according to the standards established at the practice, they should consent to participate. It is also important for immediate feedback about results to be provided so that patients and their clinicians can use the data to improve treatment.

Timing. When to administer the research protocol is another issue to be resolved in the planning stages. The initial data collection will occur either at the intake interview or during the first therapy session. Timing of the follow-up will depend on the program's objectives and symptoms to be monitored. For example, if this is an outcomes research program designed for an inpatient population, patients may be asked to complete the questionnaires as part of the intake process, at discharge, and again at periodic follow-ups for one to two years. For an outpatient research program, if the objective is to assess the progress of depressed patients in treatment, follow-up data may be collected every three to six sessions. However, if the objective is to assess depressed adolescents with suicidal ideation who are participating in an intensive home-based therapy, then data may be collected on a daily basis. Other, more general programs may be structured such that data collection will occur at more lengthy intervals, such as every three to six months.

Data Analysis and Interpretation. Once the data are collected from the various sources (patient, practitioner, other sources), the next step is data analysis and interpretation, which should be consistent with the objectives of the research program. For smaller practices that are only implementing a satisfaction survey, data may be computed by hand and consist only of means and frequencies for the various item responses and patient demographics. Reports and graphics can then be generated using existing word processing programs. However, in most cases the practice manager will want to develop an internal database and/or to participate in external databases for comparisons with similar practices. It will also benefit the practice to be able to gain access to other management information systems in order to obtain data regarding costs or utilization of other types of care.

A number of spreadsheet and database software programs exist for programming a data management system. Selection of these will depend on the size of the practice as well as existing computer technology. Practice managers can also purchase basic, preprogrammed systems in which the vendor will customize data entry and analysis. (See Appendix I.) In addition, practices may opt to invest in optical scanners, which facilitate data entry. Cost estimates for this technology can range from $1,500 to $10,000, depending on the type and quality of instrument and the company offering the features. Statistical analyses can then be conducted by importing the database, or portions of it, into statistical software programs.

Of course, the most important data analyses are those demonstrating changes in patient symptoms and/or functioning over time with therapeutic intervention. However, more complex analyses can also be performed to show which patient or treatment characteristics facilitate or hinder outcome.

In addition, it is important to analyze the differences, if any, between those patients who participated in follow-up assessments versus those who did not. Analysis of characteristics related to patients who do not easily participate in follow-up assessments may allow predictions regarding which patients will be most likely to prematurely end treatment or be noncompliant.

Unfortunately, extensive information on data analysis is beyond the scope of this chapter. It is therefore recommended that an expert in statistics and/or economics be consulted on projects in which there are multiple independent and dependent variables, so that instruments are developed appropriately and the most accurate statistics obtained. Such an individual may be located through a local university or a company specializing in biostatistical research.

Integration of Results Into the Quality Management Process

As mentioned previously, two of the primary objectives in implementing an outcomes research program are improvement in the quality of mental healthcare interventions within the practice and the development of standards of care in the mental healthcare field. Without incorporating a feedback loop into the program, there is no internal benefit to measuring treatment efficacy and certainly no integration with quality improvement goals. With outcomes data, practice managers can refine day-to-day operations, make decisions regarding the network of providers, improve programming by tailoring it to suit the needs of specific patients, track expenditures against patient progress, and redefine standards of care provided by practitioners.

In order to accomplish these aims, the following procedures should be integrated into the quality management process:

1. Reports generated from the research program should be discussed with practice managers, clinical coordinators, and utilization review staff.
2. Clinicians should be informed periodically about their performance and comments by their patients.
3. Cumulative reports noting patterns in patient progress and satisfaction should be included in the agenda of annual meetings, with recommendations regarding practice modifications, performance reviews, and quality assurance monitoring.
4. New assessment measures and questions should be added to the research protocol as additional concerns are raised by clinicians, support staff, practice managers, or insurers.

Equally important, practices should begin to share the results of outcomes studies with other practices in order to maximize the information available on mental health treatment in managed care settings and contribute to the limited scientific literature available on this topic.

REFERENCES

Attkisson, C. C., & Zwick, R. (1982). The Client Satisfaction Questionnaire. Psychometric properties and correlations with service utilization and psychotherapy outcome. *Evaluation and Program Planning* 5: 223–237.

Azar, B. (1994, May). Outcomes measurement is debated by profession. *American Psychological Association Monitor,* p. 29.

Beck, A. T., Ward, C. H., Mendelson, M., Mock, J., & Erbaugh, J. (1961). An inventory for measuring depression. *Archives of General Psychiatry* 4: 561–571.

Derogatis, L. (1985). *Brief Symptom Inventory.* Minneapolis: National Computer Systems.

Diagnostic and statistical manual of mental disorders (4th Ed.) (DSM-IV). (1994). Washington: American Psychiatric Association.

Eisen, S. V., Dill, D. L., & Grob, M. C. (1994) Reliability and validity of a brief patient-report instrument for psychiatric outpatient evaluation. *Hospital & Community Psychiatry* 45(3): 242–297.

Endicott, J., Spitzer, R., Fleiss, J., & Cohen, J. (1976). The Global Assessment Scale. *Archives of General Psychiatry* 33: 766–771.

Ihilebich, D., & Gleser, G. C. (1982). *Evaluating mental health programs: The Progress Evaluation Scale.* Lexington, MA: Lexington Books.

Mirin, S. M., & Namerow, M. J. (1991). Why study treatment outcome? *Hospital & Community Psychiatry* 42(10): 1007–1013.

Rubin, H. R., Gandek, B., Rogers, W. H., Kosinski, M., McHorney, C. A., & Ware, J. E. (1993). Patients' ratings of outpatient visits in different practice settings. *Journal of the American Medical Association* 270(7): 835–840

Selzer, M. L., Vinokur, A., van Rooijen, L. A. (1975). A self-administered short Michigan Alcoholism Screening Test (SMAST). *Journal of Studies in Alcohol* 36: 117.

Smith, G. R. (1993). Mental Health Outcomes Management Conference, Little Rock, AR (personal communication).

Spitzer, R. L., & Williams, J. B. W. (1990). *User's guide for the structured clinical interview for DSM-III-R.* Washington: American Psychiatric Press.

Ware, J. E., & Sherbourne, C. D. (1991). *The SF-36 Short Form Health Status Survey I: Conceptual framework and item selection.* Boston: New England Medical Centers Hospital, International Resource Center for Health Care Assessment.

Weissman, M. M., & Bothwell, S. S. (1976). Assessment of social adjustment by patient self-report. *Archives of General Psychiatry* 33: 1111–1115.

BEHAVIORAL HEALTH IN A MULTISPECIALTY CLINIC

Bruce Bienenstock, M.D.
Michael J. Feldman, M.D.

Psychiatry is being "remedicalized." Departments of mental health within multispecialty medical clinics are re-integrating as behavioral services move from being "carved out" to "carved in" with general medicine through capitation arrangements that include all healthcare services. The advantages and disadvantages of providing capitated services in a multispecialty setting compared to a single-specialty behavioral healthcare group are discussed in this chapter, as well as the unique features of implementing at-risk arrangements within a multispecialty medical practice.

Psychiatry began as a branch of neurology, but as psychotherapy and psychoanalysis became its primary treatment modalities it moved to the fringes of medical care. Even with the growth of consultation/liaison services, psychiatry was practiced as an independent specialty, separately housed, by individual practitioners who were not part of teams. With growing reliability and validity in diagnosis (see, for example, the publication of *DSM-III* in 1980), and advances in research, the field underwent the following changes:

1. Diagnostic accuracy enabled the field to distinguish in a reliable fashion between different psychiatric disorders, to a degree roughly comparable to the rest of medicine, taking psychiatry out of the realm of "pseudo-science."
2. Breakthroughs in the understanding of the biological and hereditary basis of mental illness put psychiatry into an equivalent framework as other medical specialties.
3. The arrival of new and effective psychiatric medicines has improved the effectiveness of psychiatric care and has "remedicalized" the field.

These changes have resulted in closer working relationships with other medical specialties. Simultaneous social and economic pressures have also changed practice styles, including:

1. shorter hospital stays;
2. specialty treatment programs;
3. less long-term individual psychotherapy and more brief, time-limited, and discontinuous psychotherapy; and
4. more family and group psychotherapy.

As the behavioral healthcare field became more complex over the past three decades, it became clear that a systematic approach to integrating biological and psychological treatment was necessary. A multidisciplinary treatment team could best provide the broad spectrum of care necessary to limit morbidity and cost. This approach to care coincided with the clinical philosophy of specialized behavioral healthcare systems, which are separate from medicine and market themselves as *carve-out* providers.

Bruce Bienenstock, M.D., is the head of the Department of Psychiatry and Clinical Psychology at the Palo Alto Medical Clinic (PAMC), the healthcare division of the Palo Alto Medical Foundation in Palo Alto, CA. During the last four years the department's multidisciplinary staff has grown from 9 to 14.5 FTEs, while referrals have increased by 19 percent annually. Among his many goals has been to help transform PAMC from a "medical arts" boutique environment to a true team-based system which is "managed care friendly." Dr. Bienenstock has worked with managed behavioral health plans and foundations to set up provider networks, and is a popular speaker at national professional conferences.

Michael J. Feldman, M.D., is Director of the Division of Mental Health at the Park Nicollet Medical Center in Minneapolis, MN. He has served in a large group practice setting since 1978, after spending three years with the United States Public Health Service in rural behavioral healthcare. Dr. Feldman has been actively involved in managed behavioral healthcare in both fee-for-service and capitated environments. He has a full-time clinical practice and is an Associate Professor of Psychiatry and of Family and Community Health at the University of Minnesota School of Medicine.

Increasingly, however, the boundary between behavioral health and general medicine is blurring. Today depression is often treated in primary medical care clinics. Behavioral healthcare professionals are treating movement disorders. The definition of *mental illness*, as it relates to medical benefits, is being debated in the courts. The remedicalization of mental healthcare has coincided with a new trend, the so-called *carve-in* era, in which behavioral healthcare and general medicine are integrated into a single system, providing continuity of care for patients. This trend acknowledges that appropriate treatment for mental illness has an offset effect on the cost and morbidity of other illnesses. Operationally this has put behavioral healthcare into the role of a primary care specialty. Patients self-refer, there is a responsive emergency service, and behavioral healthcare providers collaborate with other primary care providers.

CAPITATION AND BEHAVIORAL HEALTH DEPARTMENTS

Fee-for-service (indemnity insurance-based) behavioral healthcare providers and systems in the 1960s through the 1980s supported inefficiencies of practice by encouraging the delivery of more services and relentlessly increasing fees. Under capitation, this is no longer possible. Large, capitated multispecialty practices recognized the need to use technology to gain competitive advantage by becoming more efficient. They also needed the support systems to handle the greater information demands—both from insurance companies and from practice administrators and physicians, who increasingly have seen the need for almost instantaneous clinical and management data. In this realm separate, carved-out behavioral health departments within a multispecialty setting are at a disadvantage because:

1. their overall impact on "income" for the entire clinic is relatively small and, if not efficiently managed, they are expensive given fixed clinic overhead costs; and
2. the information necessary to manage the carved-out contracts is often incompatible with the large clinic's computer system, resulting in requests for significant and costly software modifications.

Predictably, the carve-out era gave behavioral health departments the incentive to capitate separately while attempting to remain part of the general contracts and general structure of each clinic, for the following reasons:

1. Capitation allows the behavioral healthcare department to innovate without having to be dependent on similar innovations in general medical departments.

2. Capitation forces a behavioral healthcare department to face and to resolve, if it is to succeed, the distinctions between what is the responsibility of the department versus the greater clinic, both financially and clinically.

3. Carved-out contracts allow the behavioral healthcare department to proceed without regard to the impact of the contract on the larger medical group.

The main disadvantage of separate behavioral healthcare capitation is the difficulty in determining what is a "behavioral health" versus "medical" service and, thus, which group has financial responsibility. The rapid evolution of payment systems from carved-out insurance coverage to what are now frequently described as carved-in multispecialty groups may offer the best balance in the benefit-to-cost ratio.

STRENGTHS OF THE MULTISPECIALTY SETTING

Providing behavioral healthcare in a multispecialty clinic offers many advantages. This approach to care offers:

1. the most efficient environment for the study of medical to behavioral health cost offsets, clinical algorithms, and integrated services;

2. a natural setting for joint projects in behavioral healthcare with other primary and specialty health providers;

3. access to management and culture, which naturally concentrate on systematic analysis of costs, quality, and group policies;

4. continuity of care, which allows significant organizational and fiscal advantages. Medical records are easily shared with behavioral health providers. Medical and behavioral healthcare clinicians are in frequent contact and the sense of familiarity that this breeds can translate into an outstanding and transparent program; and

5. an environment where behavioral healthcare departments in large multispecialty groups are innately affected by the clinical, cultural, administrative, and economic differences and changes within general medicine on a regular basis. This provides an opportunity for continued integration with overall healthcare delivery and the ability to advocate for the greater health needs of behavioral health patients.

Behavioral health departments can provide both higher quality and lower total-cost medical services. With the ascendance of primary care as the centerpiece of current approaches to cost containment and the need for centralized care, behavioral healthcare departments within a large clinic are in a unique position. Patients can be treated for the whole bio-psycho-social range of ailments such that behavioral health can become a primary care specialty. As more data indicate the limitations of a non-behavioral-health gatekeeper system, the need for this process should continue. Open access is necessary for behavioral healthcare departments to take their rightful place as primary care providers in the medical field.

In contrast, single-specialty, multidisciplinary groups potentially can also be quite effective, since they have the following operational advantages:

1. homogeneity of profession allows for a higher degree of common frame of reference, reducing the need for interdisciplinary education and justification in decision making; and
2. the capability to contract with multiple medical groups, corporations, governments, or carve-out companies without concern for the impact of these arrangements on the larger multispecialty group. This may be particularly important at the administrative level with regard to information systems, billing, centralized intakes, and revenue income (cost against per member per month rate, which may be distorted in comparison to other specialties within a multispecialty group).

When a behavioral health department is part of a multispecialty clinic receiving a single capitated payment, the degree that a "reasonable" part of the capitation goes to the mental department may depend on organizational politics and the strength of leadership in the department. The usual practice is to allocate a target amount, as a percentage of the entire medical premium dollar, to behavioral healthcare. This rate is often based on marketplace data for the geographic area and the benefit package, and is usually equal to or possibly somewhat less than the cost of purchasing these services outside of the group.

Since the behavioral healthcare department in a multispecialty group has integrated its overhead or administrative expense with the larger clinic, it is potentially able to take advantage of economies of scale to have a greater revenue stream and the ability to provide a broader range of care.

In summary, under capitation there are significant advantages to having an integrated healthcare delivery system that includes behavioral healthcare. The success of such a system depends in good measure on the culture within the medical group, the level of esteem in which psychiatry and behavioral healthcare are held, and the belief that the provision of mental health services are not "overhead"—but rather add to the quality of healthcare and bring down the total cost of providing care.

21

INTEGRATING EMPLOYEE ASSISTANCE PROGRAMS INTO CAPITATION

Susan L. Taylor, M.B.A.

Employee Assistance Programs (EAPs) offer a natural service extension to mental healthcare in providing preventive and acute care. EAPs can effectively partner with managed behavioral healthcare delivery systems to provide comprehensive, integrated services under capitation. They bring expertise in assessments, referrals, knowledge of community resources, crisis counseling, and population management. They also have valuable relationships with employee benefit managers, plus experience in capitation as a mechanism of payment. These strengths of EAPs are complementary to managed behavioral systems such that synergistic alliances should be formed. Based on her experience in a setting where integration under capitation has occurred, the author advises other EAPs to partner with managed behavioral healthcare programs. Steps in proposal development and sample data reporting formats are also given.

O riginally called occupational alcoholism programs (OAPs), employee assistance programs (EAPs) were established shortly after the turn of the century. These programs were staffed by nonprofessionals, usually long-term, loyal employees who were recovering alcoholics. They served employees through an employer-sponsored counseling service focused on alcohol abuse and resulting family problems. These programs were heavily influenced by the temperance movement of the early twentieth century and the emergence of Alcoholics Anonymous in the 1930s. Prior to World War II companies such as Kaiser Shipbuilding, Macy's Department Store, and Eastman Kodak established OAPs. However, interest in these programs diminished somewhat during the 1940s, '50s and '60s.

In the late 1970s the issue of substance abuse re-emerged in the United States as a major concern, with strong economic and sociological impact. Companies began to look at substance abuse and the challenge of reducing its impact on the cost of doing business. OAPs were renamed employee assistance programs (EAPs) and began marketing a "broad-brush" approach. The new EAPs developed services to assess and assist employees with a range of personal problems. Throughout the 1970s and early 1980s, EAPs grew as the Drug-free Workplace Act and other government policies heightened awareness of the impact wrought on industry by substance abuse and other personal problems.

By the late 1980s EAPs were in a difficult situation. Demand increased for accountability—showing a return on investment for company management. With shrinking resources and downsizing in a stressed U.S. economy, EAPs were called upon to justify their budgets. During this period, managed behavioral healthcare companies (MBHCs) emerged as competitors for a share of tight corporate benefit resources. The MBHCs seized the timing in the industry to capture market share, which increased pressure on EAPs to solidify their mission and identity. Many EAPs currently do not see their expertise in line with MBHCs.

The EAP field may have missed an opportunity in the 1980s to "supplant the managed care industry." Today it is becoming apparent that, rather than competing, the two fields can cooperate to create a comprehensive continuum of care for employers and employee clients. Moving beyond the fear of resource scarcity, this new chapter in behavioral healthcare is an opportunity for creativity and growth. EAPs are in a unique position to add value to any managed behavioral company's continuum of service. EAPs must focus on their strengths and realize the common goals they share with MBHCs—desiring that each client receives the care he or she needs.

Susan L. Taylor holds a Master's of Business Administration from the University of Phoenix, Albuquerque, NM, and a Bachelor of Arts degree in Psychology from the University of New Mexico, Albuquerque. She is also a certified Alcohol and Drug Abuse Counselor. Ms. Taylor has worked in the behavioral health field since 1982 as an inpatient substance abuse therapist, employee assistance counselor, and administrative director of an inpatient behavioral health/sexual trauma unit. Her combined clinical and business background complements her skills in organizational development, management development, and training. She is currently the director of the largest EAP organization in New Mexico.

CURRENT TRENDS

The goal of this chapter is to demonstrate how EAP professionals can become creative in the continuing development of the field. There is an opportunity to team with MBHCs and businesses to achieve the goal of quality care for the client within capitated environments.

EAPs should begin by taking an inventory of their strengths:

- Clinicians in EAP programs offer work-place expertise and relationships that are highly valuable to MBHCs.
- EAPs traditionally are highly experienced in assessment and referral.
- EAPs have knowledge of community resources and familiarity with accessing these services.
- EAP programs have experience in prepaid, capitated, at-risk arrangements and in whole-population management.

These are just a few of the numerous strengths of EAPs that are brought to the table when considering a partnership with an MBHC. Where such integration can be most effective and efficient will be determined in coming years.

The remainder of this chapter outlines a process of integrating EAP into capitated, managed behavioral healthcare environments. In order to participate in these environments, EAPs must develop technical operating systems to compete in the marketplace and integrate cooperatively with MBHCs.

What EAPs Bring to MBHCs

EAP providers have a unique opportunity to provide assistance to MBHCs. The following is a sample of clinical services that tie into the service continuum of managed behavioral healthcare:

- early problem identification and triage,
- crisis counseling,
- critical incident services,
- referral to community resources,
- prevention services,
- on-site/off-site services, and
- training.

Along with these service areas, EAPs have positive relationships with corporate human resource and benefit managers. Because of these relationships, EAPs are in a position to consult with the company representative and to work with the MBHC to identify opportunities for joint marketing, proposal development, efficient and cost-effective counseling services, and employer carve-outs for behavioral healthcare. EAPs have worked with companies as on-site (internal) or off-site (external) providers of assessment and referral services for many years. In the process of working as off-site providers, external EAPs have gained expertise in the area of capitated proposal and contract development. There are both clinical and operational strengths to an EAP-MBHC partnership. The following section outlines an effective process for including an EAP program in a broad capitation agreement.

How to Develop Capitated EAP Proposals

EAP services can be offered through capitation-based behavioral healthcare contracts. However, clinicians must understand the technical aspects of operating in this arena. Before an EAP and MBHC can analyze synergistic opportunities for partnership, a solid EAP proposal and contracting mechanism must be developed.

Proposal Development.   Once the needs or requests of the employer have been assessed, a proposal should be developed. This proposal should include:

- introduction and overview—describe the EAP company, mission, and service philosophy;
- a brief summary of services and expertise; and
- scope of services—including:
  consultation/policy development,
  supervisory training/coaching,
  employee orientation,
  assessment/referral,
  prevention/awareness/wellness activities,
  statistical reporting,
  cost breakdown and payment,
  utilization expectations,
  rate changes,
  program evaluation, and
  implementation plan.

References/Staff Credentials.   Many of these areas are basic to the components of standard requests for proposals from companies for EAP services. There are several issues that must be addressed by EAPs interested in joining capitated contracts.

1. Define the service. Do not try to be all things to all people. Define how many hours of supervisory training there will be during the contract period, how often, and with what limits and exceptions. How will exceptions be priced? Keep in mind that the limited amount of capitated funding must cover the services that are contracted to be provided.

2. Define assessment, referral, and crisis counseling. Some benefits managers still believe that the EAP is the managed care product provider. Differentiate the services from ongoing behavioral healthcare, but show how they complement each other in a continuum of care and—without redundancy—benefit employees and employers. Define clearly what services the EAP program will provide on and off the work site. Explain how EAP assessments will meet the system's criteria, reduce overlap, and improve access for its clients. Businesses are moving toward more teamwork in their environments. Show how the product will foster teamwork and provide the best product for them.

3. Describe clearly how the EAP and MBHC will work together. Explain the systems for the EAP to refer to behavioral healthcare. Delineate the cost savings that are inherent in EAP crisis assessment and referral as a front-end service to the MBHC's intake department. Tell how and when the EAP will refer to community resources rather than to the MBHC for treatment services. Integration between the MBHC and the EAP can be a powerful marketing tool.

4. Statistical reporting must be meaningful. Set up systems that provide the EAP, the MBHC, and the contracted company with meaningful information. Capture and report data demonstrating a return on investment for the payor. Clinicians need to learn about benefits, costs, and utilization, as well as the costs of running the EAP and of providing quality services. It is important to track the utilization of EAP services and to determine how much it costs to provide services. There are many good management information system programs available. Make sure the system can capture and report data that demonstrate quality and effectiveness. How flexible is the computer system? Is there local support? Can it be updated as the EAP grows? Is data entry simple?

The following list provides other data that EAPs, MBHCs, and client companies may find helpful.

- clinician contact summaries regarding:
  in-person counseling,
  telephone contacts,
  memos,
  discharge planning,
  no shows (look for strategies to reduce this cost),
  demographics, and
  referral source contact; and
- summaries of observable changes in clients':
  pre-EAP attendance at work,
  post-EAP attendance at work,
  performance levels (such as missed deadlines),
  behavior levels (such as concentration or irritability),
  job status,
  health plan usage,
  primary problem levels,
  secondary problem levels, and
  referral to appropriate programs.

All time and activities must be tracked by contract. Be aware of telephone consulting as a service about which data must be captured. Clinicians historically do not like paperwork, but it is important in a capitated environment to capture all costs. Activity on a case by a clinician is an expense against the limited pot of capitated money for that specific contract. Educate clinicians with statistical data and be able to show companies how

Figure 21.1 Sample Cost Breakdown

XYZ Corporation: 1,000 employees

Bid for complete EAP services

Capitation rate:

$2.50 per employee per month

$30.00 per employee per year ($2.50 X 12 months)

1,000 employees X $30 = $30,000 per year

their money has been used. Finally, it is important to break down the proposed capitation rate. Explain the expected utilization rate annually and what factors can cause the rate to change. Figure 21.1 gives an example of a cost breakdown.

Contract Cost Analysis

Once a proposal has been accepted and services are being delivered, it is important to assess contract costs quarterly. Figure 21.2 gives the quarterly costs for XYZ Corporation. The data show that, even though it is only the first quarter of the contract year, caution is in order, given that costs have exceeded those projected for the quarter. Further analysis is needed to assess whether utilization is likely to remain as high in future quarters. How much of a profit margin is needed? How well are the costs of doing business understood?

Figure 21.2 Sample Quarterly Costs

XYZ Corporation: 1,000 employees

Capitation price: $30 per employee per year

Expected utilization annually: 10 percent

$30,000 annual capitation revenue paid in monthly installments

Quarter I: *Contract Cost Analysis:*

Revenue received ($30,000/4) = $7,500

Current three-month utilization: 36 employees = 3.60 percent quarterly utilization

Projected annual utilization based on current percentage = 14.4 percent

Total hours provided by clinicians = 162

Projected annual total hours = 648

Approximate annual cost of service = 648 hours X $50* = $32,400

*The cost of $50 per hour can be a breakdown of direct and indirect costs of providing service, that is, salary of clinician, support staff, printed materials, telephones, office space, and so forth. This is just one simplified example of assessing the status of a contract.

These data and the systems to obtain them are important for the future of an EAP business. Developing the data can aid benefits managers in keeping their costs under control. EAPs must maintain a focus on accountability. Questions such as the following must be answered:

- What is the return on investment for the company?
- What interventions can be done in the work place to control utilization?
- What kind of outcomes studies need to be performed? What outcomes information will be useful and meaningful?
- How can the EAP and MBHC reduce redundancy, further integrate, and keep costs down while serving clients' needs?
- Are there other areas to improve quality?

SUMMARY

A commonly used phrase in the author's EAP is "early, positive intervention." This phrase is appropriate now as EAPs seek to redefine themselves and become accountable to those they serve. The process in the EAP field parallels many others in the healthcare industry. EAPs need to remember that they are experts in a specialized area and that their expertise can enhance the continuum of services within managed behavioral healthcare. To participate, however, it is necessary to master the arts of information gathering and accountability. A greater focus on the technical aspects of tracking and reporting costs and utilization, along with enhancing clinical skills, is necessary.

For EAP professionals, it is time to focus on "early, positive intervention" in their own programs. They need to work as partners with MBHCs and create integrated continuums of client services that are total service packages. This is an opportunity to explore the economies of scale that working together can provide. The time is right for the creative energy of change. It will be exciting over the next few years to witness the growth from these new partnerships.

22

CAPITATION IN THE PUBLIC SECTOR

Robert L. Dyer, Ph.D.

Government entities purchase over 60 percent of behavioral health services. Agencies dealing with behavioral healthcare prefer to contract with delivery systems rather than create them. Dr. Dyer draws upon his extensive public service experience to describe government-funded populations in need of programs, state initiatives now in progress, and the wide array of strategic opportunities for capitated service delivery systems. Medicaid as a driver of reform is given special attention. In addition, thorough direction is given on how to approach and work with government agencies, as compared to private insurers.

O ver 60 percent of all revenues for behavioral health services originate from government agencies (Frank & McGuire, 1994). However, knowing where the money is does not always translate into being able to access it. Many different agencies, using many different bureaucratic terms and unique methods for accessing and accounting for those dollars, act as the public's stewards. This chapter helps the reader better understand the public purchaser as a customer.

PUBLIC OPPORTUNITIES

Because each governmental agency has its own history and priorities, mental health and addictive disorders are not the sole responsibility of one oversight agency—despite the fact that each state has an agency with such a title. The mental health and/or addiction treatment authority for each state (it may or may not be the same agency) was specifically created to be the contract agency with the federal government. Until the early 1980s the federal government provided coordination of many behavioral healthcare functions through the active planning and oversight role of the National

Institute for Mental Health. Throughout the 1980s the regional offices were closed and states took over their coordinating functions. This predictably resulted in those agencies focusing their energies on individual agendas. Their primary focuses of activity were accessing federal block grants and continuing to create community-based care for individuals in state-operated institutions.

During the 1980s a number of societal phenomena created an increased demand for behavioral health services. First, the impact of addictive disorders far exceeded federal planning and funds available through block grants. Addiction care was purchased through social welfare and corrections agencies (as well as to a lesser extent by schools). Second, an explosive increase in care to children strained public welfare agencies, with over half of those children having some alcohol or drug abuse involvement. Finally, the double-digit escalation in healthcare costs, along with improved public awareness and increased behavioral healthcare offerings by traditional physical healthcare providers (hospitals and general practitioners), led to significant increases in demand for mental health services from government employees and entitlement recipients.

Today the publicly funded marketplace for behavioral health providers includes at least the opportunities summarized in Figure 22.1.

Indiana has had the unique distinction of being the median state for both population and tax contribution per citizen. Per capita tax dollars spent, for example, on behavioral healthcare were over $108. Given that the state typically provides care to those individuals in the lower 30 percent of income categories, the actual amount per individual served is considerably greater. The behavioral healthcare authority administers less than 40 percent of those dollars. In Indiana 199 federal and eight state agencies

Robert L. Dyer, Ph.D., was the Director of the Division of Mental Health for the State of Indiana. He authored the Hoosier Assurance Plan, a legislatively approved managed care reform plan for mental health and addictions. Dr. Dyer was also a member of the managed care committee of the National Association of State Mental Health Program Directors. Currently he is President of Spectrum Health, Inc., in Seattle, WA. Spectrum Health is a management services company that packages and brokers behavioral health and chronic illness care and provides marketing services for primary care and behavioral healthcare providers. Dr. Dyer is a senior associate with the Managed Care Technical Assistance Group within the National Council of Community Mental Healthcare and a former Chief Executive Officer of a large private behavioral health delivery system.

Figure 22.1 Mental Health Provider Opportunities

CONSUMER POPULATION	PROVIDER OPPORTUNITY
Federal employees	Usually as provider in a managed care network.
Veterans	Usually as contractor to a regional office or specific Veterans Affairs hospital (still largely in a fee-for-service mode).
State employees	More and more through managed contracts awarded to managed care companies.
Medicaid recipients	The norm is multiple oversight agencies (Medicaid agency, public welfare agency, public health agency, or behavioral health authority are all possible) and multiple plans. Most states separate women's and children's Medicaid, which is still largely paid with a fee-for-service model, from plans for the disabled. Separate state plan amendments or waivers usually exist for special programs serving specific populations.
Severely and persistently disabled	Usually as contract agency through behavioral health authority or its regional purchasing "boards" in those states with regional models of decision making.
Chemically addicted	Providers contract to Public Welfare Agency, Department of Corrections or state addictions authority. (To a lesser extent programs are also supported through education and county government.)
Children	Services are purchased by public welfare, corrections, and education departments at both the state and county levels, and by the behavioral health and addictions authority at the state level.

plus 92 county governments provide support just for children's care. Clearly there are many doors to "knock on" in becoming a care provider that receives public funds.

The Re-invention of Government

The pressures on government to better manage our tax resources have not gone unheeded. Almost every state has major initiatives underway to improve the coordination, effectiveness, or value of certain activities purchased or delivered by the government. These initiatives generally have similar forms. In considering a business relationship with a government agency, try to discover the agency's major initiatives: what are their goals, what form do they take, and what jargon is associated with them? The goals of most current initiatives associated with behavioral healthcare are summarized in Figure 22.2.

Figure 22.2 Current Behavioral Initiatives

GOAL	DESCRIPTION
Regionalization	Increasingly states are recognizing the benefits of local decision making about services purchased. Local boards are empowered to plan the benefits offered, determine the provider panel, and take responsibility for the oversight systems. Washington has blended state and Medicaid dollars for regional boards that administer *prepaid health plans*. These boards accept at-risk contracts to coordinate, purchase, or deliver the full range of services eligible recipients need.
Consolidation	The need for government to disassemble its conflicting rules and regulations has led to some creative projects to consolidate the purpose and funding of agencies. The Robert Wood Johnson Foundation has sponsored several consolidation projects, one of the most interesting of which is in Multnomah County, OR. There multiple agencies providing care to children came together for the first time to coordinate policy, oversight, and purchasing. Indiana and West Virginia currently are processing federal waivers to create a single consolidated system for child care services. Indiana folded 199 federal programs and eight state agencies into a single oversight agency.

(continued on next page)

Figure 22.2 (continued)

GOAL	DESCRIPTION
Privatization	Government has discovered that it is easier to purchase than to deliver care. The growth of behavioral healthcare providers, combined with the desire to improve government accountability, has made it easier to create performance contracts than to deliver services. More and more legislative initiatives are demanding choice in providers, and the old state provider "monopolies" providing care to public recipients are disappearing. Georgia is a case in point. Under legislation passed in 1993 (H.B. 100), the behavioral health authority is ordered to allow consumer choice and private providers to augment the state monopolies for behavioral health, mental retardation, and addiction treatment services paid by the authority.
Outcome Orientation	The need for government to do more than just define who should be a covered provider has become apparent. In recent history government's task was the establishment of a minimum service delivery system. Society is now demanding proof of value. Sampling for impact determines whether case management makes a difference for the client or the taxpayer. New Hampshire, Washington, and Indiana have begun routine sampling for impact. The desired impact moves beyond clinical outcomes and focuses on improving self-sufficiency—the desired outcome for the purchaser of care: the taxpayer.

Behavioral healthcare providers desiring to work with government agencies are strongly encouraged to read the book *Reinventing Government* by Osborne and Gaebler (1993). It has been used as the basis for countless initiatives and truly seems to have captured the spirit of today's reform strategies.

Medicaid, the Reform Driver

It has been difficult for state tax revenues to keep pace with medical inflation under Medicaid, which has grown at a double-digit rate every year but three since its inception in 1965. Medicaid now accounts for over 15 percent of all healthcare expenditures.

Medicaid is a voluntary program; states have a choice of participation. The federal government incentivizes that participation by providing a federal match to every state dollar, based on utilization and need. As a result, states receive from one to four dollars from the federal government for every state dollar invested. The federal program has mandatory and optional elements. The federal Health Care Financing Administration administers Medicaid and all states maintain approved state plans for their programs.

Because of the federal match, as well as the obvious need for the poor and disabled to have health insurance, all states participate in Medicaid. The rapid growth in healthcare costs has been especially troublesome to states. The average state spends 17 percent of its tax revenues on the state match for Medicaid, ranging from 4 percent (Alaska) to 34 percent (New Hampshire). Medicaid is growing at a rate of one percent of state tax revenues per year, a totally unacceptable level which consumes two-thirds of all anticipated new tax growth.

The financial pressure Medicaid places on states has resulted in more amendments and waivers to state plans recently than at any time in the program's history. States are aggressively and creatively attempting to modify their plans to serve their citizens more cost-effectively. Managed care strategies and prospective payment are the approaches favored at the current time. States are blending programs, segmenting Medicaid populations differently and changing administrative oversight. Behavioral healthcare accounts for about nine percent of Medicaid expenses. The benefits of managed care strategies have been discovered. The variety and creativity of Medicaid plans is shown by the sampling of state reforms presented in Figure 22.3.

The complexities and varieties of Medicaid state plan amendments and waivers are beyond the scope of this chapter. The reader wishing to further understand Medicaid is encouraged to read *The Medicaid Source Book* (Congressional Research Service, 1993).

Capitating Publicly Supported Care

Capitation has evolved as a popular means of coordinating care and decreasing the escalation of healthcare costs. Arizona, Indiana, Minnesota, New York, Pennsylvania, Rhode Island, and Wisconsin have created capitated programs for behavioral health populations, and many more are underway. The Monroe-Livingston Demonstration Project in Rochester, NY, launched in 1987, has been the most studied.[1]

1. Reports on the Monroe-Livingston Demonstration Project, managed by Integrated Mental Health, Inc., are available by calling 716/223-8877.

Figure 22.3 Creative Medicaid Utilization

STATE	APPROACHES
Hawaii	Two state programs surround Medicaid. Common eligibility and enrollment procedures exist for all three programs, yielding a seamless system for a wide range of citizens with different levels of coverage to reflect anticipated need.
Massachusetts	Blended traditional state behavioral healthcare and Medicaid dollars and brought in a private managed care organization to administer the plan. The state acts as customer, establishing its priorities through a performance contract with the managed care company.
Utah	Utilized traditional, state-funded nonprofit providers as preferred Medicaid providers to improve coordination between programs.
Washington	Created a special prepaid health plan for the outpatient care of its seriously and persistently disabled population, administered through the public regional boards relating to the state behavioral health authority.
Indiana	Created competing integrated service networks, blending state and Medicaid dollars and requiring performance results to stay in the provider panel.
Iowa, Oregon, Ohio, and Tennessee	All have major Medicaid behavioral healthcare reforms underway. Most states are contemplating significant changes. The joke in Medicaid is, "When you've seen one Medicaid plan—you've seen one Medicaid plan." It is a volatile environment.

Capitating publicly supported populations has brought to the forefront the need for clarity about the goals, incentives, and service needs of the programs. An early attempt in Minnesota to cover seriously and persistently disabled individuals through a private insurer was a failure. The company did not have the support systems, rehabilitation services, or case management resources to coordinate the care of the population and, as a result, the costs were much higher than anticipated. Similarly, an early program in California was changed when the managed care vendor was determined to be underserving patients because the contract incentivized cost savings without assuring quality care.

Managed care's ability to produce substantial savings appears to be lower with publicly supported populations than in the commercial world. The at-risk contracts are usually designed to deliver or secure all the care each person needs and typically are not limited as to inpatient days or yearly total dollars. Managed care's ability to coordinate care seems to offer the greatest promise. As has been shown, multiple programs coexist, each with its own incentives and disincentives, each tending to encourage cost shifting or to complicate benefits coordination. Pooled funding, common administration, and placing the risk away from government serve as incentives for government to reduce some of the onerous process regulation apparatus that was set up as a control mechanism. Administrative costs and oversight can be reduced while the array of services is broadened.

Before considering a capitation or other at-risk arrangement for a publicly supported population, the provider must have clarity on many points. Some of the more important issues are summarized in Figure 22.4.

Figure 22.4 Important Points in Capitation

CLARITY POINT	AMPLIFICATION
Eligibility	Who are the eligible recipients? Is there a clear definition?
Coverage	What are these covered members eligible to receive? What is in the benefit package? Does it include medications or physical healthcare associated with behavioral health issues (such as physical stabilization following a suicide attempt)? What is the range of care covered? How are supportive services handled (for example, residential, vocational, or educational)? Are they expected, allowed, and able to be transferred?
Competition	Who else provides care? Are there competition or "dumping" incentives accidentally built into the plan? Can consumers go outside of the provider panel and, if so, who is responsible for the bill?
Appropriateness	How is care decided? Does the consumer, provider, referral source, or government overseer get to determine appropriateness?
Dispute Resolution	How are disputes settled? What is the process and who decides? What are the range of settlements for the most common disputes?

(continued on next page)

Figure 22.4 (continued)

Coordination	What other government programs relate to or operate with the same people or concerns? Will there be pressures to coordinate or receive individuals between different programs? What is the relationship with institutional care? Do those programs relate well? Are any programs new and therefore likely to significantly influence demand?
Regulation	What are the bureaucratic process regulations influencing the care? What agencies are involved? How do they evaluate outcome? How do their requirements impact on care or costs? In return for this at-risk contract, is there any relief from regulations?
Data Reliability	How reliable are the available utilization data?
Consumer Satisfaction	What are the parameters for patient co-payment? What incentives exist that influence consumers to be compliant with the care offered?
Risk Assessment	What is the assessment of risk? Will demand change? What are the greatest financial risks? How solid can cost controls be made? What are the risks at the beginning and end of the contract (the "tail" coverage responsibilities)? How can the contract be terminated?
Treatment Integrity	Are there any factors in the contract that inherently compromise treatment standards?
Success Potential	Is it possible to be successful with the covered population?
Administrative Support	What are the reporting requirements? What is the cost of administration? Do the computer and accounting systems have the ability to handle this contract?
Payment Issues	How clear are the payment standards? When will payment be made? What happens if it is late? Can cash flow support start-up and delayed payments?

STRATEGIC OPPORTUNITIES

Given the pressures on government and the societal trends outlined above, some sectors of behavioral healthcare clearly will see significant changes in the next few years. The innovative provider will want to consider how these opportunities may be relevant to its practice. The following trends are worth considering:

Addictions. Massachusetts' blending of public behavioral healthcare and Medicaid resulted in a system more responsive to demand than either system was previously. The greatest growth in the system was in treating addictive disorders. The logic that addiction care will grow is obvious to anyone who compares expense structures of commercial and public plans. Integrated commercial plans spend one-fourth to one-third of their dollars on addiction care. Public plans cover a more risk-prone population, yet all states spend less than 15 percent of behavioral health dollars on addiction care. As plans are coordinated and blended, this sector will grow significantly. Each state's Medicaid agency, local public welfare agencies, state community corrections agency, and to a lesser extent state addictions authority are the entities where the change will occur.

Children's Care. States spend more money for children's care than for any other population. The demand for more resources for children's care occurs annually in each state's legislative session. County governments find that children's care presents significant costs. The problem is fragmentation and cost shifting among the systems responsible for oversight. States are pooling and collapsing responsibilities. The resulting systems require the specialized services shown below:

- *Institutional Clearinghouses.* These are service centers that arrange intensive and emergent care, coordinate admissions, shop for the most cost-effective care, and evaluate results.
- *Institutional Alternative Care.* As with most behavioral healthcare expenses, the greatest proportion of dollars is spent on a small percentage of recipients receiving very expensive institutional care. There is a growing recognition of the need for intensive outpatient and home-based care.
- *Case Management.* The typical child case has four case managers ranging across government agencies and purchased care contractors. Providers willing to contract on a per-case basis for delivering or coordinating total care are highly prized.

Physician-extending Services.   The dominant mode of Medicaid reform involves utilizing the primary care physician as the Medicaid gatekeeper for all specialty care. Given the historical relative lack of coordination between primary medical care and behavioral rehabilitation, Medicaid health maintenance organizations will want behavioral health practitioners in their core clinics.

Developmental Disabilities Services.   The historic deinstitutionalization of our developmentally disabled citizens merely shifted the major expenses for care from state institutions to nursing homes. There exists a great need to encourage new care models that wrap together housing, constructive activity, family involvement, and daily living skills. The limited services available are widely sought and are usually idiosyncratic to a local provider. The population of developmentally disabled individuals experiencing associated behavioral disorders currently seems doomed to an institutional existence until community-based services are created. The irony and the opportunity is that such "wraparound" community care still may be less expensive than institutional care.

Vocational Disability Services.   Of the many reasons that individuals become disabled and unable to work, behavioral disorders are prominent. Additionally, individuals with behavioral disabilities are disproportionally younger and therefore likely to consume more tax dollars. The need is for a credible program with reliable results that make the investment of intervention dollars a prudent expenditure. Currently interventions are paid on a case-by-case basis, with decisions made by case managers. Implementing a more coordinated program is an opportunity.

Early Intervention Services.   As at-risk contracts increase in number and impact on the need for improved assessment, early intervention, and prevention, then programs for at-risk populations will increase. At-risk contracts place a premium on cost-effectiveness. Clearly, more accurate assessments, impactful interventions, and improved care coordination have positive payoffs. The prospective provider must prove to the at-risk entity that it provides clinically effective services.

Community Corrections.   At a national level, society is attempting to reform the correctional system. At the same time our prison population is growing (and is already the largest percentage incarcerated of any industrialized nation) and changing our community-based programs. Over 60 percent of convicted offenders have some drug abuse issues. Corrections has recognized the need to "teach" and assure competence in basic social skills around communications, work skills, daily habits, and values. The federal government has made significant funds available to state corrections authorities to develop community-based corrections.

Performance Assurance Services.   As government moves toward a more outcomes-oriented method of conducting itself, another niche emerges: the need to develop systems and sampling methodologies that assist in resource decision making. In the past process regulations and restricted provider panels created less concern about how services were delivered or purchased. The challenge was to deliver services meeting governmental specifications. That approach is giving way to competitive provider panels that maintain status for payment eligibility by performance competition.

The outcomes desired are not those clinical outcomes with which behavioral health providers are familiar. Symptom reduction and therapist-perceived clinical improvement are replaced by performance measures that answer the purchaser's questions. Has the investment resulted in improved self-sufficiency? The public purchaser must answer to the taxpayer. Do these purchased services make a difference, or would the money have been better used for education or transportation? Providers that organize sampling processes and report card-style comparison reports will find support from government agencies.

DOING BUSINESS WITH THE GOVERNMENT

The provider that wants to do business with the government must understand the system and approach it patiently and persistently. Several factors will increase the likelihood of a long-term, successful relationship, including the following:

Do Your Homework.   Know the program you are trying to join. What are its goals? Where are expenses a concern for the public decision-maker? Are there gaps in the delivery system? Are providers routinely added or dropped from the panel? What is the size of the program? How stable are its funds? Know with whom you are dealing. Who are the decision-makers in the program? What is the decision-making process? It is a mistake to go too high or too low in these contacts. Decision-making authority is quite diffuse in government; program people, fiscal people, legal people, and sometimes political people all must do something together to start a new contract. Valuable time can be wasted "courting" bureaucrats who are uninvolved with the purchasing decisions. One state behavioral health agency to which the author provided services had more than 20 individuals with the word "director" in their titles. Find out who does what.

Remember That Government Is Not Business.   When the author left the commercial sector to become a Mental Health Commissioner, he was frequently told, "You're not in the business world anymore." The differences became apparent. Most often interaction is done with the executive branch of government. The degrees of freedom within the executive branch are set by the legislature. Desired programs may not be possible because some law stands in the way or there is no legislative basis to proceed. Capitated payments are a case in point. Most states have had to pass legislation to allow such prospective payments—which go against the normal nature of government by authorizing payment to be made before the service is delivered and documented.

Government is not organized like corporate America. The heads of agencies tend to be responsible for everything, which guarantees that they are truly responsible for very little. For example, as Mental Health Commissioner the author theoretically approved each employee's personal residential moves for all 7,000 employees of the division. Naturally, in a system so consumed with symbolic authority, delegation is the rule and so the executive branch and the legislative branch both create checks and balances, with multiple levels to the checks and balances. The support systems—fiscal, personnel, and legal—tend to have great power to stop or modify significantly, but not the power to create. With this built-in redundancy, the process is hard to define and authority is very diffuse—not an environment designed for speedy change. Pioneers must be skillful and persistent.

The provider must be willing and able to wait for processes to proceed and even for payment. The cycles of an administration impact on change. Certain times in a governor's tenure are ripe for change, and other times all expense allocations are likely to be frozen or slowed to a trickle. Payments are slow, but for service requests providers probably will be asked to respond very quickly. The operations division likely is responding to what is urgent in needing a provider's services, but the support systems are dealing with their own priorities. Government is aptly described as the place where the urgent replaces the important.

Drop the Psychobabble.   Behavioral health professionals routinely assume that government officials understand the behavioral healthcare world. That is seldom the reality. Government program heads have their own priorities and pressures. They are the customer! One must learn and speak their jargon.

Public welfare agencies are concerned about self-sufficiency, family preservation, and family reunification. They are not interested in competing theories of child psychiatry. Corrections is concerned about people not getting arrested, not the growth of their egos. Behavioral healthcare is most concerned about avoiding institutionalization. Competing outpatient technologies are much less important than minimizing inpatient recidivism.

The jargon that communicates so well at professional guild and trade meetings has little effect on the problems confronting a government department head. A strategy or proof that one can effect the goals of the agency with one's services will be effective in establishing a business relationship with that agency.

REFERENCES

Congressional Research Service. (1993). *Medicaid source book.* Washington: U.S. Printing Office.

Frank, R., & McGuire, T. (1994). Establishing a capitation policy for mental health and substance abuse services in healthcare reform. **Behavioral Healthcare** *Tomorrow* 3(4): 36–39.

Mechanic, D., & Aiken, L. (1989). *Paying for services: Promises and pitfalls of capitation.* San Francisco: Jossey-Bass.

Osborne, D., & Gaebler, T. (1993). *Reinventing government.* New York: Plume.

CASE STUDIES

SINGLE-SPECIALTY GROUP INTEGRATED WITH A MEDICAL HOSPITAL: MESA MENTAL HEALTH

Roger H. White, Jr., Ph.D.

In 1987, three individual practitioners joined together to form Mesa Mental Health Professionals, P.C. in order to create a multidisciplinary group practice that would work extensively with managed care. In eight short years, that seed has grown "from scratch" to an organization of over 70 employees in five separate offices with a statewide network of more than 100 subcontracted clinicians serving four fully at-risk contracts. Hoping that other groups will be encouraged to join the creative edge of group practice and capitation, this chapter briefly describes some of the lessons learned from the history, current operating environment, and future plans of this innovative group.

M esa Mental Health (MMH) has worked within large capitation arrangements since 1987. In addition to staff psychiatrists, psychologists, therapists, and nurses, MMH has a contracted network of over 100 providers and facilities to service capitated lives across the state of New Mexico. MMH is deeply committed to total quality management (TQM) and participatory management. A TQM program has been implemented that includes business and clinical "report cards" and numerous continuous improvement teams. MMH anticipates that it will develop through joint ventures into a regional provider and case management system.

FORMATION

Factors Leading to Formation. In early 1985, two solo practice psychologists began an office-sharing arrangement. Both strongly believed that survival as behavioral healthcare practitioners necessitated actively working with the managed care environment that was prominent and growing rapidly in

Albuquerque. In 1987 a psychiatrist who also shared this belief joined, with the result that the group incorporated as a business. (See Figure 23.1.) Four ideas drove the formation of the group:

1. The most efficient delivery of behavioral health services would require a multidisciplinary approach, using physicians, psychologists, and Master's-prepared clinicians in an integrated, full-service delivery system.
2. In the future it would be important to integrate behavioral health and general medicine.
3. At a time when clinicians were starting to scramble to be on the different health maintenance organization (HMO) and preferred provider organization provider panels, it made sense to seek not to be on the various lists, but to be *the* list, for example, to become the exclusive provider for insurers and employers.
4. Rather than continuing to operate as individual practitioners, it was important for the founders to become an incorporated business. This required that each be a partner, draw a salary, and allow him- or herself to be overruled by the others, at times, in the interest of the group.

Development of the Medical Hospital Relationship. Although the original plan did not call for creating a formal relationship with a hospital, in its first capitation arrangement MMH subcapitated with a local freestanding psychiatric hospital to provide the professional component to inpatient services. Later MMH sought and obtained the full capitation contract for facility costs and professional fees and began buying services from the hospital. This relationship with the freestanding psychiatric hospital was terminated after three years due to differences in the business objectives of the

Roger H. White, Jr., Ph.D., is a native New Mexican, born and raised in Los Alamos. Dr. White received his B.S. degree, cum laude, in psychology, from the University of New Mexico, and his M.A. (1970) and Ph.D. (1983) degrees from the University of Colorado in Boulder, CO. He was in full-time private practice, in Albuquerque, NM, from 1984 to 1993, when he joined Mesa Mental Health. His specialty is brief psychotherapy with adolescents and adults.

Figure 23.1 History of Mesa Mental Health Professionals, Inc.

1987	Incorporation as Mesa Mental Health Professionals, P.C.
1988	First capitation contract for professional services only; second capitation contract for inpatient professional services only; opened second office.
1989	First full-risk capitation contract—15,000 covered lives; first utilization review contract with a major employer.
1990	Terminated inpatient professional-services-only contract; initiated hospital negotiations for primary medical hospital affiliation.
1991	Expanded professional- services- only contract to a full-risk contract —total covered lives now 45,000; opened third office; formally affiliated with medical hospital; first employer carve-out under full-risk capitation, adding 4,500 covered lives.
1992	Fourth full-risk capitation contract—total covered lives now 95,000.
1993	Expanded to statewide network; began negotiating to acquire an EAP service.
1994	Acquired EAP service; expanded statewide network; began preparing for site visit/certification by National Committee for Quality Assurance, to occur in 1995.

two organizations—essentially whether to keep beds filled or to be managed care and group practice oriented in the future by shifting treatment to ambulatory care settings.

The group had learned, however, that long-term stability indeed required a relationship with a hospital, ideally one with the full range of medical services, which could meet MMH's desire to work closely with general medicine in clinical delivery and marketing. It was also recognized that such a relationship needed to maintain some very important elements of autonomy. MMH did not wish to become owned by the hospital and believed that growth could best be stimulated by working together without joint ownership.

In 1991 MMH entered into a relationship with Presbyterian Healthcare Services (PHS), a local and regional medical-surgical hospital group with a psychiatric program. The hospital system was to provide inpatient and partial hospital programs while MMH provided physicians for the psychiatric medical directorships and a full continuum of outpatient services to complement the hospital's programs. Additionally, MMH agreed to use PHS for the psychiatric admissions generated from MMH's three capitated contracts, and PHS was to consider using MMH as a capitated, exclusive provider for its own HMO. In 1992 MMH became the capitated behavioral health provider for the HMO owned by PHS.

Although this relationship has functioned well over three years, honest struggles continue around the efficient and equitable alignment of financial incentives. The near-term future of this relationship includes trying to formulate a true alignment of financial incentives without damaging the autonomous nature of the relationship and without hindering MMH's entrepreneurial interests. For example, PHS recognized that its employee assistance program (EAP) was not viable, and so this program was transferred to MMH to own and operate. MMH has no interest in ownership of psychiatric units and is actively working with PHS to design an appropriate method for downsizing the hospital's programs to make them more financially sound.

MANAGEMENT STRUCTURE

Ownership.   The three clinicians who formed the group continue as its owners. Their motivation was to create a growing, innovative business entity and clinical delivery network. They originally organized the ownership structure to encourage all physician and Ph.D. clinicians who joined the group to buy in, by taking a lowered salary, after three years. Over time, however, it became apparent that there were misaligned visions between the original shareholders and the three other clinicians who opted for ownership. The new shareholders seemed more interested in profits, and less interested in expansion and attention to business matters, than the original owners.

The new owners were adversely affected by two negative aspects of ownership—assuming responsibility for the business debts of an expanding organization (by 1992 MMH had incurred $250,000 in operating debt plus a building mortgage of over $500,000), and having to share leadership. The latter factor led to recognition of the need for clear management positions —which could not include all six owners. Resolution of these problems, during 1992 and 1993, produced a strong and unified upper management, with a clearer purpose: "We are here, because this is the kind of business we want to be in, rather than being here only for profit." Unfortunately, this resolution resulted in the later owners selling back their stock, and two of them leaving MMH. Clarifying and unifying the visions of ownership and goals of the business was a painful, but necessary, process.

Board of Directors.   Until 1994, the owners and the Board of Directors were the same. As the organization grew, the need to differentiate among the owners (shareholders), the Board of Directors, and management intensified. In late 1993 the shareholders decided that the goal of participatory management could best be furthered by having two employees sit on the board as full voting directors of the corporation. Today the board consists of the three owners and two employee-elected directors, one each from the support staff and the clinical staff. Employee directors hold a term of one year and may be re-elected. The board meets monthly and the nonowner members of management attend in advisory, nonvoting roles.

The functions of the board are to:

1. oversee the Executive Director;
2. approve major policy issues, including the annual budget and management's goals and objectives; and
3. protect the vision and mission of the organization.

The board has consistently decided not to include any outside experts in a membership role.

Management Structure.   Since being an owner historically has not necessarily been accompanied by the desire, ability, or appointment to be in management, a formal management structure with defined roles was needed. This structure for MMH is shown in Figure 23.2. Due to the small size of the organization, especially at first, there has always been some overlap between the roles that one person may fill. Currently, approximately 20 percent of the more than 70 employees are involved in management at one or more levels.

Management Roles.   The shareholders—the owners—provide the general business direction for the organization. Ultimately, they are responsible for the broader vision that guides the group. The Board of Directors was discussed above. The Executive Director, in concert with the management team, is responsible for general business strategy and organizational planning. Although the Executive Director is a physician, it was decided early in the organizational structuring that the goals of a multidisciplinary organization were best met not by seeking medical dominance but rather by establishing equality among the professional groups. Therefore the specific position of Medical Director was deemed not appropriate. Instead, the

Figure 23.2 Management Structure (Including General Functions)

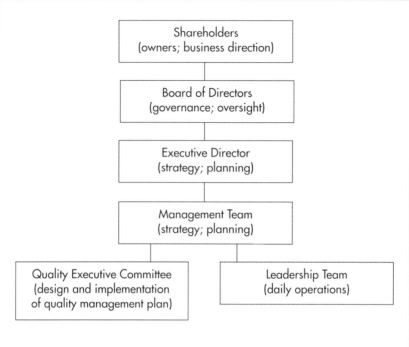

MEMBERSHIP

Shareholders: The three owners.

Board of Directors: The three owners plus one elected employee each from the clinical staff and the support staff.

Management Team: Executive Director, Clinical Director, Network Services Director, EAP Director, Quality Program Manager, and Administrator.

Quality Executive Committee: Quality Program Manager, Executive Director, Clinical Director, Administrator, Utilization Management Coordinator, EAP Director, and one representative each from the clinical and support staff.

Leadership Team: Executive Director, Clinical Director, Administrator, Network Services Director, Lead Receptionist, Business Office Manager, Clinical Office Team Leader from each of the four offices, EAP Director, Utilization Management Coordinator, and Quality Program Manager.

group created a business/administrative head (Executive Director) and, for the clinical portion of the business, a Clinical Director who reports to the Executive Director. In MMH, the current Clinical Director is a Ph.D. psychologist.

The Management Team is responsible for overseeing the Quality Executive Committee and the leadership team. The management team consists of the Executive Director, the Clinical Director (who directs internal clinical staff and functions), the Administrator (who directs financial and management information system functions), the EAP Director (who runs the employee assistance division), the Quality Program Manager (who directs the Quality Executive Committee, described below), and the Network Services Director (who manages the clinical intake system, capitation contractual relations, and contracted network providers).

The Quality Executive Committee is responsible for the design and implementation of the TQM plan for the entire organization. As such, it champions and coordinates the many continuous improvement teams, the outcomes research, and the quality indicators used to report on the functioning of the business and the clinical delivery system. It is notable that all full-time employees are involved in a continuous improvement team.

The Leadership Team includes representatives from all major facets of the organization (management team plus office team leaders and key support staff) and is responsible for the entire organization's daily operations. Meetings of the leadership team are divided into time for acknowledging outstanding effort by employees, sharing by each supervisor about activities in their area, and decision making about operational matters.

CAPITATION FUNCTIONING

Services Provided Under Capitation.   Currently, MMH has four full-risk capitation contracts involving both outpatient and inpatient services for approximately 95,000 covered lives. These contracts obligate the group to provide administrative services (claims processing, utilization management, provider credentialing, and network development throughout the entire state of New Mexico) as well as providing direct clinical services in outpatient, partial hospital, and inpatient settings. (See Figure 23.3.)

Contract Development.   The first contract, obtained in 1988, was a subcapitated arrangement with a private hospital for management, inpatient, and outpatient professional services. The next step (1988) was a second capitation contract to provide only inpatient professional behavioral health

Figure 23.3 Practice Summary

I. **Business Structure**
Year Founded: 1987
Owned By: Gayle Zieman, Ph.D., Robert Ericson, Ph.D., and Steve Sehr, M.D.
Business Status: For-profit, Subchapter S Corporation
Vision/Mission Statement: Mesa Mental Health is dedicated to developing and providing innovative behavioral health services to improve the well-being of residents throughout the Greater Southwest. We will continue to affiliate nationally in promoting the exchange of knowledge and vision to advance quality healthcare.
Number of Offices: 5
Geographic Area Served: State of New Mexico

II. **Clinical Staffing**
Total Employed Clinical Staff (in FTEs):
Master's-Degreed Therapists: 14.0
Psychologists: 7.5
Nurses/Physician's Assistants: 1.6
Psychiatrists: 6.5
Others: EAP Clinicians—6.0
Total Number of Subcontracted Network Providers:
Master's-Degreed Therapists: 66
Psychologists: 34
Psychiatrists: 10
Others: 0

III. **Capitation Functioning**
Number of Contracts: 4
Total Covered Lives: 115,000
Capitation Revenue as Percentage of Total: 74
Total Contracts in Group's History: 6
Mean Utilization Statistics: (varies across four capitation contracts; ranges given)
Penetration Rate (percentage of enrollees accessing treatment): 2.9 to 4.0
Outpatient Length of Treatment (in visits): 4.2 to 7.4
Hospital Days/1,000 Members: 21.0 to 28.0 (include outpatient hospital days at 0.5 day)
Hospital Admits/1,000 Members: 2.0 to 4.0 (include outpatient hospital admits at 0.5)

services for the population of the largest local HMO. In 1989, MMH took on its first full-risk contract—which continues today. One contract begun in 1990 is a direct employer "carve-out," in which MMH provides the full range of behavioral health services to the company's employees and their dependents, plus providing on-site EAP services. With the 1994 acquisition of New Mexico's largest EAP provider from PHS, MMH's hospital partner, EAP services are rapidly becoming fully integrated with traditional clinical delivery, and it has become possible for each to market the other.

There is a strong interest within management to develop more administrative service only (ASO) contracts, which do not include being at risk for utilization of clinical services, and other management-only services, in addition to more capitation arrangements.

Utilization Management.   Each of MMH's capitation contracts includes responsibility for the management of service utilization. Initially, utilization management (UM) was managed in the traditional manner: concurrent case review and authorization of a limited number of sessions at multiple times throughout an episode of care. Over time, this philosophy has changed. Currently, UM is managed according to the following fundamental ideas:

1. It is important for UM to be clinically rather than administratively driven.
2. It is important to avoid micromanagement of individual cases.
3. External subcontractors submit an initial treatment plan with an estimated length of treatment of from one to twenty sessions. The UM Coordinator approves or denies each request, with the Clinical Director available for second opinions and the Executive Director used for appeals.
4. Internal providers submit no treatment plans for review.
5. UM is organized more around population management and working with each clinician, rather than on the management of services per patient.

EFFECTS OF CAPITATION ON GROUP CLINICAL AND BUSINESS FUNCTIONING

Clinically, capitation at MMH has effectively put the control of services into the hands of the people delivering the services. In doing so, however, it has forced a shift in thinking: providing individual services does not result in revenue generation, but must be viewed as an expense. Although it is possible to think that under capitation the motivation is *not* to provide services, the truth is that in order to stay in business *not* providing services is akin to "shooting oneself in the foot"—since clinical situations simply get worse. Successful functioning within capitation contracts at MMH has required a high level of efficiency, prevention, and quality. The desire for efficiency and quality, within limited resources, has often forced confrontations between clinical philosophies and treatment and resource realities. This has placed time and energy pressures on management and clinicians alike to maintain quality while encouraging clinical openness, flexibility, and creativity.

From both clinical and business perspectives, capitation has increased the need for accountability. As such it has forced endless instances of trying to blend the clinical and legal needs for confidentiality with the clinical, legal, and business needs for data. From the business perspective, capitation has created predictability in cash flow. However, it has added new expenses for the development of systems and services, some of which traditionally were done by insurance companies. Developing this new dimension has produced positive results. The data generated by these new systems has been useful internally.

MMH does not desire to return to a fee-for-service payment structure, but instead enjoys the autonomy and creativity that are allowed under prepaid, at-risk arrangements.

CLINICAL DELIVERY SYSTEM

Continuum of Care Provided. Even though capitation contracts provide coverage for acute care or medically necessary care only, MMH provides a full continuum of care, which often expands the definitions of acute and medically necessary care to include the functional treatment of many chronic and ongoing conditions. Over time, it has become apparent how very important to the delivery system is developing prevention and psychoeducational services, even though these technically are not covered benefits.

Staff Mix and Styles of Practice. All disciplines—physicians, psychologists, therapists, physician's assistants, and psychiatric nurses—are represented among the 34 clinical staff. Psychiatrists primarily provide medication and inpatient management and actively share on-call and medical hospital consultations with the psychologists. Nurses and a part-time physician's assistant provide support services to the psychiatrists. All clinicians are responsible for providing emergency services to their own patients on weekdays. Group psychotherapy has not been used extensively, but increasingly is being used as groups are organized more around patient functioning levels rather than by gender or symptoms. As the information systems continue to develop, better knowledge related to managing patients by the different behavioral health disciplines and levels of care will emerge.

Network Arrangements and Subcontracted Providers. MMH has always had a network of clinicians in private practice who are subcontracted to provide care for capitated patients. Currently, there are approximately 110 subcontractors statewide. This arrangement is driven by three basic needs:

1. covering different geographical areas including numerous rural locations;
2. having subspecialty services available when needed without having to employ specialists—for example, specialists who can provide neuropsychology services or signing for the hearing impaired; and
3. being able to meet MMH's standard of providing rapid access to care.

Quality and legal liability requirements mandate that a key component to a successful network is a thorough credentialing process. Credentialing and recredentialing of providers is approximately a half-time position for a clerical staff person.

Intake and New Patient Procedures. The intake process has become a centerpiece of MMH's organizational commitment to access, responsiveness, and customer service. Intake not only determines the flow of work through the organization, but it has the potential to make or break the organization from both clinical and business perspectives. Emergency cases receive a face-to-face evaluation on the same day with a psychiatric nurse who has psychiatric and psychological backup. Urgent cases are scheduled within 48 hours, and routine cases within 10 working days.

During the first five years of MMH's experience with capitation, every new patient was seen for a face-to-face triage, with the focus on case management and treatment matching. Patients often saw this as an unproductive additional step in receiving care, and clinicians often did not use the history gathered in the triage to the extent desired. As a result each new patient now receives a 10 to 15 minute telephone triage, with the same focus.

MANAGEMENT INFORMATION SYSTEMS

Computer systems are an integral part of managing the myriad details of the business. (See Chapter 16.) The management information system (MIS) is continually evolving. At a practical, day-in, day-out level, it is challenged with handling a rapidly growing database and demands for more refined data manipulations. The capability of the MIS seems to lag continually behind the demand for more sophisticated data.

For the first two years, MMH's capitation system was managed on a massive, cumbersome, in-house-developed spreadsheet system plus accounting and billing programs, all run on a network of Macintoshes. Later, an in-house-developed relational database for the Macintosh network was used for two years to manage capitation. In 1991, billing and scheduling were moved to a Unix platform with a wide area network between the three separate offices in Albuquerque.

Currently, billing and scheduling remain as described above. Capitation management, accounts payable, and utilization management are managed on a DOS local area network system. In 1992 MMH purchased capitation software, which had been originally designed to run a small HMO and was modified to handle MMH's preauthorizations, the concurrent and retrospective UM of subcontracted providers, accounting, claims processing, and statistical reporting. On the immediate horizon is refined electronic downloading of enrollment data from insurers for capitated populations, and electronic transfer between the traditional billing software and the capitation system.

QUALITY IMPROVEMENT

Management.   In late 1992, MMH set out to develop a comprehensive quality management plan. Implementation of this plan began in 1993, with two basic focuses:

1. Internal management and improvement had to become clearly and fundamentally data driven.
2. Culturally, a metamorphosis was necessary to change from a hierarchical business to a team participatory process. Enormous time and resources have been focused on staff training and implementation in this area.

The business required clear guidelines to direct future growth. The MMH Board of Directors, with input from the whole organization, developed clear vision and mission statements along with a set of corporate values, which were introduced to staff at a two-day retreat.

Delivery of Clinical Services.   Quality improvement in clinical care is essentially a process of developing the tools necessary to monitor clinical processes and then using the data to make continual improvements. Many of the necessary tools are not available yet. Current internal mandates for data and improvement processes are to:

1. reduce the variability in clinical services;
2. develop standards of care and specific procedures for specific events (for example, assessment of suicidal risk) or conditions; and
3. develop data for decision algorithms to be used in the provision of clinical services.

MMH is a participant in the Outcomes Management Program of the Council of Behavioral Group Practices (see Chapter 19 and Appendix H). The outcomes data are crucial for tracking clinical indicators of functioning, including: length of time from first contact to first appointment, re-admission rate for inpatient services, rate of patient complaints, and levels of symptom reduction, daily functional improvement, and general health status up to one year after entering treatment.

FUTURE DIRECTIONS

MMH desires to continue to be an innovative leader in behavioral health-care delivery systems and behavioral health management. Participation nationally in education and dialogue among behavioral healthcare systems is also a strong commitment. Specific short-term business goals include:

1. expanding the MMH delivery system more thoroughly throughout the state of New Mexico, while maintaining ownership of the delivery system;
2. developing more ASO management contracts;
3. aggressively meeting external regulatory demands, such as those from the National Committee for Quality Assurance;
4. implementing thoroughly the corporate vision, mission, and values in all aspects of the business;
5. being recognized as the quality expert in behavioral health;
6. expanding management and educational consultation services;

7. consolidating the MIS into one computer network with a single operating system, while implementing complete UM software and a fully computerized patient record; and

8. developing as part of a regional network, including joint ventures with other organizations as regional and national partners in sharing financial and expertise resources.

LESSONS LEARNED

Formation of the Group.   Keep ownership small and cohesive. Do not go for size. Be sure, in the beginning, that the shareholders, to a person, have bought into the vision for the group. The beliefs, principles, and visions of the shareholders must be very clearly aligned.

Management Structure.   Develop the management team, including well-defined management roles and an expert business manager, as soon as possible. The group must have the tools and expertise to change and to know where it stands financially and clinically at any point in time. Clinicians need to learn to let go of "hands-on" control over the business. Not everyone can be in management. At least in the beginning, some people will need to perform multiple roles. The team approach to developing change is slower, but much more effective, especially in improving systems and gaining employee satisfaction. Have a healthy foundation of ethics and vision, including strong business ethics.

Capitation Arrangements.   Capitation is actually easier than most people think, so do not be afraid to do it. Never contract for just a piece of the continuum of care; seek full at-risk contracts. Have the data system in place before starting the contract, to know where the money is going. Be very clear about which services are to be provided and which services are not covered by the contract. (See Chapter 13.) Articulate and plan for as many scenarios in the flow of treatment as possible. Do not be lax in relationships with payors; apply resources to maintain relationships on an ongoing basis. From a business standpoint, it is very important to be responsive to both contract payors and patients.

Clinical Delivery System.   Engage a hospital partner early in the process. Have physician employees who are part of the group culture, rather than buying physician services on a piecemeal basis. Try to have clinical productivity expectations in place before expanding the number of employee clinicians. A blended model with a core of employed clinicians and a network of subcontracted clinicians can work fairly well, although it is important to be sure that incentives are aligned, that is, the subcontractors are incentivized to be efficient and conscious of quality in their care. It is important to be creative—explore subcapitation, tiered payment structures, and episode-of-care payments.

Management Information Systems.   Plan globally from the beginning. Build from the perspective of a single cohesive system. Avoid fragmentation.

Quality Improvement.   A quality program in today's healthcare environment is a requirement, not a choice. Do as much planning ahead as possible. Quality programs are very difficult and costly to implement, especially in terms of time and energy. It is very important to obtain full participation and full "buy-in" from all levels of the organization. Do not forget to include the support staff.

SINGLE-SPECIALTY GROUP INTEGRATED WITH A MEDICAL CLINIC: PACIFIC APPLIED PSYCHOLOGY ASSOCIATES

Gregory Alter, Ph.D.

The formation of Pacific Applied Psychology Associates (P.A.P.A.) afforded an opportunity to go beyond a narrow approach to treatment defined by a specific clinical school of thought while paying attention to the organizational issues that foster sensible, humane care. Managed care presented the chance to innovate. P.A.P.A. was founded in 1982 with the intent to develop a treatment setting that made optimal use of time-sensitive treatment, social and organizational psychology, and the principles of health maintenance. By 1986 a strategic alliance with a medical group was established, and similar alliances have continued for P.A.P.A. as an exclusive, capitated provider. Today P.A.P.A. has ten offices, with several more planned, and the group serves 200,000 capitated lives.

A generation of psychotherapists began asking some challenging questions early in the 1960s. Why did the people who paid for treatment rarely ask how long it might take and how much it might cost? And if a patient had the temerity to ask about the parameters of treatment, why did so many clinicians act as though that person was either resisting treatment or asking a hostile question? Few people dared to ask anything about their medical or psychotherapeutic treatment, causing the author to wonder, "Why not?" How strange it was that so little discussion of radically differing approaches to treatment ever occurred outside of the classroom! After graduation, psychotherapists seemed to find a niche, along with others who thought within the confines of the approach they had already learned.

FORMATION

Pacific Applied Psychology Associates (P.A.P.A.) was founded in 1982 with the intent of going beyond this narrow approach and developing a treatment setting that would make optimal use of time-sensitive psychotherapeutic treatment, incorporate methods from social and organizational psychology, and provide services to health maintenance organization (HMO) members. (See Figure 24.1.) In 1986 when the original partnership became incorporated as P.A.P.A., Inc., the corporation lacked any capitalization other than the revenue generated by the professional practice. The two founding partners treated the majority of the patients and subsidized the growth of the practice into managed care. P.A.P.A. has always been an independent, "freestanding" provider organization.

The partners retained corporate control while implementing a collaborative decision-making model for day-to-day operations. Since P.A.P.A. started with few staff and a small amount of managed care business, and grew slowly over several years, the group had the opportunity to refine clinical and programmatic thinking while the partners maintained a good deal of personal control over its services.

P.A.P.A.'s founders believed that opportunities would arise for psychologists as leaders in healthcare reform, and were confident in their vision that this system of care could be created—even if there was doubt about its immediate economic viability.

MANAGEMENT STRUCTURE

Formation of an independent group provider organization has been more than a 40-hour-a-week job. In the field of managed behavioral healthcare, professional practice can hardly be conducted within the confines of a 40-hour week because of external requirements to appropriately document and communicate about treatment. As P.A.P.A., Inc., grew to serve over

Gregory Alter, Ph.D., is Chief Operating Officer of Pacific Applied Psychology Associates (P.A.P.A.). His predoctoral work was in community mental health and deinstitutionalization. Dr. Alter has worked in the managed mental healthcare field exclusively since receiving his doctorate in Social/Clinical Psychology from the Wright Institute in 1979. As co-founder of P.A.P.A., Dr. Alter has specialized in training models applicable to multidisciplinary managed care clinicians and in management information system applications for small provider group development. His consulting experience ranges from small community agencies to nationwide managed care organizations. Dr. Alter also currently serves on the California Psychological Association's Committee on Reimbursement and Managed Care.

Figure 24.1 History of Pacific Applied Psychology Associates

1982	Formation of a partnership aimed at medical group subcontracting for professional services. Fairfield Medical Group capitates HMO outpatient mental health and substance abuse professional services for 5,000 covered lives.
1985	Fairfield Medical Group subcapitates inpatient professional services and expands to over 10,000 covered lives; Oak Hill Medical Group capitates professional services for 30,000 lives. Expansion of fee-for-service business, including MCOs, by 30 percent per year.
1986	Pacific Applied Psychology Associates (P.A.P.A.) incorporates.
1987	Oak Hill Medical Group closes. P.A.P.A. enters a capitation contract with Hill Physicians Medical Group (1,500 lives). Fremont Medical Group closes just as it agrees to capitate with P.A.P.A.
1990	Two capitation contracts now total 75,500 lives. Expansion to four offices and staff differentiation into departments.
1993	Hill Group grows to 135,000 covered lives. Now eight offices, 350 network providers, and 20 staff providers.
1994	After 13 years, Fairfield Group terminates contract with 30 days notice. Hill Group expands to replace loss. P.A.P.A. seeks equity partners to aid in rapid regional expansion and considers public-sector contracting. Two hundred thousand covered lives with almost no clinical complaints. Outpatient lengths of stay are under five visits and inpatient lengths of stay are less than eight days.

50,000 capitated lives, opportunities arose to begin differentiating organizational tasks meaningfully.

Fortunately, P.A.P.A. had established a strategic alliance relatively early (1986) with an outside organization (Hill Physicians Medical Group). This alliance allowed P.A.P.A to link its growth to Hill's regional growth and need for a single source of behavioral healthcare services. It also presented the opportunity to observe how the Hill group managed its entry in the managed healthcare arena.

While a close collaborative relationship with a primary contractor was emphasized, business development was also pursued with major national managed care organizations (MCOs). Clinical and administrative staff both had to learn about the diverse contractual obligations that P.A.P.A. had

Figure 24.2 Management Structure—Pacific Applied Psychology Associates

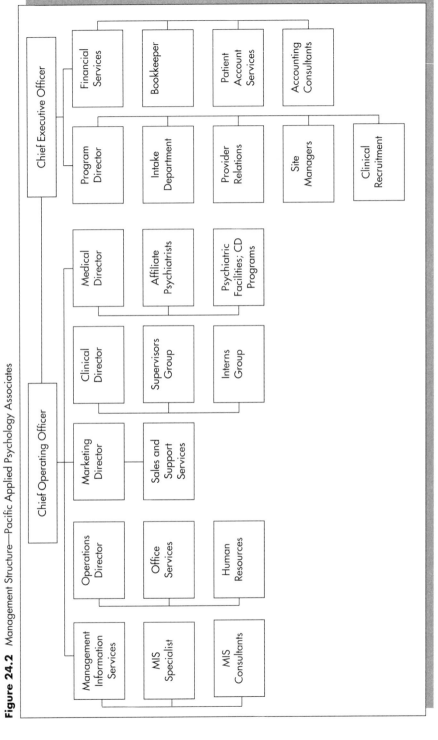

assumed. Balancing the benefits of diversification and growth with the need to maintain coherence in contracting activities is a constant challenge.

P.A.P.A., Inc., began with two office locations, in Berkeley and Fairfield, CA, and has since grown to ten offices, with several more planned throughout Northern California. The expansion in geographic scope and number of patients treated required corresponding shifts in management. (See Figure 24.2)

Clinical program management includes intake, site management, and provider network relations—under the direction of the Program Director. Financial services, facilities management, human resources, and office operations are under the direction of the Chief Executive Officer. Financial services provide payor and patient billing, accounts collection, management reporting, and patient clinical record management. Business development and planning are under the direction of the two principals.

Supervision.   P.A.P.A. is distinguished by being an independent, freestanding, outpatient-based provider group which employs a unique approach to supervision to accomplish organizational objectives. The group uses the efficient treatment strategies of a managed care company without the degree of waste entailed by an elaborate case management bureaucracy that reviews, from a distance, each individual case.

Each clinician and administrative staff member receives adequate individual and group supervision to accomplish the primary objectives of his or her position. As the total number of employees has grown, the supervision process has been formalized to an increasing degree, including written agendas, process notes, and action plans—which include routing, typically, to at least one additional layer of management.

Clinical supervision consists of overseeing both the administrative and clinical treatment components of care. Usually, individual supervision requires about one hour per week, with new employees requiring more supervision and the senior staff less. Group supervision and training are also used to improve clinical effectiveness and efficiency.

The administrative component of clinical care includes all of the functions typically under the purview of quality assurance and utilization review. The variety of the supervision tasks includes: review of length of treatment in light of treatment goals, appropriateness of referral to psychiatry or a hospital, relations with the primary care physician, supervisee performance of administrative tasks (such as charting and collections), and staff interpersonal relations.

The clinical treatment component of supervision includes many features familiar to mental health professionals from their training. Additionally, the supervision must assess and encourage the supervisee's focus on time-effective treatment strategies and modalities. The supervisor encourages additional training in specific modalities necessary to remedy a deficiency—which may emerge during a review of a particular case—or to provide a new service to an emergent patient group.

Contrary to what those unfamiliar with supervision of peer professionals might expect, P.A.P.A. has always enjoyed the support of the professional staff in obtaining quality supervision. Access to supervision is viewed as an opportunity and an advantage in achieving one's professional goals and in gaining job satisfaction. The emphasis of all supervision is on the consultative quality of the interaction, rather than the authority of the supervisor over the supervisee. Supervisees are encouraged to gain emotional support and practical assistance from their supervisors and from the supervisory "hour." Supervision actually encourages efficiencies outweighing the direct costs to the group as a business.

Supervision of operational staff has developed concurrently with the differentiation of operations teams. P.A.P.A. started with no support staff other than very part-time reception assistance by the nurse of an affiliated medical group. Operations teams emerged as the amount of work increased in each operational area: reception, intake, clerical, billing and collections, human resources, and information systems. Additionally, a number of specific tasks are outsourced to independent contractors: bookkeeping, computer network maintenance, and software programming. As with the clinical staff, all operations staff expect and receive supervision adequate to allow full assessment and discussion of their positions and assignments. Any failure, either by supervisor or supervisee, to give or receive supervision is viewed as a problem to be remedied.

Rapid expansion has strained the fabric of the supervision model, in that optimal supervision requires supervisors who have been fully acculturated with the P.A.P.A. philosophy of care and are familiar with the organization's history and direction. Layering of supervision, with more experienced supervisors lending assistance to newer supervisors and a formal mechanism of interviews and orientation in place for supervisory positions, is intended to mitigate some of the challenges created by expansion.

"Departments," which previously may have consisted of only one individual, have now grown to be too large for a single general operations meeting, especially with a number of staff working at clinical sites around Northern California. Therefore, the structure of the supervisory meeting has grown to encompass meetings for the individual operations teams, as well as the operations group as a whole.

Each clinical site employs the part-time services of a Site Manager and/ or Site Coordinator, a clinician who oversees the logistical and clinical operations of each site and ensures adequate communication with the central Berkeley office. A Site Coordinator serves as an assistant to the Site Manager, while smaller clinical sites require only a Site Coordinator in order to function. Reception and clerical tasks are analyzed on a site-by-site basis, with as much support function turned over to the central office as the particular situation will allow. This system of managing sites has allowed the group to achieve a degree of integration unavailable via any other mechanism.

CAPITATION FUNCTIONING

In P.A.P.A.'s beginning years, 1982 to 1986, the massive restructuring of behavioral healthcare lying ahead was apparent, but it was not at all clear who would pay for the new approaches to service delivery. The partners endured with a good nature the disparaging comments of colleagues while aggressively seeking out their first capitated contracts. When financial risk was assumed by P.A.P.A. for the amount of care to be delivered, the dismay of colleagues often verged on barely concealed scorn!

But in this regard there was information to counterbalance the scorn and the anxiety of the founders' families. The research on outpatient psychotherapy showed that therapy use falls within a rather narrow range, even if no effort is made to shorten the duration of treatment. Personal practice experience supported this research, and made the partners prone to trust it. With little negotiation and no fanfare, P.A.P.A., Inc., signed a one-page agreement with Fairfield Medical Group in 1982 to provide behavioral health services on an exclusive, capitated basis. The contract called for P.A.P.A. to be the exclusive provider of mental health services between February, 1982, and June, 1994. By the termination of that contract P.A.P.A. was capitated for 15,500 lives for outpatient mental health and substance abuse services, the management of inpatient professional services, consultation to the medical departments, and inpatient substance abuse rehabilitation management.

The level of background research and analysis done by P.A.P.A. in 1982 before entering into new capitation arrangements will no longer suffice. For example, P.A.P.A. assumed risk in its first capitated contract with no historical knowledge of utilization rates, breakouts by employers, or negotiation regarding how risk might be minimized.

From 1982 through 1985 P.A.P.A. pursued contractual arrangements with medical groups in Alameda, Contra Costa, and Solano counties in Northern California. The business plan called for development of at-risk, exclusive provider relationships to manage and provide the full continuum of mental health and chemical dependency services. (See Figure 24.3.)

Figure 24.3 Practice Summary

I. Business Structure
Year Founded: 1982
Owned By: Gregory Alter, Ph.D., and Neil Dickman, Ph.D.
Business Status: Professional Corporation
Vision/Mission Statement: P.A.P.A. specializes in managed mental
healthcare services. We provide education, consultation, and
treatment to meet a broad spectrum of individual, family, and group
needs. Some people seek help for a well-defined problem that can be
solved quickly. Others seek ongoing support for change in several
aspects of their lives. We respect each person's right to participate in
the choice of treatment approach that best meets his or her specific
needs. We design an individual therapeutic response to each unique
situation. Such flexibility results from a command of several therapeutic disciplines.
Number of Offices: 10
Geographic Area Served: Northern California region

II. Clinical Staffing
Total Employed Clinical Staff (in FTEs):
Master's-Degreed Therapists: 16
Psychologists: 14
Nurses/Physician's Assistants: 0
Psychiatrists: 0.5
Others: 0
Total Number of Subcontracted Network Providers:
Master's-Degreed Therapists: 25
Psychologists: 35
Psychiatrists: 165
Others: 0

III. Capitation Functioning
Number of Contracts: 1
Total Covered Lives: 200,000
Capitation Revenue as Percentage of Total: 60
Total Contracts in Group's History: 3
Mean Utilization Statistics:
Penetration Rate (percentage of enrollees accessing treatment): 2.5
Outpatient Length of Treatment (in visits): 4.5
Hospital Days/1,000 Members: 13 (include outpatient hospital days at
0.5 days)
Hospital Admits/1,000 Members: 2.33 (include outpatient hospital
admits at 0.5)

Between 1984 and 1986, P.A.P.A. contracted with the Oak Hill Medical Group of Oakland to be its exclusive, capitated provider of behavioral services. In 1986, upon termination of the Oak Hill agreement and the closure of the Oak Hill Medical Group, P.A.P.A. developed an agreement with the Hill Physicians Medical Group to be its exclusive behavioral healthcare provider, including the development of a provider network and office locations sufficient to meet expected demand throughout Northern California. Under that agreement, the number of covered at-risk lives has grown from 1,500 to over 200,000. All professional services are capitated. In contrast to what actually happened in the group's growth and development, its original business plan called for a gradual entry into the at-risk market!

Since 1982 P.A.P.A. has developed its MCO contracting strategy of beginning with individual provider contracts and moving toward group provider agreements, and more recently to case-rate and subcapitated arrangements. Simultaneously, P.A.P.A. has developed an emphasis on providing services through the most efficient combination of salaried and networked providers, making full use of the most modern behavioral and management information system (MIS) technologies. Approximately 80 percent of the patients are serviced by salaried employees. Except in scale, P.A.P.A.'s management of care has met or surpassed the standards developed by all of the national, single-specialty MCOs. The specific focus on at-risk behavioral healthcare contracting within an integrated staff/network provider mix, and on fostering use of the most advanced treatment methods, has resulted in widespread acknowledgement of P.A.P.A. as a premier independent behavioral healthcare provider in Northern California.

Rather than abandon traditional fee-for-service business, P.A.P.A. has retained and expanded its fee-for-service clientele. By emphasizing the professional qualifications of licensed psychologists to provide assessment, as well as treatment by psychologists and Master's-level therapists, P.A.P.A. has maintained a viable presence in the shrinking fee-for-service market.

As the marketplace for managed behavioral care developed, P.A.P.A. has become increasingly sophisticated in its approach to planning, marketing, and service delivery. As economies of scale have emerged, P.A.P.A. has enjoyed increasing opportunities to demonstrate profitability. Perhaps more significant than current profitability is the group's minimal outstanding indebtedness—which demonstrates the rigorous approach to fiscal management employed by P.A.P.A. A growth rate of 30 percent per year in gross revenues has been sustained since inception. Prior to 1993, net profits were distributed as salary, without any retained earnings. Current projections target net before-tax retained earnings at 4 percent of gross revenues.

CLINICAL DELIVERY SYSTEM

The P.A.P.A. clinical delivery model grew out of the experience of the two founders, especially related to their years of working with the persistent, severely mentally ill in community treatment settings, as well as the wealth of knowledge brought by the growing clinical staff.

Much of what can be said succinctly about P.A.P.A.'s clinical delivery model is contained within a clinician's handbook, which forms the basis of treatment. P.A.P.A. employs a variety of therapeutic modalities (individual, group, couple, and family psychotherapies) to address the needs of a diverse client population. Therapists attempt to integrate the use of specific therapeutic strategies and techniques with a psychodynamic understanding of the client. They are cognizant of the importance of the therapeutic relationship and attempt to use interpersonal processes in understanding and helping clients. Educational tools may be offered in treatment, such as books, tapes, videos, referrals to seminars, and didactic discussions within the therapy hour. Therapists routinely consult with and refer to physicians, psychiatrists, and other health professionals who may be involved in the client's treatment. They are also aware of resources in the community, which may figure prominently in a client's care, and they fully utilize these resources when appropriate.

It is important that therapists recognize their role in a managed care system. They accept fiduciary responsibility both to their clients and to third-party payors to fully disclose the financial aspects of treatment. Patients and their families receive relevant information regarding fees charged by P.A.P.A. and the terms of any applicable insurance or third-party payor coverage. Limitations and exclusions from coverage are fully explained and P.A.P.A.'s clinical staff make reasonable efforts to assist each patient in receiving the treatment that will be most beneficial. Conflicts of interest between P.A.P.A.'s relationships with patients and third-party payors are fully disclosed and efforts are made in such cases to resolve the conflict.

MANAGEMENT INFORMATION SYSTEMS

P.A.P.A. began developing its information systems in 1982 when first considering the variety of forms needed to process charges and treatments provided. In 1984, while the volume from Fairfield Medical Group was still extremely small, P.A.P.A.'s computerization began, primarily to produce summary data which were based on different sorting and filtering criteria.

In order to gain experience with the emerging technology in an affordable way, the author developed a prototype practice management software system, using a flat file database. With this system necessary bookkeeping was done to manage the nascent capitated and fee-for-service business. In addition, the unique capabilities of that text-oriented database allowed templates for all office forms and form letters to be developed.

In early 1990 the author again searched for a new platform for a practice management system that could expand with P.A.P.A.'s rapid growth and was affordable (less than $10,000). Since no software offered all of the features needed, software allowing for additions and modifications to its code was purchased. The decision was made to run on mainstream hardware platforms (IBM-compatible computers), and to stay with established software vendors. The advice followed was to spend the maximum amount affordable on hardware to run the computing-intensive data application. A local area network, which could be maintained by in-house staff, was installed.

Despite the headaches attendant upon any complex system of machinery, that overall purchasing strategy has been successful. To add functionality to the purchased software, contract programmers have been employed to do modifications. Such modifications, however, have been costly and quite difficult to implement successfully. Additionally, P.A.P.A.'s medical software vendor was pushed to upgrade the software for managed care. Of critical importance has been the addition of ad-hoc query software to the database to allow for custom searches, sorts, and reports, whether financial or clinical. The importance of the ability to query the database cannot be overemphasized. Have an efficient query tool!

"Group-ware" applications enabling the sharing of patient, scheduling, and billing information over regular phone lines, while allowing for reading database information and entering data directly, are particularly encouraging for the future. These will make it possible to share essential company documents among the offices and to use the same system for electronic mail. P.A.P.A. is also considering clinical decision-support software and/or automated diagnostic software, which offers an intriguing view of the humane possibilities for computerized patient records and clinical profiles.

In the area of information systems, the question: "Do you build your own or buy a ready-made system for practice management?" has been answered at P.A.P.A. by buying an off-the-shelf practice management system as a base and building on it. In reality, hybrid systems such as this will continue to be the norm, even as more comprehensive practice management software vendors attempt to attract behavioral group practices. The pace of change in both hardware and software guarantees that today's total solution will be tomorrow's half-baked answer!

FUTURE DIRECTIONS

P.A.P.A., Inc., will continue to expand in the near future with several more offices planned for Northern California. To balance the benefits of diversification and growth, contact has been made with several public-sector mental health departments—since California is ambitiously seeking to employ managed care technology in public programs. The development of these public-sector relationships fosters additional areas of management growth at P.A.P.A., such as creating clinical supervision and training appropriate to capitated contracts covering the chronic, severely mentally ill population.

As P.A.P.A. continues to grow, there will be many opportunities to shape the professional climate, such as opportunities to expand the integration of behavioral healthcare into the broader healthcare arena. P.A.P.A. will continue to innovate in areas of practice where other, more highly reimbursed professional healthcare specialties have yet to venture.

Although P.A.P.A. has already been a substantial force in the regional market for doctoral training internships, its role will expand into the development of a graduate and postgraduate training curriculum. P.A.P.A. will become a greater force in shaping professional practice education, particularly through online computer-based multimedia courses and conferences.

P.A.P.A. also intends to enhance its position in the behavioral healthcare marketplace by developing strategic partnerships with all market sectors. Among the most important considerations is the fact that, until now, P.A.P.A. has been excluded from any of the savings enjoyed by insurers and contracting medical groups for reduced inpatient facility costs.

To assist with capital needs while maintaining the freedom to chart an independent business course, P.A.P.A. will find appropriate venture partners. It will maintain its percentage of regional market share while expanding into additional markets geographically, and will seek greater profitability to attract the capital necessary for such expansion. Since vertical integration is already in progress, it can be expected that any partnership will likely involve attempts to reshape business activities in a progressive mode, such as integrating private, for-profit hospital companies and public-sector, not-for-profit institutional providers. Currently, the venture capital markets show little interest in behavioral healthcare, but as vertical integration and renewed efficiency are demonstrated, the small profit margins on large volume will be more likely to attract investors.

Even in the midst of increased competition and stress in the healthcare marketplace, P.A.P.A.'s staff members will pay ever greater attention to the mood and culture of their organization, setting an example for the healthcare delivery systems of which they are a part by caring for each other as healthcare providers as much as they care for the needs of their patients. As P.A.P.A. continues to succeed in these endeavors, opportunities will arise to assist in the development of the general system of medical care. Lessons learned in behavioral healthcare will be applied to the total practice of medicine, emphasizing behavioral and lifestyle approaches to wellness. In small ways, this will reverse some of the overwhelming cultural prejudice against the world of emotions and their effects on both physical and psychological well-being.

Lessons Learned

Objectives and History.   At-risk contracting is feasible for many, if not all, behavioral healthcare providers. It offers providers the greatest control over the services provided and maximum creativity over clinical programming. It is a learned business skill, quite different from clinical practice. It is possible to maintain a valued clinical career and an ethical stance toward patients, combined with a for-profit business structure—and succeed.

Management.   Rapid change plus increased productivity and lower profit margins would seem to detract from the time to plan, reflect, and enjoy one's work. Therefore, pay even greater attention to the process of planning, giving even more time to quiet reflection. Find a way to share some joy in the midst of treating clients' most painful conflicts, especially with colleagues—who may really need the sustenance.

Professional Goals and Business Success.   Consider how one's continued managed care professional activity will address the most important concerns for the provision of services to patients. In formulating and refining a vision of "best professional practices," recognize how one's professional growth will foster the group's business success.

Clinical Delivery.   Behavioral healthcare has an accumulated body of knowledge in both organizational development and clinical practice, which is being expanded upon rather than abandoned in the development of managed care. Pay attention to your strengths. Articulate those strengths within the group to make your personal contribution.

Contract Negotiations. The behavioral provider group must take a decisive role in defining the services to be covered under capitation. Articulation of the scope and quality of the services to be covered under capitation by a licensed behavioral healthcare provider will establish the basis for a long-range marketing strategy, as well as for contractual negotiations. The role of the healthcare provider, rather than an attorney or healthcare administrator, is central in forging new contractual relationships. Nonhealthcare specialists—from lawyers and marketing consultants to bankers and venture capitalists—can certainly provide assistance, but someone within the group must take a decisive role in presenting the group and negotiating on its behalf with the various organized healthcare delivery systems needing its services.

Information Systems. Whatever is bought now will require modification later. Do not assume that paying more will add value to the information system. However, do assume that you should spend the most you can on hardware: behavioral health is computing-intensive, and last year's fast computer will not support tomorrow's integrated, graphically oriented software. Realize that practice management software will cost tens or hundreds of thousands of dollars. Pay as much attention to the other aspects of office automation as to the practice management software, because the MIS is more comprehensive than just a computer and a practice management system. And remember, no matter what anybody says to the contrary, paper will remain a staple, both as input and output, for some time to come!

FUTURE DIRECTIONS FOR BEHAVIORAL HEALTHCARE

Acceptable levels of cost-effectiveness will only be achieved in groups with over 50,000 to 100,000 covered lives under capitation. However, regional differences will provide opportunities for smaller groups to form, develop effective business strategies, and either combine with larger groups or move into larger markets. Generic psychotherapy services will be less important than the provision of specialty services such as mobile crisis intervention and non-hospital-based acute care alternatives.

HMO services may supersede carve-out MCOs as the dominant caregivers in large states with major metropolitan areas. MCOs will continue to service large national employers and areas in which managed care has not matured sufficiently to force medical groups to attend to behavioral healthcare. Payor-provider partnerships will emerge from being buzzwords, and provider morale will benefit substantially.

The author encourages those clinicians ready to help shape the future of behavioral healthcare to join the already established group practices. Involvement among the various groups across the country will make the frustrations more bearable, and the satisfactions more palpable.

25

MENTAL HEALTH DIVISION WITHIN A MULTISPECIALTY GROUP: PALO ALTO MEDICAL CLINIC

Bruce Bienenstock, M.D.

Multispecialty clinics throughout the United States have undergone radical changes in the last few years, including a marked shift toward managed care and capitation. To function clinically and cost-effectively, virtually every system and procedure has had to change. This chapter documents how the Palo Alto Medical Clinic has responded to capitation as a mental health department within a large medical group. The group is described, as are the steps that were followed to make the necessary changes.

In the 64 years since its formation, the Palo Alto Medical Clinic (PAMC) has become the leading healthcare provider in the greater Palo Alto area. The growing staff currently consists of over 160 physicians, while the number of allied health professionals is also growing rapidly. There are now two satellite clinics, both of which have behavioral healthcare clinicians.

FORMATION: HISTORY AND CULTURE OF PAMC

The clinic began in 1930 as a partnership between two physicians. Original members were all physicians and members of the clinical faculty at Stanford. Throughout the 1970s and 1980s psychiatrists in the Division of Psychiatry generally used short-term treatment models and hospitalized patients only under the most extreme of circumstances. They also spent a great deal of time with their medical and surgical colleagues, and participated in the group effort to provide the best and most cost-effective multidisciplinary medical care available. (See Figure 25.1.)

With the agreement in 1980 to contract with TakeCare (a health maintenance organization (HMO) that leaders at the clinic had helped to

Figure 25.1 History of Palo Alto Medical Clinic (PAMC)

1930	PAMC formed as a partnership between two physicians.
1980	Contract with TakeCare, an HMO created partially with leadership from PAMC. Clinical thinking changes to include finances, revenue, and productivity, leading to the strategic decision to create the Palo Alto Medical Foundation to separate business functions from the clinic.
1991	Change occurs from PAMC's multiple practice design of the past to become a "true group." Decision is made to proceed with the assessment of specific developmental goals. A full patient satisfaction survey is conducted.
1991	Teams are organized to work on the following projects: systematic triage, timely intake, an organized quality management system, an organized utilization management process, clinical standards, a consolidated mental health record, and a unified information system.
1992	A local provider network underbids the Division of Psychiatry and PAMC loses the mental health component of a supposedly "safe" contract.
1994	A TQM process is started to centralize utilization review with outside providers. A full business plan is under development.

found), a new perspective about finances, revenue, productivity, and work became necessary. The need to regulate or manage was clear, but there were no methods in place to achieve this.

Bruce Bienenstock, M.D., is head of the Department of Psychiatry and Clinical Psychology at the Palo Alto Medical Clinic (PAMC), the Health Care Division of the Palo Alto Medical Foundation in Palo Alto, CA. During the last four years his multidisciplinary staff has grown from 9 to 14.5 FTEs, while referrals have increased by 19 percent annually. Among his many goals has been to help shift PAMC from functioning as a cluster of boutique providers with a "medical arts" mentality to a true team which is "managed care friendly." Dr. Bienenstock has spoken at national conferences and worked with managed behavioral health foundations to set up provider networks.

Through the 1980s and until recently, all of PAMC's contracts were negotiated from the viewpoint of their value for the whole organization (as some psychiatric benefit was almost always included in the plan). There were few financial incentives to control utilization other than a hospital *risk pool*, an amount of money set aside at the beginning of each contract year, part of which would be returned if hospital utilization and costs were below an agreed-upon standard.

MANAGEMENT STRUCTURE

PAMC is the Health Care Division of the nonprofit Palo Alto Medical Foundation (PAMF). The foundation handles all contracting, marketing, billing, human resources, finances, and facilities, while the clinic employs the providers of care. (See Figure 25.2.)

In the mid-1980s PAMC made the strategic decision to form PAMF. The functions of the clinic and the foundation were separated because

Figure 25.2 Management Structure—Palo Alto Medical Clinic

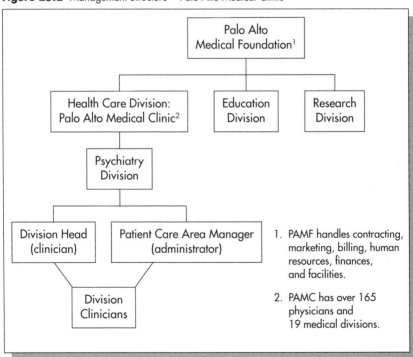

this separation would generate the flexibility required for contracting with different insurers. Separation was a wise choice, based on an appreciation of the rapidity of change, the possibilities of HMO failures, and the need to be able to switch directions without feeling hostage to a single health plan.

However, this choice produced unexpected results. While there tended to be some uniformity across health plans in general medical benefits, each plan had its own unique behavioral healthcare guidelines and methods for behavioral utilization review.

By the summer of 1991 the Division of Psychiatry was ready to change from PAMC's traditional multiple practice design to become what Dr. Paul Buongiorno (1991) has called a "true group," a cohesive group able to function independently with high flexibility and readiness for change. This change in the division was set in motion by shifts in payor sources over the course of the 1980s. From 1984 to 1989 the local county's insurance mix changed from 75 percent indemnity and 25 percent HMO/preferred provider organization (PPO) coverage to 65 percent HMO/PPO and 35 percent indemnity.

The implications of this shift were significant. The clinic's fee-for-service business was dropping rapidly while revenue from PPO and HMO business was increasing dramatically, along with notable increases in Medicare and special contracts patients.

CULTURAL EVOLUTION WITHIN THE DIVISION OF PSYCHIATRY

In response to these changes, the Division of Psychiatry's leaders attended two conferences on HMO psychiatry, which led to the conclusion that the division had to become a model for cost-conscious care. There was also a belief that in the near future some form of capitated system was likely for the division. A further realization was that HMO psychiatry relied on a broad multidisciplinary approach and staffing, in which psychiatrists would be used primarily for their strengths in dealing with medical issues, medications, and particularly complicated cases. All of these issues crystallized the awareness that the PAMC mental health department had to change its operations substantially. As if to give more impetus to such change, a competitor from the community came to TakeCare, the clinic's main managed care contract, and offered to provide care for the HMO's psychiatric patients on a capitated basis, and at a lower rate than the Division cost!

In late 1991 the decision was made to pursue the following developmental goals:

- develop a mission statement;
- evaluate the current status of the professional staff;
- assess divisional needs with regard to:
  the medical administration,
  the physicians at PAMC,
  contracts, and
  the Education Division;
- investigate other psychiatric clinics;
- survey patient satisfaction; and
- develop an implementation plan.

Members of the division from all specialties were involved in learning about the operations of three other psychiatry divisions based in large multispecialty clinics, which agreed to help PAMC. Findings from these other psychiatry divisions led to the understanding of what PAMC needed, namely: leadership, staff training, education about new types of reimbursement and insurance coverage, strong ties to nonpsychiatrist physicians, and integration of medical and psychiatric treatment programs.

A team developed a patient satisfaction questionnaire to survey patients about their experiences with individual therapists and global issues such as how they experienced the billing process. It was important to know things such as how they felt they were handled by office staff, and how easy or difficult they found it to park.

The conclusions from this Patient Satisfaction Survey were:

- Patients were happy with their professional care, but they were not happy with parking and with many of the division's operations.
- Patients found it difficult to reach us by telephone and at times to make appointments, and they sometimes felt that phone calls were not returned promptly.
- Access for emergencies and urgent cases was thought to be only fair at best.
- Fee-for-service patients were being turned away in an attempt to cover the needs of the capitated patients that the division was obligated to see.
- There was no systematic method to understand how many staff from the different behavioral health specialties were needed.

Simultaneously, another local provider network came to PAMC and underbid the division's services. The clinic thus lost the behavioral health component of a supposedly "safe" contract. All of these events led in 1992 to a full review of the division's strengths and weaknesses. The conclusions from this audit were:

- Patients, referral sources, the medical leadership and administration, and contracting insurance companies were satisfied with the quality of the clinical work done in the division.
- Referral sources were concerned about access while the therapists in the division increasingly felt burdened by paperwork, lack of clinical guidelines, and lack of administrative support at almost all levels.
- There were no algorithms to guide internal utilization management except for general definitions of "crisis intervention" and "medical necessity." These shortcomings increasingly were placing ethical, clinical, and potentially medical-legal barriers in front of the delivery of care.
- The division remained totally dependent on whatever psychiatric benefits were available in the general contracts written at the level of PAMF. There was increasing evidence that the psychiatric benefits in these contracts were *not* secure, and that the behavioral health benefits were often the most limited among the medical specialties. The newer *carve-out* managed care behavioral health benefits were sometimes more generous than those from HMOs, but were administratively far more complicated and time-consuming.
- The division had access problems.
- There was very little financial information available about the division and little was being collected in a systematic fashion. Other than global costs, there was almost no information available about utilization patterns, and no system to track costs.
- Systems for handling emergency care were based on practice patterns from the past, which were much more leisurely and required less paperwork.
- The intake process had been improved by making social workers responsible for intake and triage. However, they came to think that their time was poorly utilized, in that most intakes were relatively routine, and could be better spent seeing patients.
- There was no consensus as to the future of carve-out behavioral health managed care at the highest levels of the institution.
- The satisfaction of the staff, in the midst of these increasing demands, was becoming as crucial a factor to the overall success of the division as the satisfaction of patients and referral sources.

IMPLEMENTING CONTINUOUS IMPROVEMENT

The studies and conclusions described above occurred simultaneous with the early growth of the carve-out movement in prepaid behavioral healthcare. While research had shown that significant changes were needed to satisfy current "customers," the division also believed that significant vulnerability remained to future changes in the marketplace.

Given the broad changes needed at all levels of the division, the decision was made to focus on very specific areas, followed by education for division staff as well as the medical and administrative leadership in each area. By doing so, it was expected that there would be observable changes in behavior as the staff became educated. A system of ad hoc committees, some using total quality management (TQM) methods (see Chapter 10) and some operating much more simply, was created to assess and develop changes in the required areas. While each recommended change appeared to be small, the composite of the changes was huge.

Teams were formed to work on the following projects:

- a systematic and timely intake and triage system;
- an organized quality management system including treatment algorithms and peer review;
- an organized utilization management process;
- clinical standards for caseload and case-mix issues;
- a consolidated behavioral healthcare record; and
- a unified information system to track referrals, utilization, and credentialing information.

Example of a Continuous Improvement Team

As an example of this process, the following steps occurred in the creation of an intake and triage system. Prior to the clinic contracting with HMOs, all intake and triage decisions had been made by a psychiatrist on call. This system began to break down as the number of emergencies and urgent cases seemed to grow and the overall length of treatment decreased. Social workers were hired to help in developing an intake and triage system, but without success.

A TQM team was created to address the many clinical and administrative issues necessary to create a smooth system. The process was facilitated by a psychiatrist and a social worker who had taken two-day intensive training as facilitators in this area. Using standard TQM techniques, a flow chart of the current processes for handling routine, urgent, and emergency calls was created to identify the sources of delay in the system. The flow charts demonstrated many obstacles to obtaining initial appointments.

The next step for this team was to agree that its mission was to reduce appointment scheduling time by reducing the steps needed to make an appointment for a routine referral, and to collect data to assess the problem. Next the team focused on the primary cause of delays: there were too many steps and too many people involved in the procedure, with a process that was too complicated, and with frequent duplication of effort. The team decided to integrate the multiple processes and to decrease the number of people and steps involved by:

- having one intake coordinator to field intake phone calls;
- centralizing the scheduling of initial appointments; and
- having a separate telephone line for intake, with a full-time staff person to answer the phone, book initial routine appointments, and collect insurance information. The intake staff person was assigned to assess the emergency or routine nature of each call and make appropriate referrals.

A variety of conflicting demands, however, became apparent. The intake coordinator required access to the clinic's mainframe computer for insurance and registration information and needed a database containing intake and referral information, such as information about contracted affiliate network providers (called clinical "associates"), in order to make clinically appropriate referrals.

To achieve "buy-in" from the other division members, a series of meetings was arranged. The other staff members readily agreed to the system—seeing it as a way to reduce phone calls and frustration, as well as to collect new patient data. Upon obtaining the division's support, the team met with the heads of Family Practice, Internal Medicine, Specialty Internal Medicine, Pediatrics, and Urgent Care. The proposed system was greeted very positively by these departments, as they had all found access to psychiatry to be confusing for themselves and their patients.

After the new system was installed and its effectiveness was measured, the team, division staff, and all referral sources (including several managed care organizations) expressed great satisfaction with the changes. The team was extremely successful in realizing its mission.

In addition to the TQM process used in developing an intake and triage system, teams have also created products in the other identified areas of difficulty: organizing a full quality management system, developing treatment algorithms (currently being done with the Department of Pediatrics), establishing a peer review process, organizing a utilization management process, developing clinical standards, creating a single behavioral health chart for each patient, and progressing on a unified patient information database. A complaint policy has also been established. Complaints are viewed as tools for quality improvement, and a standardized procedure is used in their investigation.

The TQM process is now being used to collect data in three areas of concern to our patients: night and weekend call response, daytime call response, and policies and procedures regarding cancellations and interruptions due to emergencies. The results of these findings will be used in modifying existing systems. A committee is also completely redesigning our insurance policies and procedures for a patient handout.

In addition, the division has developed the following:

- yearly performance appraisals of all staff,
- biannual customer satisfaction surveys,
- a plan to create a new compensation formula in which incentives are aligned with the requirements of managed care and capitation,
- a commitment to joining the Council of Behavioral Group Practices' multisite outcomes study (see Chapter 19 and Appendix H),
- ongoing education of all staff, and
- a division manual of policies and procedures.

FUNCTIONING UNDER CAPITATION

The division continues to see the bulk of its commercial business through the broader contracting and capitation arrangements negotiated by PAMF for the entire PAMC. The division's involvement in capitation ranges from a careful focus on utilization within several HMOs, for which PAMC provides the entire range of multispecialty group care, to risk-sharing arrangements with several single-specialty managed behavioral health plans. As medical information systems become more fully developed, particularly in regard to managing on a "cost" versus "revenue" basis, and as staffing increases to accommodate new business, the division looks forward to going fully at risk alone.

PAMC has used a number of methods to educate physicians, nurses, psychologists, and social workers about the economics of practice under capitation. (See Figure 25.3.) As a result the importance of tracking the number of new patients, by therapist and globally, and the number of follow-up appointments, is now understood by many mental health clinicians.

As Goldstein (1994) has correctly pointed out, managed behavioral healthcare requires a great deal of integration. The division is moving in

Figure 25.3 Practice Summary

I. **Business Structure**

Year founded: 1930

Owned by: Palo Alto Medical Clinic

Business Status: The Palo Alto Medical Clinic is the Health Care Division of the Palo Alto Medical Foundation, a nonprofit 501(c) organization. It is a community-based, multispecialty group practice.

Vision/Mission Statement: The mission of the Palo Alto Medical Foundation is to provide and integrate quality healthcare, health education, and biomedical research to improve the health status of our region. The Department of Psychiatry is committed to giving the highest quality of care possible in the context of the clinic's increasing managed care environment.

Number of Offices: 3

Geographic Area Served: mid-San Francisco Peninsula

II. **Clinical Staffing**

Total Employed Clinical Staff (in FTEs):

Master's-degreed Therapists: 9.2

Psychologists: 1

Nurses/Physician's Assistants: 0

Psychiatrists: 6.5

Other: 0

(continued on next page)

---

that direction. A current focus, for example, is upon establishing a centralized utilization review system with contracted outside providers. By bringing utilization review into the division, an improved information flow between outside providers and those making utilization decisions is expected, along with improvement in quality and a decrease in costs. The utilization patterns will be studied in a multidimensional fashion, including tracking care by procedure (CPT code), diagnosis, and therapist. The utilization patterns will become TQM tools for designing pathways and criteria, as well as for learning from one another.

In addition, it is vital in a capitated environment to know the costs of care. How much does it actually cost for a social worker or psychiatrist to see a patient? What does it cost per hour for each type of therapist to run a group therapy session? These analyses are vital in determining which contracts are appropriate to each setting. They are informative as to the relative

Figure 25.3 (continued)

Total Number of Subcontracted Network Providers:
Master's-degreed Therapists: 13
Psychologists: 14
Psychiatrists: 25
Others: 4 (MFCC)
Affiliated Group Practices: 4

III. Capitation Functioning
Number of Contracts: 7
Total Covered Lives: 57,000
Capitation Revenue as Percentage of Total: 45
Total Contracts in Group's History: 11
Mean Utilization Statistics:
Penetration Rate (Percentage of enrollees accessing treatment): 4.69
Outpatient Length of Treatment (in visits): 4.5 (exclusive of medication visits, which average 4.0)
Hospital Days/1,000 Members: 16.2 (include outpatient hospital days at 0.5 day)
Hospital Admissions/1,000 Members: 1.9 (include outpatient hospital admits at 0.5)

costs of each type of behavioral health professional, and the relative costs of contracting versus employing clinicians.

The division is now in the process of tracking the following data: average length of stay for hospitalizations, number of psychiatric admissions, number of psychiatric hospital days, and days per thousand admissions. Comparisons by provider are being developed and tracked on a relational database.

FUTURE DIRECTIONS

One of the keys to the future of the division has been the decision to write a specific business plan. With all of these studies and changes, the Division of Psychiatry has come to see itself as ready to be a leader in managed care within PAMC, and it is time to again move toward greater integration with the entire clinic.

A joint effort has been established between the various management entities to study the fiscal merits of contracts and to write a specific business plan for the division. Expectations for this plan are that it will offer an outside consultant's view of the division's strengths and weaknesses, which should provide an analysis of opportunities in the local marketplace and a view of what the competition is doing. It should also provide guidance with regard to possible mergers, both within the local market and with regional integrated delivery systems such as Sutter Health in Sacramento. The goal for the division is to be able to solely contract on a fully at-risk basis.

Other future activities of the division will include:

- continued local integration and collaboration;
- expanded efforts to integrate behavioral healthcare throughout the multidisciplinary group practice of PAMC, to the point of making it an essential element;
- expanded services to meet "niche" needs;
- reduced costs through innovation and team efforts;
- becoming a model for cost-effective, superior quality, diversified behavioral healthcare;
- choosing local collaborations with systems and individuals having similar values and principles;
- balancing the cost of independence with the cost of complexity;
- collaboration and integration on a Northern California and statewide basis;
- defining a strategic direction for the behavioral health component of the Sutter Health system; and
- supporting alliances between colleagues in Northern and Southern California with whom we have been fostering relationships.

LESSONS LEARNED

Group Culture

- Work with individuals who can see the positive aspects of capitating behavioral healthcare benefits.
- Find a value set that the group can embrace.
- Leadership and management must be valued and nurtured from the beginning.
- Individuals with skills and commitment in these areas are essential for the birth and development of a group process.

- Work toward a "true group" model, very much in line with Deming's 14 points (Aguayo, 1991). Understand the necessity and value of conflict.

Market

- Focus your efforts on areas of strength; that is, work from strength, not from weakness or fear of competitors—who will proceed as they see best for themselves, whether you are there or not.
- Understand what potential customers, including hospitals, employers, insurers, and the community, want and will pay for.
- Focus on a geographic area you can service well.

Services

- Understand the need for a continuum of care, while also understanding that it is sometimes more effective and/or cost-efficient to buy rather than own.
- Have the basic operating systems in place and understand their costs before contracting.

Collaboration

- Understand that while non-behavioral-health colleagues may be allies in healthcare delivery, they have their own legitimate and sometimes contrary interests. Negotiate, negotiate, negotiate.
- Understand and be able to justify why capital expenses in behavioral healthcare are worthwhile to the total organization. Present clinical and financial data.

REFERENCES

Aguayo, R. (1991). *Dr. Deming, the American who taught the Japanese about quality.* New York: A Fireside Book; pp. 124–125.

Buongiorno, P. M. (1991, September). Organization and operations: How to manage group practices in a managed care environment. Symposium panel discussion conducted at **Behavioral Healthcare *Tomorrow*** conference, Boston, MA.

Goldstein, L. S. (1994, February). Merge the streams. Presentation at *Managing Capitation in Behavioral Health Networks* conference, Washington, DC.

26

University-based Single-Specialty Group: University Managed Care

Allen S. Daniels, Ed.D.

The Department of Psychiatry at the University of Cincinnati has been responsive to trends in the changing healthcare market. The need to preserve a significant role for clinical programs was identified proactively, and the financial needs of the institution were addressed through the initiation and development of a managed care program. The outcome has been a clinically and financially successful venture. While the experience is directly relevant for academic departments, it is also applicable to other larger institutions wishing to enter managed care and capitation.

A cademic medical centers are uniquely positioned to develop and provide managed behavioral healthcare. They achieve this status through their comprehensive service delivery systems and their potentially integrated provider groups. Options exist for departments of psychiatry to develop service and provider systems for existing insurance companies, or to create their own managed care programs. The determination of directions is mediated by a strategic assessment of existing market opportunities and by departmental objectives.

The Department of Psychiatry at the University of Cincinnati College of Medicine began with the development of a group practice (University Psychiatric Service), specializing in the delivery of managed behavioral healthcare. Over time the department also created University Managed Care, a full spectrum administrator of managed care programs. These innovative resources were each established to meet the requirements of a rapidly changing healthcare market. This case study illustrates the process by which academic behavioral healthcare departments can accommodate the requirements of an evolving market.

FORMATION

University Psychiatric Services (UPS) began operation in 1983 as a managed care group practice within the University of Cincinnati's Department of Psychiatry, in affiliation with the department's ambulatory behavioral healthcare clinic. The initial goal of this program was to expand the funding source for resident training, which at the time was jeopardized by the ambulatory clinic's independence from the University Hospital. The plan was to develop clinical programs that would be available to employers or insurers through contractual agreements. This service was created as an independent and freestanding entity from other clinic and department programs in order to preserve its autonomy and flexibility in responding to potential business opportunities.

The initial UPS contract was for an innovative carve-out of outpatient behavioral health benefits for the University of Cincinnati, a self-insured employer. Faculty members were offered a restructured benefit plan which created incentives for both members and providers to use time-limited, focused interventions. The construction of this benefit package also provided coverage for extended psychotherapy as needed. Approximately 20 percent of the employee group elected this option. The results of this program were quite favorable, and the contract ran until 1987, when the health benefit was incorporated as a comprehensive preferred provider organization (PPO). Other PPO arrangements were established with large employer groups and employee assistance programs in the area.

As a result of the benefit transition to a full-service PPO, UPS was awarded a contract to serve as the point-of-service access and outpatient utilization review agent for the mental health and substance abuse components of this new program. Triage and preauthorization for services were provided by UPS clinical coordinators. In July, 1990, UPS also began a contractual arrangement with a health maintenance organization (HMO)

Allen S. Daniels, Ed.D., is Senior Vice President of Operations for University Managed Care and Executive Director of University Psychiatric Services. Both of these organizations are affiliated with the Department of Psychiatry at the University of Cincinnati, OH, and University of Cincinnati Medical Associates. Dr. Daniels is also Assistant Professor of Clinical Psychiatry at the University of Cincinnati, and a clinical social worker with extensive experience in the operation of academic group practices and the development of managed care programs in an academic setting.

Figure 26.1 History of University Managed Care

1983	Department of Psychiatry organizes University Psychiatric Services (UPS) as a "simulated group practice." UPS is composed of faculty and community practitioners, and serves as a panel for the University's faculty health plan.
1987	UPS is awarded University PPO contract for triage and outpatient utilization management.
1990	UPS contracts with University of Cincinnati's HMO for utilization management and preauthorization, and begins full capitation negotiations—vying with American Biodyne, which has a hospital utilization of 5 days/1,000 while the University's utilization is 80 to 100 days/1,000 (HMO industry average is 25 to 30 days/1,000).
1991	University Managed Care (UMC) is formed to accept HMO capitation contracts for faculty. Devoted staff are hired; 12,000 covered lives are under capitation. UPS serves as staff model while a community IPA panel is also available.
1992	13,000 University lives are added under utilization review contract to replace primary care physician gatekeeper authorization for behavioral health services.
1993	University HMO is sold to Blue Cross/Blue Shield and existing BC/BS patients are added to capitation. 40,000 MetLife point-of-service lives are added for triage and utilization management.
1994	UMC manages 35,000 capitated lives for full behavioral healthcare coverage. University Health Plan HMO's behavioral health costs are reduced by 50 percent.

affiliated with the PPO and the university. This involved 24-hour-a-day preauthorization and utilization management services for all inpatient care. UPS also served as the anchor practice for the PPO's ambulatory care. In early 1990 discussions began between the HMO and UPS regarding development of a full-risk capitation program.

University Managed Care, Inc., (UMC) was formed by the Department of Psychiatry in late 1990 for the purpose of managing the delivery of behavioral healthcare services to subscribing group contracts. UMC commenced operation on July 1, 1991, with a capitated responsibility for 12,000 HMO lives. It has since grown to include both capitated and point-of-service managed care responsibilities. (See Figure 26.1.)

MANAGEMENT STRUCTURE

The structure of group practice management in academic health centers varies on a continuum from centralized to decentralized organizational models. (See Figure 26.2.) One alternative is a unified practice structure in which all departmental practice corporations are integrated into a single entity. At the other extreme is a confederation of independent practices, which may share some common features but are largely autonomous. UPS and UMC at the University of Cincinnati exist in an academic practice culture that has some components of integration, but remain largely autonomous. UMC's capitation contracts are the largest volume of prepaid contracts held in the medical center.

The Department of Psychiatry's practice corporation is Psychiatric Professional Services Inc. (PPSI). PPSI, the parent organization for UPS, is a not-for-profit corporation directed by a President—who must also be the Chairman of the Department of Psychiatry. UPS is a multidisciplinary practice which utilizes both faculty from the department and clinicians employed by the practice. This group is affiliated with the other service delivery components, and it generates clinical and faculty income support for the department.

UMC is a for-profit corporation for federal tax purposes and a nonprofit corporation under the laws of the State of Ohio. It is managed under the direction of a Board of Trustees, with the President being the Chairman of the Department of Psychiatry. A primary mission of UMC is to develop managed behavioral healthcare contracts that support the academic practice. UMC has a contract with UPS to provide comprehensive clinical and utilization review services for all of its agreements. UMC also contracts with the Department of Psychiatry's practice corporation to provide all management services. As the scope and role of UMC's contracts expand, an increased autonomy between these corporations is likely.

CAPITATION FUNCTIONING

When UMC began full-risk capitation with a local HMO in 1991, enrollment totaled approximately 12,000 lives, including those from midsized companies throughout the geographic service area. For UMC, UPS provided a staff-model service delivery system. A community-based panel of providers and facilities was also available. (See Figure 26.3.) Together these resources provided a geographically accessible resource for the greater Cincinnati metropolitan area.

Figure 26.2 Management Structure —University Managed Care

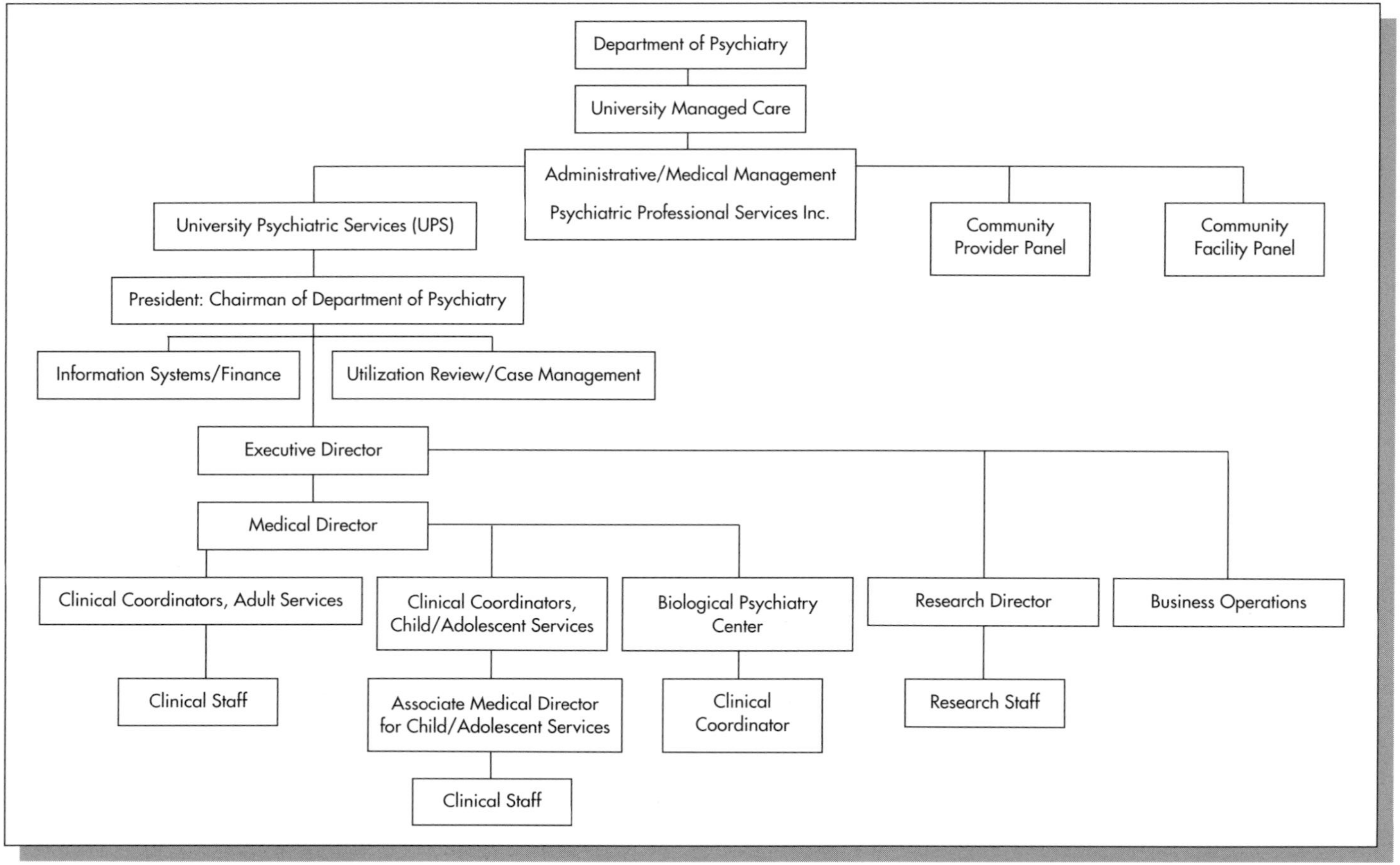

In January, 1992, UMC assumed responsibility for a point-of-service plan covering ambulatory utilization review for an additional 13,000 HMO members. This program was designed to replace the primary care physician as the gatekeeper for mental health and chemical dependency referrals. This system was implemented because the primary care physician gatekeeper process limited access to mental health and substance abuse services.

Figure 26.3 Practice Summary

I. Business Structure
Year Founded: University Psychiatric Services (UPS)—1983
University Managed Care (UMC)—1991
Owned By: Department of Psychiatry, University of Cincinnati
Business Status: UPS—not for profit; UMC—for profit
Number of Offices: 3
Geographic Area Served: Southwestern Ohio

II. Clinical Staffing
Total Employed Clinical Staff (in FTEs): 20.5
Master's-Degreed Therapists: 8
Psychologists: 6
Nurses/Physician's Assistants: 1.5
Psychiatrists: 5
Others: 0
Total Number of Subcontracted Network Providers:
Master's-Degreed Therapists: 10
Psychologists: 15
Psychiatrists: 20
Others: 0

III. Capitation Functioning
Number of Contracts: 3
Total Covered Lives: 80,000
Total Contracts in Group's History: 5
Mean Utilization Statistics:
Penetration Rate (Percentage of enrollees accessing treatment): 2.2
Outpatient Length of Treatment (in visits): 5.4
Hospital Days/1,000 Members: 26 (include outpatient hospital days at
   0.5 day)
Hospital Admits/1,000 Members: 1.8 (include outpatient hospital admits
   at 0.5)

In July of 1993 UMC also assumed full-risk responsibilities for Blue Cross/Blue Shield of Ohio's HMO Health Ohio members in the Cincinnati service area, when the local HMO was sold. A collaborative role in the development of a provider network for the PPO was also assumed. UPS became the anchor practice for both of these programs. In October, 1993, UMC also began providing full-risk capitated services for MetLife HMO members, as well as point-of-service review and triage for approximately 40,000 additional MetLife members.

UMC is currently pursuing a spectrum of program developments. These include new partnerships with insurance programs in the community, and an expanding role in the evolving public behavioral health delivery system.

CLINICAL DELIVERY SYSTEM

For all UMC contracts, a select panel of facilities and providers has been developed. UMC contracts with facilities that are affiliated with the insurance plans. A core staff-model practice is available through UPS, which has three locations in the metropolitan area. A panel of community providers is available to offer broad geographical accessibility.

The core clinical services are provided by UPS. This practice also provides all utilization management and emergency triage services for UMC members, including a 24-hour emergency service known as the Psychiatric Emergency Service (PES), which is part of University Hospital and remains open at all times. PES is extremely valuable in the evaluation and management of crisis situations. The facility has the capacity to hold and observe patients for up to 23 hours, and is staffed by a full complement of behavioral health professionals. PES also has the capacity to provide short-term substance detoxification services. Inpatient psychiatric and substance abuse care is provided through a network of hospitals and facilities. UMC has comprehensive contracts with a continuum of resources. These contracts are primarily based on comprehensive per-diem rates for inpatient usage, and structured program rates based on discounted program costs.

MANAGEMENT INFORMATION SYSTEMS

Initially UMC was confronted with the start-up requirements for an information system, with limited resources for development and an unclear determination of need. Well aware of the significance of accurate information in the management of prepaid populations, UMC was advised that several options were available. These included the purchase of a practice management (billing) system, the purchase and modification of a small HMO package, or custom development. At the time there was a dearth of available systems (see Chapter 16). The clinical practice had an established relationship with an outside vendor for billing and accounts receivables. Based on the assumption that any existing system would require customization, the course of custom development was pursued.

The initial UMC information system was established on a database management program. A local programmer was used to write a limited system to track utilization for information and claims management. For an initial population of 12,000 lives this was effective. As needs outgrew the capacity and sophistication of the system, the option was available to join the larger Medical Associates group within the university and initiate the design and implementation of a managed care application. This is a comprehensive practice management information system integrating the modules of billing and accounts receivables, patient scheduling, and the managed care functions.

This new resource provided UMC with the fundamental components of an information system necessary for a capitated delivery program. These elements include enrollment, referrals, claims, and premium billing. The enrollment module tracks the monthly covered lives and the scope of capitated members. The referrals module supports the UMC medical management system and allows for the authorization of care. Automated claims are paid based upon established linkages between members, employer groups, and benefit plans. The premium billing component allows for the custom billing of self-insured groups. The implementation of this system has allowed UMC to accurately track the information necessary to manage a prepaid population and to provide its insurance partners with sophisticated data.

QUALITY IMPROVEMENT

The focus on the quality of services that are provided in clinical care has emerged as a central component in managed care, as well as in the emerging certification of practices and insurers. The guidelines of the National Committee for Quality Assurance (NCQA) are rapidly becoming the benchmarking standard for quality improvement programs. Quality improvement programming for UMC has followed a course similar to that of the practice's evolution. As a practice affiliated with an academic medical center, one of its primary mechanisms for quality improvement has been in the area of outcomes evaluation.

The quality of clinical programs can be assessed in two ways; the quality indicators are the outcomes of a clinical intervention and the satisfaction of the patient. UMC has supported the evaluation of both in its clinical delivery system (see Chapter 19). In order to facilitate the commitment to quality improvement, two staff positions are dedicated to this task—the Director of Utilization Management and Quality Assurance and the Director of Outcome Research. These individuals, who are also a part of the clinical staff, bring a unique commitment to the importance of quality assessment. Their efforts have also led to the creation of a multisite clinical evaluation protocol initiated by the Institute for Behavioral Healthcare's Council of Behavioral Group Practices (see Appendix H). This project supports the establishment of benchmarks for the evaluation of quality and the continuous improvement of clinical outcomes.

LESSONS LEARNED

The development of a group practice is an evolving process that occurs through both opportunity and commitment. Successful groups share a common culture, which supports clinical practice and provides mutual rewards for the participants. In an academic setting, the goals of the participants may be varied and the mission of these clinical organizations frequently are unclear. In addition, the priorities for faculty members often are different from those promoted through clinical practice. The combination of these factors creates an environment in which it is often difficult to foster an integrated group practice.

Most academic departments of psychiatry have a broad spectrum of clinical services available through their teaching programs. While these resources are often developed for public behavioral healthcare systems, they are also well suited for managed care programs. The task for an academic department is the development of the group culture of integration.

In order for an academic department to emerge in the managed care environment, four areas of development must be evident. These include:

- coordination of the delivery system,
- structures for medical management,
- information systems that support managed care and prepayment, and
- quality improvement systems.

Each of these resources must be vested within the full commitment of the department's leadership.

The coordination of the delivery system is essential for any program to succeed. It requires a commitment for these resources to become vertically integrated systems of care. When a clinical system assumes prepaid risk for a member population, it is necessary that all segments of the organization be prepared to do whatever it takes to accommodate the clinical needs of the member. The UMC program has developed a core group practice and a network of community facilities and providers. In the development of this network, it has been important to cultivate a resource of providers and facilities able to meet the needs of our constituent populations.

The components of a medical management system encompass a continuum of resources. These include 24-hour access to clinical service, utilization review, utilization management, treatment authorization, and claims payment. These resources commonly are not available within existing group or academic computer programs. Therefore, they represent one of the largest areas of start-up commitment for an emerging managed care delivery system. In our experience it has been important to identify key individuals who are able to take on the responsibilities of leadership and medical management, and expand their range of daily responsibilities.

Information systems support the structure of the medical management component of a managed care program. Most existing practices have some limited capacity for billing and accounts receivable. However, these are not sufficient tools for the assumption of risk and the management of care.

The final component of an evolving practice and delivery system is the quality improvement program. The delivery system must have mechanisms to track the quality of clinical outcomes and support the culture of quality improvement in a continuous fashion. This approach is facilitated in a number of ways, but must include clinical outcomes and patient satisfaction.

FUTURE DIRECTIONS

The future of academic-based group practices lies in their ability to accommodate the requirements of rapidly evolving healthcare systems. In those markets where there is a predominance of existing managed care plans, it will be important for an academic department of psychiatry to find a role within the available delivery systems. For departments in less developed markets there is an opportunity to create managed care products and actively compete in the evolving health systems. Ultimately, as larger multi-specialty healthcare delivery systems evolve and as public and private sectors consolidate, it will be particularly important for academic departments of psychiatry to seek and achieve full integration.

For UMC and UPS, the future is already in transition. Based on an existing foundation of capitated contracts, expansion is in process. This evolution includes the development of strategic partnerships that will support the long-term stability of these organizations. Such relationships include an expanded role with the multispecialty medical group for the University of Cincinnati, and the consolidation of several local hospitals into a health facility alliance. In addition, other strategic partnerships are forming within larger delivery systems and insurance plans. The goal is to seek status as the anchor for expanding delivery systems in the areas of behavioral health and managed care support.

The future of healthcare and the delivery of behavioral healthcare are in a period of rapid transition. Academic departments of psychiatry historically have been slow to respond to the evolving needs of the commercial healthcare market. At the current crossroads, these departments will need to quickly adopt a proactive stance to implement programming that fosters their continued viability. University Managed Care and University Psychiatric Services offer models for this process.

APPENDICES

A

GLOSSARY OF
MANAGED CARE TERMS

Access   An individual's ability to obtain medical services on a timely and financially acceptable basis.

Administrative Loading   The amount above the actual cost of healthcare services (called pure premium) in premium costs necessary to cover administration, marketing, and profit.

Administrative Service Only (ASO)   A management service contracted to control a health plan's costs, conduct utilization review, and pay providers. Same as Third-Party Administrator and Pass Through.

Administratively Necessary Day   A day of stay that is necessary not for clinical reasons but rather for disposition or discharge planning and transfer.

Adverse Selection   Enrollment that disproportionately creates adverse risk, such as a more impaired population with higher healthcare utilization.

Any Willing Provider   A provision, often legal, requiring that any provider with appropriate credentials be allowed to join a closed panel.

At-Risk   Any financial arrangement or contract in which a provider or health plan assumes exposure for the costs of services needed by a population of enrollees.

Average Adjusted Per Capita Cost (AAPCC)   The estimated amount it would cost to provide services through a fee-for-service model; used to determine Medicare rates for HMOs.

Average Daily Census (ADC)   The mean number of patients daily in a hospital.

Average Length of Stay (ALOS)   The mean length of hospital stays in days for a population of enrollees.

Benefit Package   A contractually defined set of healthcare benefits that are covered under an insurance, HMO, or capitation plan.

Beta Risk   A form of direct financial risk, especially under capitation, resulting from the cost of catastrophic cases, especially when the number of covered lives is too small to compensate for outliers.

Biased Selection   The distribution of relatively healthy versus unhealthy individuals in an insured population. See Adverse Selection.

Capitation   A method of payment for healthcare in which the provider is prepaid a fixed amount, usually monthly, for each member of a health plan regardless of whether that member accesses services. The fixed rate pays for all services necessary for the population regardless of actual utilization or costs.

Capitation Rate   For insurers, the monthly revenue requirement from premiums per member per month to cover the health plan's costs. For providers, the rate paid per month under a capitation arrangement to provide care to a fixed population. See Per Member Per Month.

Carve-out   Removing specific health services to be managed separately from the standard medical coverage, for example, a carve-out for mental health.

Case Management   The handling or directing of a patient's treatment as to which services are needed and how they should be provided.

Case Mix   The blend of diagnoses and/or treatment types (for example, inpatient and outpatient) for a particular provider, facility, group practice, or health plan.

Case Rate   A flat rate fee schedule based on a fixed amount per patient, often by diagnosis, and especially for inpatient care. See Fixed Rate and Diagnostic-Related Group.

Closed Panel   A fixed group of clinicians from which enrollees must choose.

Combined Provider Organization (CPO)   See Hospital-Physician Organization.

Community Rating   The method of setting premiums, mandated for federally qualified HMOs, in which the HMO uses a community-wide premium rate or equivalency formula for determining premium rates to members in a defined service area, based on the average family size, mix of single versus family contracts, and community standards.

Community Rating by Class (CRC)   A variation of community rating, allowed as of 1989, in which premiums charged to members can be set by age, sex, marital status, family size, industry, and smoking/nonsmoking status.

Comprehensive Medical Plan (CMP)   An HMO-like plan for Medicare beneficiaries only, usually employing capitation.

Concurrent Review   A form of utilization review conducted during the provision of services (such as during an inpatient treatment period) to determine if the services meet the insurer or third party's requirements to justify payment for the services provided.

Consolidated Omnibus Budget Reconciliation Act of 1985 (COBRA)   A federal statute requiring employers to extend the option to continue healthcare insurance to employees who would otherwise lose such coverage due to layoffs, termination, divorce, separation, or death; extensions are for 18 months if due to layoff and 36 months if due to divorce, separation, or death.

Coordination of Benefits (COB)   An insurance provision, when an insured member is covered by more than one insurer, of defining which insurer is responsible for primary payment and which is responsible for secondary payment. This coordination prevents double reimbursement.

Co-payment   A cost-sharing arrangement whereby the insured beneficiary pays a fixed fee at the time of service, augmenting the amount paid to the provider by the health plan. The co-payment does not vary with the provider's charge for the service.

Cost Sharing   A provision of a health plan which requires the insured to pay some portion of the costs for services. Deductibles and co-payments are forms of cost sharing.

Demand Risk   A form of direct financial risk, especially under capitation, resulting from enrollees demanding more treatment than is necessary.

Diagnostic-Related Group (DRG)   A prospective payment arrangement under which services are paid on a case rate or fixed rate, based on retrospective data about costs for treating certain diagnoses.

Dual Choice Provision   A legal mandate, prior to 1991, that employers with more than 25 insured employees must, if requested by employees or insurers, offer both an indemnity plan and an HMO plan. Also called Dual Option.

Due Diligence Review   An employer or insured's review of a provider panel to determine if the panel is adequate to meet expected healthcare needs and if providers meet community standards.

Economic Credentialing   Determining clinical qualifications or privileges based solely or primarily on financial criteria.

Employee Retirement Income Security Act of 1974 (ERISA)   An act that exempts the health plans of self-insured employers from many state laws (including freedom-of-choice laws).

Enrollee   The individual enrolled in a health plan or a dependent of the enrolled individual who is also covered by the plan. Same as Member.

Exclusive Provider Organization (EPO)   A closed panel of providers contracted on a fee-for-service or capitation basis.

Exclusivity Clause   A legal provision binding a provider to contract only with a single health plan.

Experience Rating   A system of setting insurance premiums reflecting the cost and utilization experience of a particular group or employer.

Family Mental Health Practitioner (FMHP)   A therapist identified for mental health treatment as the primary practitioner for an individual or family, like a primary care physician in routine medical care.

Federally Qualified   An HMO that has met the standards determined by the HMO Act of 1973 or its many amendments. Plans are no longer mandated to be federally qualified.

Fee for Service   An indemnity plan arrangement of paying a percentage of providers' billed charges, often with a maximum based on a usual, customary, and reasonable fee determination.

First-Dollar Coverage   A health plan coverage which has no deductible amounts; in some cases a co-payment may be required.

Fixed Rate   A payment-for-services arrangement in which the provider is paid a certain amount per case, often by diagnosis, for providing services regardless of the actual amount of services used or needed. See Case Rate and Diagnostic-Related Group.

Gatekeeper   A provider, usually a primary care physician, who preauthorizes access to treatment.

Group Model   A health plan that provides healthcare services through group practices contracted to the HMO and paid on a salary, fee-for-service, incentive, or capitation basis.

High Touch   Any service with apparent high human contact from the perspective of the patient or enrollee.

Holdback   See Withhold.

Hospital-Physician Organization (HPO)   A joint venture between a hospital and a group of providers to market or contract with one or more health plans. Same as Physician-Hospital Organization (PHO).

Incurred But Not Reported (IBNR)   Financial liabilities or claims for services for which a health plan or capitated provider has become responsible, but which have not yet been reported or submitted to the health plan or capitated provider for payment.

Independent Practice Association (IPA)   A group of healthcare providers who are often in solo private practices, organized together by contract to facilitate participation in more than one healthcare plan. Also called Independent Practice Organization (IPO).

Integrated Mental Health System (IMHS)   An HMO-like health plan for the chronically mentally ill.

IPA Model   A health plan organized to provide services through one or more independent practice associations (IPAs), which are contracted to the health plan and paid on a fixed rate, fee-for-service, incentive, or capitation basis.

Lag Factor   The percentage of claims incurred during a set time period relative to the claims processed and paid during the same period.

Last-Dollar Coverage   An insurance coverage without a maximum or lifetime limit to the benefits payable.

Length of Stay (LOS)   The days used in a hospital stay.

Lock-in Requirement   See Closed Panel.

Managed Care Organization (MCO)   Any group conducting or implementing healthcare through managed care concepts of service preauthorization, utilization review, and a fixed network of providers. In mental healthcare the term is often used to refer to a utilization review organization.

Management Information System (MIS)   The computer and data management system.

McCarran-Ferguson Act   Legislation enacted in 1945 that prohibits most antitrust actions against insurers.

Medically Necessary   Determination by a health plan as to whether a service is necessary for medical reasons or patient functioning.

Medigap   The coverage difference between Medicare and supplemental insurance.

Meltdown Scenario   A phenomenon of spiraling adverse selection when high users of services repeatedly continue to select a particular health plan (usually an indemnity plan) while the low users of service select another plan (usually a managed care plan).

Member   See Enrollee.

Moral Hazard   A form of direct financial risk resulting from enrollee dishonesty, carelessness, or lack of judgment.

Morbidity Risk   A form of direct financial risk resulting from the actual degree or amount of psychopathology and psychiatric morbidity in the population.

Network Model   A health plan that provides healthcare services through a network of independent practitioners and group practices contracted to the HMO and paid on a salary, fee-for-service, incentive, or capitation basis.

Omnibus Budget Reconciliation Act of 1986 (OBRA '86)   A Congressional act taking effect in 1991 that prohibits HMOs from making payments directly or indirectly to providers as an inducement to reduce or limit services to Medicare or Medicaid patients.

Open-Ended Plan   Opposite of closed panel. See Open Panel.

Open Enrollment   A period of time during which new subscribers or employees of a particular employer may elect a new health plan or switch plans.

Open Panel   A large group of clinicians from which the subscribers can select for their healthcare.

Outlier   An enrollee requiring or using distinctly more or less service than is typical for patients with a given condition or illness. Usually defined as two standard deviations from the mean.

Out-of-Area Benefits   The benefits an insurance plan provides when members are outside the geographically defined limits of the plan. These always include emergency services.

Out-of-Plan Benefits When services are authorized to be provided by a clinician or facility outside of a plan's closed panel, or beyond the standard limits of the plan benefit.

Overutilization Unnecessary or excessive services offered by providers or demanded by enrollees.

Pass Through Same as Administrative Service Only and Third-Party Administrator.

Penetration In marketing managed care plans, the percentage of possible subscribers actually enrolled in a particular plan or set of plans. In the provision of care or capitation, the percentage of possible enrollees accessing care.

Percentage of Premium A fixed rate used to prepay a capitation contract based on a percentage of the total subscriber premium dollars paid to the health plan. An alternative capitated payment arrangement to per member per month.

Per Member Per Month (PMPM) The fixed rate used to prepay a capitation contract monthly based on the number of enrollees.

Physician-Hospital Organization (PHO) See Hospital-Physician Organization (HPO).

Point of Service (POS) A health plan that allows enrollees to choose a clinician from an HMO or PPO panel of providers, or to select a nonpanel provider who will be reimbursed by a standard indemnity form of coverage.

Preauthorization An authorization made under utilization review by an insurer or third party, before the provision of services, designating the services to be paid by the insurer or third party. Also called Prior Authorization, Precertification, or Predetermination.

Precertification See Preauthorization.

Preferred Provider Organization (PPO) A type of health plan that contracts with providers to provide services at a fixed discount while enrollees are given a financial incentive to use the contracted providers.

Prepaid Group Practice (PGP) A group practice paid on a capitation basis.

Prepaid Health Plan (PHP) An insurance arrangement in which subscribers pay the insurer in advance for access to a specified set of healthcare benefits. HMOs are prepaid health plans.

Price Elasticity The relationship between price and utilization of services, for example, the higher the cost of co-payments, the lower the use of services. Also called Price Responsiveness.

Price Responsiveness See Price Elasticity.

Price Risk A form of direct financial risk, especially under capitation, which is the variance between the capitation bid price and the actual cost of providing services.

Primary Care Physician (PCP) A subscriber's designated physician for basic medical care; usually a family practitioner, pediatrician, internist, or obstetrician-gynecologist.

Professional Review Organization (PRO)   A group of professionals, often providers, assigned to review an insurer's performance; heavily used by Medicare.

Prospective Payment System (PPS)   Any payment system in which the amount to be paid to the provider is set before services commence.

Qualified   See Federally Qualified.

Quality Assurance   A program to set standards for and monitor the quality of care provided.

Recredentialing   A retrospective reviewing and renewing of the credentials or clinical privileges for a provider, based on that provider's past performance.

Re-insurance   Insurance carried by a health plan, insurer, or provider group under capitation to guard against excessively high costs or patient utilization.

Resource-based Relative Value Scale (RBRVS)   A fee schedule and service coding system for Medicare phased in over a four-year period beginning in January, 1992.

Retrospective Review   A form of utilization review conducted after the provision of services to determine if those services meet the requirements of the insurer or third party to justify payment for services provided.

Rider   A legal addendum or provision that modifies, by either expanding or decreasing, the agreement of a health plan to cover certain services or conditions.

Risk Bands   Utilization strata fixing changes in capitation payments for very high or low utilization. Also called Risk Corridors.

Risk Pool   An arrangement whereby part of a provider's payment is withheld and returned in proportion to the financial well-being of the health plan. See Withhold.

Risk Sharing   Any arrangement in which business entities, such as providers of services and an insurer, share in being at-risk for the costs of services to a population of enrollees.

Safe Harbors   Federal guidelines issued in July, 1991, for the Anti-Kickback Statutes of 1972 and 1977 regarding businesses that deal with Medicare and Medicaid; these restrict provider ownership to 40 percent where professional activities affect financial gain.

Self-Insurance   The type of insurance that is in place when a group, employer, or organization assumes its own risk for the costs of healthcare services.

Sentinel Effect   The alteration of clinical or administrative practice as a result of knowing that review or monitoring is occurring.

Service Area   The defined geographic area within which a health plan agrees to provide direct services.

Skimming   A type of risk stratification that occurs when a health plan seeks to enroll only the healthiest or lowest risk subscribers as a means of controlling risk and costs. Also called Creaming.

Social Health Maintenance Organization (S/HMO) An HMO that provides social and preventive services to a geriatric or other special-needs population with unique long-term care requirements.

Staff Model A health plan that employs its own providers.

Stop-Loss In a capitation contract, the maximum expense the provider can incur before the capitation rate structure changes; like a risk band except that it only addresses the upper limits of expenses. For subscribers, the upper amount for which a co-payment is due before the health plan assumes full coverage for costs incurred.

Subscriber The person in whose name an HMO or PPO policy is issued.

Tax Equity and Fiscal Responsibility Act of 1982 (TEFRA) Among other medical insurance provisions, this law allows HMOs to contract with Medicare on a capitated basis.

Third-Party Administrator (TPA) A fiscal intermediary or agent that pays claims on behalf of a payor. Same as Pass Through and Administrative Service Only.

Triage The assessment of patient need and assignment to appropriate care.

Triple Option A health plan offering indemnity, PPO, and HMO plans.

Usual, Customary, and Reasonable (UCR) A fee structure for services based on assessment of prevailing fees in a particular community or region.

Utilization The amount of services used by a patient or patients.

Utilization Management (UM) The management of patients' utilization of services, often for purposes of determining need for preauthorization or treatment. UM may be prospective, concurrent, or retrospective.

Utilization Review (UR) The review of patients' utilization of services, often for purposes of determining need for treatment. UR may be prospective, concurrent, or retrospective.

Utilization Review Organization (URO) A business entity that provides utilization review for insurers or employers. A URO may also credential providers and pay claims on an administrative service only (ASO) basis.

Verification of Coverage A procedure for checking an enrollee's status with a particular health plan, usually prior to beginning services, as a part of preauthorization and utilization review.

Withhold A portion of a provider's fee retained by a health plan as a part of a risk-sharing arrangement. The provider receives all or a portion of the withhold periodically based upon the financial performance of the health plan. See Risk Pool.

Wraparound An arrangement between an HMO and a more traditional insurer to offer non-HMO medical insurance products to the HMO and its subscribers.

MANAGED CARE RESOURCES

I. ORGANIZATIONS

American Association for Partial
Hospitalization
901 N. Washington St., Suite 600
Alexandria, VA 22314-1535
703/836-2274.

American Board of Certified Managed
Care Providers
P.O. Box 11625
Clearwater, FL 34616
813/531-6666.

American Health Information
Management Association
919 N. Michigan Av., Suite 1400
Chicago, IL 60611-1683
800/383-2973.

American Managed Care and Review
Association
1227 25th St. NW, Suite 610
Washington, DC 20037
202/728-0506.

American Psychiatric Association
1400 K St. NW
Washington, DC 20005
800/343-4671 (Managed Care Hotline).

American Psychological Association,
Practice Directorate: Legal and
Regulatory Affairs
1200 17th St. NW
Washington, DC 20036-3090
202/247-7600.

Computer-Based Patient Record
Institute
919 N. Michigan Av., Suite 1400
Chicago, IL 60611-1683
800/383-2973.

Council of Behavioral Group Practices
c/o Institute for Behavioral Healthcare
1110 Mar West St., Suite E
Tiburon, CA 94920
415/435-9754.

Foundation of the American College
of Healthcare Executives
840 Lakeshore Drive
Chicago, IL 60611
312/943-0544.

Group Health Association of America
1129 20th St. NW, Suite 600
Washington, DC 20036
202/778-3200.

Health Outcomes Institute
2001 Killebrew Drive, Suite 122
Bloomington, MN 55425
612/858-9188.

Institute for Behavioral Healthcare
1110 Mar West St., Suite E
Tiburon, CA 94920
415/435-9821.

InterStudy
2901 Metro Drive, Suite 4000
Bloomington MN 55425
612/858-9291.

Medical Group Management
Association
104 Inverness Terrace E.
Englewood, CO 80112-5306
303/397-7872.

National Association of Managed Care
Physicians
1601 Trapelo Rd.
Waltham, MA 02154
617/290-0400.

National Center for Managed Health
Care Administration
University of Missouri-Kansas City
5100 Rockhill Rd.
Kansas City, MO 64110-2499
816/235-1489.

National Committee for Quality
Assurance
1350 New York Av., Suite 700
Washington, DC 20005
202/628-5788.

Utilization Review Accreditation
Commission
1130 Connecticut Av. NW
Washington, DC 20036
202/296-0120.

II. PERIODICALS AND DIRECTORIES

Accountability News for Health Care Managers
Atlantic Information Services
1050 17th St. NW, Suite 480
Washington, DC 20036
800/521-4323.

AMCRA Monitor
American Managed Care and Review
Association
1227 25th St. NW, Suite 610
Washington, DC 20037
202/728-0506.

Behavioral Healthcare *Tomorrow* Journal
1110 Mar West St., Suite E
Tiburon, CA 94920
415/435-9848.

Business Insurance
The Crain Syndicate
740 Rush St.
Chicago, IL 60611-2590
800/678-9595.

Capitation Management Report
National Health Information, L.L.C.
P.O. Box 670505
Marietta, GA 30066-0126
800/597-6300.

CCH Monito
CCH Inc.
4025 W. Peterson Av.
Chicago, IL 60646-6085
800/435-8878.

Directory of Managed Care Organizations
American Managed Care and Review
Association
1227 25th St. NW, Suite 610
Washington, DC 20037
202/728-0506.

Directory of Partial Hospitalization Programs
American Association for Partial
Hospitalization
901 N. Washington St., Suite 600
Alexandria, VA 22314-1535
703/836-2274.

Employee Benefit News
1483 Chain Bridge Rd., Suite 202
McLean, VA, 22101
703/448-0520.

Executive Report on Managed Care
Managed Care Information Center
Dept. 14, 3100 Highway 138
Wall Township, NJ 07719-1442
800/516-4343.

Group Practice Managed Healthcare News
201 Littleton Rd., Suite 100
Morris Plains, NJ 07950-2932
201/285-0855.

Health Care Competition Week
Capitol Publications, Inc.
1101 King St., Suite 444
Alexandria, VA 22314-2968
800/345-1301.

Health Care Reform Week
United Communications Group
P.O. Box 90608
Washington, DC 20090-0608
800/929-4824.

Health System Leader
Bader & Associates
P.O. Box 2106
Rockville, MD 20847-2106
301/468-1610.

Health Systems Strategy Report
Capitol Publications
1101 King St., Suite 444
Alexandria, VA 22314
800/655-5597.

HMO Magazine: Directions in Managed Health Care
Group Health Association of America
1129 20th St. NW, Suite 600
Washington, DC 20036
202/778-3200.

Hospital Management Review
COR Research, Inc.
P.O. Box 40959
Santa Barbara, CA 93140.

The InterStudy Competitive Edge
InterStudy
P.O. Box 4366
St. Paul, MN 55104
612/858-9291.

The InterStudy Quality Edge
InterStudy
P.O. Box 4366
St. Paul, MN 55104
612/858-9291.

Managed Care Information Base
Managed Care Information Center
Dept. 14, 3100 Highway 138
Wall Township, NJ 07719-1442
800/516-4343.

Managed Care Law Outlook
Capitol Publications
1101 King St., Suite 444
Alexandria, VA 22314
800/655-5597.

Managed Care Outlook
Capitol Publications
1101 King St., Suite 444
Alexandria, VA 22314
800/655-5597.

Managed Care Report
American Academy of Child and Adolescent Psychiatry
Public Information Office
P.O. Box 96106
Washington, DC 20090
202/966-7308.

Managed Care Week
Atlantic Information Services
1050 17th St. NW, Suite 480
Washington, DC 20077-5862
800/521-4323.

Managed Care Yearbook
Managed Care Information Center
Dept. 14, 3100 Highway 138
Wall Township, NJ 07719-1442
800/516-4343.

Managed Healthcare
7682 Old Oak Blvd.
Riverton, NJ 08077
800/949-6525.

Managed Health Care Directory
Managed Care Information Center
Dept. 14, 3100 Highway 138
Wall Township, NJ 07719-1442
800/516-4343.

Medical Group Management Journal
Medical Group Management Association
104 Inverness Terrace E.
Englewood, CO 80112-5306
303/397-7872.

Medical Outcomes and Guidelines Alert
Faulkner & Gray
Eleven Penn Plaza
New York, NY 10001-2206
212/967-7060.

*National Directory of Managed Care
Companies and Employee Assistance
Programs*
Professional Health Plan
5856 College Av., Suite 206
Oakland, CA 94618
800/428-7559.

Open Minds
Open Minds
44 S. Franklin St.
Gettysburg, PA 17325-9959
717/334-0538.

*Report on Healthcare Information
Management*
Capitol Publications
1101 King St., Suite 444
Alexandria, VA 22314
800/655-5597.

*Report on Medical Guidelines and
Outcomes Research*
Capitol Publications
1101 King St., Suite 444
Alexandria, VA 22314
800/655-5597.

St. Anthony's Ancillary Capitation Report
St. Anthony's Publishing
P.O. Box 96561
Washington, DC 22090
800/632-0123.

*St. Anthony's Health Care Capitation
Report*
St. Anthony's Publishing
P.O. Box 96561
Washington, DC 22090
800/632-0123.

St. Anthony's Physician Capitation Report
St. Anthony's Publishing
P.O. Box 96561
Washington, DC 22090
800/632-0123.

*The Singer Report on Managed Care
Systems and Technology*
Charles Singer and Company
401 Edgewater Place, Suite 580
Wakefield, MA 01880-9830
617/246-7585.

State Health Watch
Subscription Services Dept.
704 Stony Hill Road, Suite 154
Yardley, PA 19067-5507
215/295-2304.

Washington Health Report
Faulkner & Gray, Inc.
Eleven Penn Plaza
New York, NY 10117-0373
800/535-8403.

III. BOOKS

Alternative health services delivery systems manual (1991). Washington: Practice Directorate, American Psychological Association.

Austad, C., & Berman, W. (Eds.) (1991). *Psychotherapy in managed health care: The optimal use of time & resources.* Washington: American Psychological Association.

Berwick, D., Godfrey, A., & Roessner, J. (1990). *Curing health care: New strategies.* San Francisco: Jossey-Bass.

Boland, P. (1991). *Making managed healthcare work.* New York: McGraw-Hill.

Clarke, R. L., Coddington, D. C., Keen, D. J., & Moore, K. D. (1992). *The crisis in health care: Costs, choices and strategies.* San Francisco: Jossey-Bass.

Coile, R. C. (1989). *The new medicine: Reshaping medical practice and health care management.* Gaithersburg, MD: Aspen Publishers.

Duhl, L. J., & Cummings, N. C. (1992). *Health services: Coping with crisis.* New York: Springer.

Feldman, J. L., & Fitzpatrick, R. J. (1992). *Managed mental healthcare: Administrative and clinical issues.* Washington: American Psychiatric Association Press.

Feldman, S. (1991). *Managed mental health services.* Springfield, IL: Charles Thomas.

A guide for establishing programs for assessing outcomes in clinical settings (1994). Chicago: Joint Commission on Accreditation of Healthcare Organizations.

Health care alliance & network sourcebook. (1994). New York: Faulkner & Gray.

Insider's guide to managed care: A legal and operational road map (1990). Washington: National Health Lawyers Association.

Kongstvedt, P. R. (1988). *The managed health care handbook.* Gaithersburg, MD: Aspen Publishers.

Patterns in HMO enrollment (1991). Washington: Group Health Association of America.

Poynter, W. (1994). *The preferred provider's handbook.* San Francisco: Jossey-Bass.

St. Anthony's capitation reference manual. (1994). Reston, VA: St. Anthony's Publishing.

St. Anthony's capitation utilization and rate guidebook: 1994-95 edition. (1994). Reston, VA: St. Anthony's Publishing.

St. Anthony's guide to capitation contracts. (1994). Reston, VA: St. Anthony's Publishing.

Winegar, N. (1992). *The clinician's guide to managed mental healthcare.* New York: Haworth Press.

Woody, R. H. (1991). *Quality care in mental health: Assuring the best clinical services.* San Francisco: Jossey-Bass.

C

PROVIDER SUBCONTRACT GUIDELINES

The following items generally must be covered in a full contract designed to subcontract outpatient services to a network provider. Professional legal advice should be sought in the development of a contract of this nature.

1. *Term:* The period of time covered by the contract must be clearly stated. The renewal process should also be well defined.

2. *Services to Be Provided and Fees to Be Paid:* The covered services (such as health psychotherapy or psychotropic medication management) that the provider is to provide should be specified. It is most important to specify any services that will not be covered, for example, marital therapy. The provider should also be bound not to discriminate in providing services based on age, sex, race, religion, ethnic origin, or handicap. The fee structure is usually presented in an appendix or attached exhibit. How client co-payments will be handled must be spelled out carefully.

3. *Provider Qualifications:* The training, licensure, and malpractice insurance requirements expected of the provider must be covered in detail. These may take the form of a reference to meeting the requirements set forth in a full credentialing policy and procedure. (See Appendix D.)

4. *Preauthorization and Utilization Review:* How clients will be referred to the provider and how the provision of services will be authorized must be carefully delineated. Also specified must be the regulations governing authorizations after the initial one and what reporting procedures are required to keep the contractor knowledgeable about each referred patient's treatment status.

5. *Access to Treatment:* The contract should clearly delineate within what time period after referral an appointment must be offered to new patients, what office hours are acceptable to the contractor, and what emergency availability is expected from the provider.

6. *Client Records:* The specifications for how medical records are to be kept must be articulated, including meeting the Freedom of Information Act and Titles XVIII and XIX of the Social Security Act. Retention and ownership of records should be addressed, as well as requirements for the sub-

contractor to maintain confidentiality. Usually there is a provision for the subcontractor to obtain a release of information on a routine basis from each client for the release of treatment information to the contractor.

7. *Quality Assurance:* The requirements for the provider's participation in contractor review of patient charts, peer review, and outcomes management should be addressed.

8. *Independence of the Subcontractor:* It is most important to specify that the subcontractor is not an employee or agent of the contractor and has freedom in choosing how to practice and to associate with other payors.

9. *Termination:* Any contract must describe how the agreement can be mutually or unilaterally terminated and under what conditions, such as insolvency of either party or unethical treatment or behavior. Requiring the provider to assist in assuring continued care for needy patients during any transition is most helpful.

10. *Notification and Assignment:* The agreement should clarify that it cannot be transferred or assigned to anyone else and should clearly state the parties' addresses to be used in communication.

D

Sample Provider Credentialing Forms

APPLICATION FOR PROFESSIONAL STAFF
MEMBERSHIP AND PROVIDER PARTICIPATION

GENERAL INSTRUCTIONS

- Please complete the application in full. You may include a Curriculum Vitae with your application. Please do not reference the CV on the application itself.
- Please TYPE OR PRINT all responses.
- Attach additional sheets if necessary.
- Include a photocopy of the following: State license; proof of professional liability coverage (including limits and expiration date); special professional certifications; list of continuing education programs attended over the past (___) months and CMEs received; proof of board certification (physicians only) or eligibility (residency certificate); and DEA certificate/registration (physicians only).

PERSONAL INFORMATION

Last Name _____ First Name _____ MI____

Maiden Name (if applicable) _____

Home Address_____

City_____ State_____ Zip_____

Telephone: Home:_____

Birth Place_____ Birth Date_____ U.S. Citizen ___Yes ___No

PRACTICE/GROUP INFORMATION

Practice Name (if applicable) _____

Main Office _____

City_____ State_____ Zip_____

Telephone: Office: _____ Emergency: _____ FAX:_____

Office/Location #2: _____

City_____ State_____ Zip:_____

Telephone: Office: _____ Emergency: _____ FAX:_____

Office/Location #3: _____

City_____ State_____ Zip_____

Telephone: Office: _____ Emergency: _____ FAX:_____

NOTE: If you have more than three (3) locations, please list additional locations on a separate typewritten sheet, making sure to include all information indicated above.

Under what number do you bill? (Please Check ONE)

Tax ID: _____ Tax ID#: _____ SS#: ____ SS#: _____

Medicare #: _____ Medicaid #: _____

Other Insurer #: _____ Insurer: _____

Other Insurer #: _____ Insurer: _____

• Preferred Patient Access Phone #: _____

• Preferred Administrative Issues Phone #: _____

• Preferred Billing/Collections Phone #: _____

EDUCATION

Undergraduate School_____

Address_____ City_____

State_____ Zip_____ Degree_____

Attended From_____ To_____

Medical/Graduate School_____

Address_____ City_____

State_____ Zip_____ Degree_____

Attended From_____ To_____

Internship _____

Address_____ City_____

State_____ Zip_____ Percent Full-time_____

Attended From_____ To_____

Type of Internship_____

Director/Advisor Name_____

Residency 1 (Physicians)/Internship 2_____

Address_____ City_____

State_____ Zip_____ Percent Full-time_____

Attended From_____ To_____

Type of Residency/Internship_____

Director/Advisor Name_____

Residency 2 (Physicians)/Internship 3_____

Address_____ City_____

State_____ Zip_____ Percent Full-time_____

Attended From_____ To_____

Type of Residency/Internship_____

Director/Advisor Name_____

CERTIFICATION/LICENSES/REGISTRATION
PROFESSIONAL SOCIETY MEMBERSHIPS/FELLOWSHIPS

Certifications

1. Board/Certifying Body: Name_____

    Certified? Yes____ No____ Eligible? Yes____ No____

    Certification Date_____ Expiration Date_____

Physicians

Flex_____ Date Taken_____ ECFMG#_____

2. Board/Certifying Body: Name_____

    Certified? Yes____ No____ Eligible? Yes____ No____

    Certification Date_____ Expiration Date_____

Physicians

Flex_____ Date Taken_____ ECFMG#_____

3. Other Certification (National/State/Professional)_____

    _____

Certification Date_____ Expiration Date_____

Physician Applicants:

If you have not taken the Board Certification examination, do you plan to take it in the future? Yes___ No___

If yes, when:_____

Licenses

Do you hold State License(s)? Yes____ No____

1. License #_____ Expiration_____ Type: _____

    Issuing State: _____ Date license was first issued:_____

2. License #_____ Expiration_____ Type: _____

    Issuing State: _____ Date license was first issued:_____

3. License #_____ Expiration_____ Type: _____

    Issuing State: _____ Date license was first issued:_____

Physician Applicants

DEA# : _____ Expiration_____

Professional Society Memberships/Fellowships_____

_____

_____

CHRONOLOGY OF PROFESSIONAL CAREER

- List all present and prior, in chronological order, most recent first.

- After Internship/Residency or Postgraduate Degree, account for all time periods including military service, travel, or periods of illness.

Professional Practice

1. Practice/Organization_____

Address_____

City_____ State_____ Zip_____

Associate/Supervisor_____

Telephone _____ Date From_____ To_____

2. Practice/Organization _____

Address _____

City_____ State_____ Zip_____

Associate/Supervisor_____

Telephone _____ Date From_____ To_____

3. Practice/Organization_____

Address _____

City_____ State_____ Zip_____

Associate/Supervisor_____

Telephone _____ Date From_____ To_____

4. Practice/Organization_____

Address _____

City_____ State_____ Zip_____

Associate/Supervisor_____

Telephone _____ Date From_____ To_____

Hospital Affiliations

1. Hospital_____

Address _____

City_____ State_____ Zip_____

Staff Category_____

Date From_____ To_____

2. Hospital_____

Address _____

City_____ State_____ Zip_____

Staff Category_____

Date From_____ To_____

3. Hospital_____

Address _____

City_____ State_____ Zip_____

Staff Category_____

Date From_____ To_____

REFERENCES

Name three (3) individuals who have personal knowledge of your current clinical abilities, ethical character, and ability to work cooperatively with others and who will provide specific written comments on these matters upon request (professional references only).

1. Name_____

Organization_____

Address_____

Title_____ Phone _____

2. Name_____

Organization_____

Address_____

Title_____ Phone _____

3. Name_____

Organization_____

Address_____

Title_____ Phone _____

DISCIPLINARY ACTIONS

Have you ever had any of the following denied, revoked, suspended, reduced, limited, or placed on probation, or have you voluntarily relinquished any of the following in anticipation of any of these actions, or are any of these actions now pending? If yes, provide full explanation on a separate sheet.

- License, in any state   ( )Yes   ( )No

- DEA Registration   ( )Yes   ( )No

- Other Professional Registration/License   ( )Yes   ( )No

- Academic Appointment   ( )Yes   ( )No

- Medical/Hospital Staff Membership   ( )Yes   ( )No

- Clinical Privileges   ( )Yes   ( )No

- Prerogatives/rights on any medical staff   ( )Yes   ( )No

- Other institutional affiliation status   ( )Yes   ( )No

- Professional society membership   ( )Yes   ( )No

- Professional liability insurance   ( )Yes   ( )No

- Have you ever been involved in any suit, including arbitration?   ( )Yes   ( )No

- Have you had any other professional sanction?   ( )Yes   ( )No

- Have you had any professional action against you which was resolved by monetary settlement?   ( )Yes   ( )No

- Are there any medical incidents for which you have been contacted by an attorney regarding potential malpractice liability (settlement request, writ of summons, etc.)?   ( )Yes   ( )No

- Within the past five years, have you ever been convicted of, or pleaded guilty to, a criminal offense, including a verdict of guilty following a plea of nolo contendere?   ( )Yes   ( )No

- Have you had any Medicaid, Medicare, or other governmental or third-party payor sanctions?   ( )Yes   ( )No

PRACTICE PARAMETERS

• Type of Practice: (check one)

Single Discipline Group_____   Multidisciplinary Group_____   Solo_____

• What is your response time (in days) from the point of first contact to first appointment? _____

• Indicate the number of new referrals you will be able to accept per week: _____

• Indicate routine office hours: _____

• Would you be available for same day crisis assessments,
  if necessary?   ( )Yes   ( )No

• Would Saturday and/or evening appointments be available?   ( )Yes   ( )No

• Are you currently a participating provider with any other
  managed care plans (HMO, PPO, managed fee-for-service
  network)?   ( )Yes   ( )No

Please list the other networks in which you currently participate:_____

_____

• Do you have twenty-four (24) hour on-call availability for
  your patients?   ( )Yes   ( )No

If yes, respond to the following.

a) Do you utilize an answering service?   ( )Yes   ( )No

Service Phone #: _____

b) Do you utilize a digital pager?   ( )Yes   ( )No

Pager Phone #: _____

c) Do other providers furnish on-call back-up?   ( )Yes   ( )No

If yes:
Are they members of your group?   ( )Yes   ( )No

Are they _____ Network members?   ( )Yes   ( )No

CONDITIONS OF APPLICATION

By making this application, I hereby:

- signify my willingness to appear for interviews in regard to my application, if necessary;

- authorize all representatives of _____ to consult with my prior associates and others who may have information bearing on my professional competence, character, ethical qualifications, and ability to work with others;

- consent to the inspection by all representatives of _____ of all documents that may be material to an evaluation of my qualifications and competence;

- release from liability all representatives of _____ for their acts performed and statements made in good faith and without malice concerning my application and my credentialing and qualifications;

- release from liability any and all individuals and organizations who provide information to _____ with good faith and without malice concerning my professional competence, ethics, character, and other qualifications for staff appointment and clinical privileges;

- pledge to maintain an ethical practice, to provide for the continuous care of my patients, and to refrain from delegating the responsibility for care of my patients to any person not equally qualified to undertake that responsibility;

- acknowledge that I, as an applicant for participation, have the burden of producing adequate information for a proper evaluation of my professional, ethical, and other qualifications for such participation and for resolving any doubts about such qualifications;

- acknowledge that any significant misstatements in or omissions from this application constitute cause for denial of participation or cause for summary dismissal from _____; and

- certify all information given by me to the foregoing questions and statements in this application to be true and correct without omissions of any kind.

_____   _____
Signature   Date

_____

Name (please print)

All information supplied will be kept in strictest confidence. _____ will employ all reasonable safeguards to protect the Applicant's privacy.

REQUEST FOR PROFESSIONAL STAFF/PROVIDER PRIVILEGES

Privileges are granted to clinicians to become members of the Provider Network on the basis of academic preparation, training, practical experience, and recommendations regarding competency and performance. Different clinical privileges require specific training and experience. Please review the following privileges in light of your training, experience, and level of competency. Indicate the privileges you desire. In determining re-appointment, the Credentials Committee will consider information from peer review, utilization review, quality management, and other programs in recommending continuation of clinical privileges.

Requested		Credentials Committee Approval and Date
_____	Adult Psychiatry	_____
_____	Child and Adolescent Psychiatry	_____
_____	Chemical Dependency Detoxification and Treatment	_____
_____	Medication Management	_____
_____	Individual Psychotherapy	
	Child	_____
	Adolescent	_____
	Adult	_____
_____	Group Psychotherapy	
	Child	_____
	Adolescent	_____
	Adult	_____
_____	Family Psychotherapy	_____
_____	Psychological Testing	_____
_____	Neuro-psychological Testing	_____
_____	Biofeedback	_____
_____	Other (Specify_____)	_____

I am requesting the clinical privileges noted above. I agree to abide by the Contractual Stipulations, Rules and Regulations of _____.

SIGNATURE:_____

DATE:_____

CLINICIAN PEER EVALUATION

_____ has applied for provider privileges at/with _____.
He/she has indicated in his/her application for appointment that he/she would
like you, _____, to be a peer reference. Privileges are granted to
clinicians on the basis of academic preparation, training, practical experience, and
recommendations regarding competency and performance. Different clinical
privileges require different levels of training and experience. The accompanying
privilege request form shows you the clinical privileges requested. In light of his/
her training, experience, and level of competency, please rate the clinician on a
scale of 1 to 5, with 5 representing excellent and 1 representing poor. If you have
no experience with the clinician in any area indicated, check "Don't Know." The
Credentials Committee will consider information from peer review, utilization
review, quality management, and other programs in determining re-appointment
and clinical privileges.

Privileges:	Don't Know	Competency Rating				
1. Adult Psychiatry	_____	5	4	3	2	1
2. Child and Adolescent Psychiatry	_____	5	4	3	2	1
3. Chemical Dependency Detoxification and Treatment	_____	5	4	3	2	1
4. Medication Management	_____	5	4	3	2	1
5. Individual Psychotherapy	_____	5	4	3	2	1
Child	_____	5	4	3	2	1
Adolescent	_____	5	4	3	2	1
Adult	_____	5	4	3	2	1
6. Group Psychotherapy	_____	5	4	3	2	1
Child	_____	5	4	3	2	1
Adolescent	_____	5	4	3	2	1
Adult	_____	5	4	3	2	1
7. Family Psychotherapy	_____	5	4	3	2	1
8. Psychological Testing	_____	5	4	3	2	1
9. Neuro-psychological Testing	_____	5	4	3	2	1
10. Biofeedback	_____	5	4	3	2	1
11. Other	_____	5	4	3	2	1

Comments on back of form.

I acknowledge that I am aware of no medical or emotional problems that would
interfere with this practitioner's ability to deliver services.

SIGNATURE:_____DATE:_____

E

INSURER NEEDS ASSESSMENT TOOL

HOW TO USE THE NEEDS ASSESSMENT TOOL

The Needs Assessment Tool is an excellent way to begin building a database about a health insurance company (HIC). The managed behavioral healthcare delivery system (MBHDS) can proactively use this tool to gather information for making appropriate business decisions about which HICs it wishes to pursue. This tool can be used annually for a currently capitated arrangement between the MBHDS and the HIC to ensure that the HIC database remains current, and that present and projected needs are being serviced successfully by the MBHDS.

In gathering the information, the MBHDS needs to understand that it is similar to a sales process and may take several months. The information may be obtained from one or more contacts over a series of months by telephone or direct personal contact. Do not be discouraged if it takes longer than anticipated. Remember, the purpose is to build a database from which better decisions can be made, while introducing one's organization to key decision-makers at the HIC.

In gathering information using the Needs Assessment Tool, opportunities for the organization will be discovered. Each MBHDS has specific strengths and may on a short- or long-term basis add value to the products offered by the HIC. Review the information gathered and examine those areas where there are opportunities.

While gathering the information outlined in this Needs Assessment Tool, it is helpful to visualize an inverted pyramid. Much of the information gathered during the initial phase of the interview process is general, represented by the wide opening at the top of the inverted pyramid. It is a challenge to identify the repeating themes of the answers filtering down through the pyramid in response to increasingly focused questions, but it is within such information that opportunity lies.

INFORMATION NEEDED

A. *General.*
1. Current providers:
   a. who, how long,
   b. scope of services provided,
   c. satisfied (cost, quality, membership satisfaction);
2. Total membership:

      a. national,
      b. local;
   3. HIC management team (local):
      a. CEO/executive director,
      b. medical director,
      c. provider relations,
      d. marketing,
      e. national/regional contacts,
      f. key decision-makers (local/national).

B. *Products.*
   1. HMO;
   2. PPO;
   3. Point of service (in/out of network plan);
   4. Other;
   5. Local membership by product;
   6. Benefit:
      a. current basic package product,
      b. number of benefit plans offered by product;
   7. Future product plans (EAP, long- or short-term disability management, Workers' Compensation, prevention programs, and so forth).

C. *Current Operations.*
   1. Referral process (self- or PCP referral);
   2. Utilization management process:
      a. current method,
      b. projected change;
   3. Appeal/grievance process;
   4. HIC's expectations for access:
      a. patient (that is, 24-hour coverage, 7 days a week),
      b. geographical.

D. *Financial.*
   1. Reimbursement type by product (fee for service or capitation):
      a. HMO,
      b. PPO,
      c. POS,
      d. other;
   2. Risk (shared versus 100 percent responsibility by MBHDS; percentage of sharing).

E. *Total Quality Management.*
   1. Current program;
   2. Participative or delegated;
   3. External accreditation:
      a. National Committee for Quality Assurance,
      b. Utilization Review Accreditation Commission;

    4. Credentialing/recredentialing of MBHDS providers, delegated/non-delegated;

    5. Provider profiling, delegated/nondelegated;

    6. Potential/desire for outcomes studies.

F. *Management Information System.*

    1. HIC current system (mainframe versus PC/LAN-based);

    2. Expectations for online capabilities:

       a. eligibility interface,

       b. benefit information by plan,

       c. authorizations;

    3. Data needs of HIC:

       a. utilization management reports, frequency,

       b. HEDIS,

       c. employer-specific breakout;

    4. Electronic claims capability.

F

Capitation Management Information System Vendors

1. American Health Management and
   Consulting (AHMAC)
   140 Allens Creek Rd.
   Rochester, NY 14618
   716/461-4236
   Product: AHMAC MIS

2. DataBreeze, Inc.
   199 S. Addison Rd., Suite 100
   Wood Dale, IL 60191
   708/766-9555
   Product: Prepaid Manager

3. Fred Rothenberg & Associates, Inc.
   21243 Ventura Blvd., Suite 241
   Woodland Hills, CA 91364
   818/999-5021
   Product: EZ-CAP

4. Medipay, Inc.
   620 S.W. 5th, Suite 610
   Portland, OR 97204
   800/879-6334
   Product: MBHCmicro

5. Psychological Health Technologies
   8300 Utica Av., Suite 259
   Rancho Cucamonga, CA 91730
   909/945-5662
   Product: PsychVision

6. UNI/CARE Systems, Inc.
   3150 Livermore, Suite 115
   Troy, MI 48083
   313/689-9890
   Product: UNI/CARE

G

SAMPLE MANAGEMENT INFORMATION SYSTEM REPORTS

EXPLANATION OF BENEFITS

From: The XYZ Capitated Group
    4000 Medical Loop
    Anywhere, USA
To Provider: Harold Goodock, Ph.D.
    100 Hospital Lane
    Anywhere, USA

PT	ID	Insurer	Plan	CPT	Date	Hosp	*Exp	Pt Co-pay	Dx	Due Prov
Sample, Joe	111223333	HMO1	Best	90844	09/02/94	N		10.00	300.40	75.00
Sample, Joe	111223333	HMO1	Best	90844	09/12/94	N		10.00	300.40	75.00
Sample, Joe	111223333	HMO1	Best	90843	09/23/94	N		7.50	300.40	45.00
Sample, Joe	111223333	HMO1	Best	90847	09/30/94	N		10.00	300.40	75.00
									Total Due	$270.00
Enhelp, Ima	444556666	HMO1	Mid	90801	09/01/94	Y		0.00	296.20	85.00
Enhelp, Ima	444556666	HMO1	Mid	90843	09/02/94	Y		0.00	296.20	52.50
Enhelp, Ima	444556666	HMO1	Mid	90843	09/04/94	Y		0.00	296.20	52.50
Enhelp, Ima	444556666	HMO1	Mid	90843	09/05/94	Y		0.00	296.20	52.50
Enhelp, Ima	444556666	HMO1	Mid	90847	09/08/94	Y	2	0.00	296.20	85.00
Enhelp, Ima	444556666	HMO1	Mid	90843	09/09/94	Y	2	0.00	296.20	52.50
Enhelp, Ima	444556666	HMO1	Mid	90843	09/10/94	Y	2	0.00	296.20	52.50
Enhelp, Ima	444556666	HMO1	Mid	90847	09/11/94	Y	2	0.00	296.20	85.00
									Total Due	$517.50
Better, Tom	666778888	HMO1	Mid	90844	09/15/94	N		20.00	309.28	65.00
Better, Tom	666778888	HMO1	Mid	90844	09/22/94	N		20.00	309.28	65.00
Better, Tom	666778888	HMO1	Mid	90843	09/29/94	N		10.00	309.28	42.50
									Total Due	$172.50
Wurss, Even	888990000	HMO2	Low	90801	09/21/94	Y	8	42.50	305.00	42.50
Wurss, Even	888990000	HMO2	Low	90843	09/22/94	Y	8	26.25	305.00	26.25
Wurss, Even	888990000	HMO2	Low	90843	09/24/94	Y	8	26.25	305.00	26.25
Wurss, Even	888990000	HMO2	Low	90843	09/27/94	Y	8	26.25	305.00	26.25
Wurss, Even	888990000	HMO2	Low	90843	09/29/94	Y	8	26.25	305.00	26.25
Wurss, Even	888990000	HMO2	Low	90844	09/30/94	Y	8	42.50	305.00	42.50
									Total Due	$190.00

PT	ID	Insurer	Plan	CPT	Date	Hosp	*Exp	Pt Co-pay	Dx	Due Prov
Patient, Yung	000112222	HMO2	Top	90830	09/16/94	N		15.00	314.00	70.00
Patient, Yung	000112222	HMO2	Top	90830	09/16/94	N		15.00	314.00	70.00
Patient, Yung	000112222	HMO2	Top	90830	09/16/94	N		15.00	314.00	70.00

Grand Total Due: $1360.00

*Explanation Codes
[2] In partial hospital program
[8] 50% Behavioral Health/Addiction Treatment Benefit

Statement Date: 10/09/94

Utilization Report—Behavioral Health Services
Provider Network: The XYZ Capitated Group
4000 Medical Loop
Anywhere, USA
To Health Plan: Superduper Health Plan
100 Anywhere Lane
Anywhere, USA
Report Period 1/1/94 to 12/31/94

	1st Qtr.	2nd Qtr.	3rd Qtr.	4th Qtr.	YTD
Enrollment (mean ave.)					
Total	31,500	33,000	31,125	33,000	31,125
Subscribers	9,000	9,400	9,460	10,000	9,465
Dependents	21,000	21,600	22,040	22,000	21,660
Enrollees Accessing Services					
Total	1,205	1,221	1,176	33,000	31,125
Subscribers	9,000	9,400	9,460	10,000	9,465
Dependents	21,000	21,600	22,040	22,000	21,660
Accessing Outpt. Services					
Total Treated	294	311	317	302	1224
Subscribers	98	101	109	97	405
Dependents	196	210	208	205	819
% of Total Enrolled Treated	.93	.94	1.01	.88	3.61
Subscribers	.22	.23	.26	.22	1.30
Dependents	.58	.56	.62	.57	2.63
Ann'lized Access/1000 Enrollees	9.33	9.42	10.11	8.84	36.13
Subscribers	8.22	8.02	8.25	8.61	33.41
Dependents	10.12	9.97	10.76	9.41	39.54
Mean Encounters/Enrollee	7.66	7.50	7.32	7.22	7.43
Subscribers	5.88	6.01	5.90	5.89	5.92
Dependents	8.21	8.03	8.09	8.13	8.11
Accessing Inpt. Services					
Total Admitted	13	20	18	29	80
Subscribers	4	6	5	9	24
Dependents	9	14	13	20	56
Ann'lized Admits/1000 Enrollees	.41	.61	.58	.88	2.57
Subscribers	.39	.43	.38	.52	1.63
Dependents	.45	.81	.77	.97	3.28
Mean LOS/Enrollee	8.41	8.01	8.56	9.05	8.53
Subscribers	6.23	6.01	5.90	5.89	5.92
Dependents	10.31	10.78	10.92	11.07	10.77
Accessing Outpt. Hosp. Services					
Total Admitted	14	21	20	28	83
Subscribers	5	6	5	8	24
Dependents	9	15	15	20	56

	1st Qtr.	2nd Qtr.	3rd Qtr.	4th Qtr.	YTD
Ann'lized Admits/1000 Enrollees	.44	.64	.64	.84	2.57
Subscribers	.36	.34	.61	.59	1.69
Dependents	.51	.68	.69	.97	3.22
Mean LOS/Enrollee	7.21	8.11	7.96	9.25	8.53
Subscribers	5.96	6.22	5.68	5.85	5.92
Dependents	10.38	9.88	10.92	10.59	10.48

Date 01/15/95

Profit and Loss Statement
Capitation for the Superduper HMO
The XYZ Capitated Group
Report period: 01/01/95 to 06/30/95

	1st Qtr.	2nd Qtr.	3rd Qtr.	4th Qtr.	YTD
Enrollment (mean ave.)					
Total	31,500	33,000			32,250
Cap PMPM	2.87	2.87			2.87
Revenue					
Capitation Payments	90,405.00	94,710.00			185,115.00
Co-payments	16,272.00	17,047.00			33,319.00
Stop-Loss Payments	1,650.00	1,740.00			3,390.00
COB payments	856.00	1,110.00			1,966.00
Misc. income	276.00	00.00			276.00
Total	109,459.00	114,607.00			224,066.00
Expenses					
Inpt. Per Diems	38,768.00	39,466.00			78,234.00
Outpt. Hosp. Per Diems	14,458.00	14,558.00			29,016.00
Inpt. Prof. Costs	9,540.00	10,008.00			19,548.00
Outpt. Hosp. Prof. Costs	6,376.00	6,422.00			12,798.00
Outpt. Services—Staff	10,258.00	11,184.00			21,442.00
Outpt. Services—Network	2,640.00	3,118.00			5,758.00
Utilization Management	7,800.00	7,800.00			15,600.00
Intake/Triage	5,680.00	5,680.00			11,360.00
Shared General Overhead	6,846.00	6,846.00			13,692.00
Taxes	2,312.00	2,683.00			4,995.00
Total	104,678.00	107,765.00			212,443.00
Profit/Loss	4,871.00	6,842.00			11,623.00
% of Revenue	4.45	5.97			5.19

Date: 07/15/95

H

SAMPLE OUTCOMES STUDY DESIGN

OUTCOMES MANAGEMENT PROGRAM

The following outcomes management system was developed as a cooperative project by the eight group practices represented on the Steering Committee of the Council of Behavioral Group Practices (CBGP), a group practice consortium sponsored by the Institute for Behavioral Healthcare. The project leaders were Gayle Zieman, Ph.D., from Mesa Mental Health in Albuquerque, NM, and Allen Daniels, Ed.D., and Teresa Kramer, Ph.D., from the University of Cincinnati, OH.

The protocol was pilot-tested for three months in the eight practices (geographically spread across the country in seven states), and then was made available to all 62 practices of the CBGP in October, 1994. A national database for the project has been developed within the Department of Psychiatry at the University of Cincinnati. (For information on membership in the CBGP, see Appendix B or call 415/435-9754.)

A. *Goals and Purposes of the Outcomes Management System.*
 1. To aid behavioral group practices in their clinical quality improvement efforts and in using and meeting National Committee for Quality Assurance (NCQA) and HEDIS (Health Plan Employer Data Information Set) requirements, as well as other quality standards and clinical indicators of interest.
 2. To provide a psychometrically sound, comprehensive, and cost-effective outcomes research protocol for outpatient treatment that offers reliable and valid core data assessing:
    a. the short- and long-term effectiveness (symptom cessation/reduction and functional improvement) of behavioral health treatment provided,
    b. impact of behavioral health treatment on physical health,
    c. patient satisfaction with the care provided, and
    d. features within the care delivery system that are functioning well or in need of improvement.
 3. To provide a core protocol to which practices can add questions or specialized assessments (such as supplemental evaluations of patients with specific diagnoses).

    4. To create a standardized outcomes protocol with a comparative national database that will permit benchmarking between groups.

B. *Specifications.*

    1. The clinical assessment covers both mental health and addiction treatment.

    2. The protocol is designed to be implemented by a group with multidisciplinary staff, multiple offices, subcontracted affiliate practitioners, and adolescent as well as adult patients.

    3. The protocol is expandable to evaluate the outcomes of treatment with children and other special groups.

    4. The assessment is cost-effective, less than $5 per assessment (national database and data analysis costs not included).

    5. Assessment forms allow for manual scoring or optical scanning.

    6. Integrated statistical analysis software is available at a moderate cost to all CBGP members.

    7. The protocol is amenable to modular use, such that individual practices have the option of using all or parts of the protocol.

    8. Whenever possible, assessment tools are in the public domain or available at no fee per administration.

    9. The protocol can be completed by patients in 20 minutes or less.

C. *Method.*

    1. Protocol instrumentation:

       a. cover letter—custom-designed by each practice.

       b. Beginning Services Survey—survey at initial session, which:

          i. assesses patient satisfaction with access to treatment and expectations from treatment (developed by the CBGP), and

          ii. gathers demographic data (Personal Characteristics questionnaire developed by Health Outcomes Institute, formerly InterStudy; see Appendix I).

       c. Satisfaction Survey—a comprehensive survey used during ongoing treatment and post treatment. Four subscales:

          i. overall satisfaction (Client Satisfaction Questionnaire, Larsen, et al., 1979; Attkisson & Zwick, 1982),

          ii. satisfaction with psychotherapy and therapist,

          iii. satisfaction with medication and physician, and

          iv. satisfaction with office functioning.

         (Questions for last three scales developed and tested by the CBGP.)

       d. Behavior and Symptom Identification Scale (BASIS-32)—behavioral health and addiction treatment symptom and daily function screening tool (Eisen, et al., 1994). Five subscales:

          i. daily living function,

          ii. relation to self/others,

          iii. depression/anxiety,

          iv. impulsive/addictive behavior, and

          v. psychosis.

e. Health Status Questionnaire 2.0 (HSQ, essentially the same instrument as the SF-36, in the public domain)—a comprehensive survey of perceived health status and daily functioning (from Health Outcomes Institute; see Appendix I). Currently in wide use in medical and behavioral healthcare settings nationally. Eight subscales:

  i. health perception,
  ii. physical functioning,
  iii. limitations attributed to physical health,
  iv. limitations attributed to emotional problems,
  v. social functioning,
  vi. mental health,
  vii. bodily pain,
  viii. energy/fatigue.

f. Progress Evaluation Scale (PES)—daily life functioning measure (Ihilebich & Gleser, 1982). The PES may also be used as a rating by clinicians of patient functioning. Seven subscales:

  i. family interaction,
  ii. occupation,
  iii. getting along with others,
  iv. feelings and moods,
  v. use of free time,
  vi. problems, and
  vii. attitude toward self.

g. Treatment Events Checklist—treatment data retrieved from patient chart or office MIS (developed by the CBGP). Four subareas:

  i. diagnoses,
  ii. treatments (including medications),
  iii. adverse events (since beginning treatment), and
  iv. ending to treatment.

2. Assessment administration schedule:

a. pretreatment—patients complete packet before first treatment session.

b. follow-up: 3 months, 6 months, 12 months (practices may assess more frequently or for longer periods if so desired). Packets are administered by mail regardless of length of treatment. A letter or telephone call is to be used one week after mailing as a reminder/motivator to complete and return the packet.

3. Patient sampling—random selection of at least 8 percent of a practice's clinical population completing all four assessment administrations. Return rate on mailed assessments is expected to be 30 percent. To gain 8 percent overall completion, estimate that 33 percent of all patients treated within a group practice will need to be included.

REFERENCES

Attkisson, C. C., & Zwick, R. (1982). The client satisfaction questionnaire: Psycho-metric properties and correlations with service utilization and psychotherapy out-come. *Evaluation & Program Planning* 5: 233–237.

Eisen, S. V., Dill, D. L., & Grob, M. C. (1994). Reliability and validity of a brief pa-tient-report instrument for psychiatric outpatient evaluation. *Hospital & Community Psychiatry* 45(3): 242–297.

Ihilebich, D., & Gleser, G. C. (1982). *Evaluating mental health programs: The Progress Evaluation Scale.* Lexington, MA: Lexington Books.

Larsen, D. L., Attkisson, C. C., Hargreaves, W. A., & Nguyen, T. D. (1979). Assess-ment of client/patient satisfaction: Development of a general scale. *Evaluation & Program Planning* 2: 197–207.

OUTCOMES MANAGEMENT RESOURCES

1. Centers For Mental Healthcare
   Research
   University of Arkansas for Medical
   Sciences
   4301 W. Markham
   Little Rock, AR 72205
   501/686-5600
   Product: Outcomes systems development and implementation.

2. Health Outcomes Institute
   2001 Killebrew Dr., Suite 122
   Bloomington, MN 55425
   612/858-9188
   Product: Outcomes systems development and implementation.

3. Intermountain Health
   Center for Behavioral Healthcare
   Efficacy
   36 S. State St., 22nd Floor
   Salt Lake City, UT 84111
   801/442-3493
   Product: Outcomes systems development and implementation.

4. Medical Outcomes Trust
   P.O. Box 1917
   Boston, MA 02205
   617/426-4046
   Product: Information on outcomes systems and data.

5. National Committee for Quality
   Assurance
   1350 New York Av., Suite 700
   Washington, DC 20005
   202/628-5788
   Product: Quality standards and certification of programs.

6. National Computer Systems
   5605 Green Circle Dr.
   Minnetonka, MN 55343
   612/939-5000
   Product: Computerized scoring
   and reporting technology for multiple assessment instruments.

7. New Standards, Inc.
   1080 Montreal Av., Suite 300
   St. Paul, MN 55116
   800/755-6299
   Product: Outcomes systems development and implementation.

8. RAND Corporation
   Health Policy Sciences
   1700 Main St.
   Santa Monica, CA 90407
   310/393-0411
   Product: Information on outcomes systems and data.

9. Response Technologies, Inc.
   3399 South Country Trail
   East Greenwich, RI 02818
   401/885-6900
   Product: Computerized scoring
   and reporting technology for multiple assessment instruments.

10. Strategic Advantage
    1784 Dupont Av., S.
    Minneapolis, MN 55403
    612/374-5995
    Product: Outcomes systems devel-
    opment and implementation.

11. Treatment Research Institute
    One Commerce Square
    2005 Market St., Suite 1020
    Philadelphia, PA 19103
    800/335-9874
    Product: Outcomes systems
    development and implemen-
    tation.

12. University of Connecticut Health
    Center
    c/o Hal Mark, Ph.D.
    Department of Community
    Medicine
    Farmington, CT 06030
    203/679-3279
    Product: Outcomes systems devel-
    opment and implementation.

13. Velocity Healthcare Information
    10907 Red Circle Dr., Suite 130
    Minnetonka, MN 55343
    800/844-5648
    Product: Computerized scoring
    and reporting technology for mul-
    tiple assessment instruments.

INDEX